Transistor-Transistor Logic

by

George Flynn

Howard W. Sams & Co., Inc.
4300 WEST 62ND ST. INDIANAPOLIS, INDIANA 46268 USA

SECOND EDITION
FIRST PRINTING—1978

International Standard Book Number: 0-672-21572-1
Library of Congress Catalog Card Number: 78-63124

Printed in the United States of America.

Preface

The use of digital logic devices probably started with industrial control systems and telephone networks, where relays were used to perform logic or switching. Long before that, of course, the abacus was used for purely mathematical operations.

With the parallel development of electronic digital computers and semiconductor technology, digital logic devices really began to stand out. Circuit designers took a new look at how to do things. Soon digital instruments and complex systems began to appear: digital voltmeters, frequency counters, sophisticated control systems for military aircraft, special-purpose digital computers, and control systems for complex weapons and space probes. Finally, we have digital wrist watches, and this will not be the end of the line.

Underlying the end products are the semiconductor logic devices that perform the digital functions of signal generation, counting, adding, subtracting, multiplying, shifting, encoding, decoding, remembering or storing, multiplexing, comparing, etc. The first group of semiconductor circuits developed to perform the basic digital functions became known as Resistor-Transistor Logic, or RTL. Hardly was RTL well launched when Diode-Transistor Logic, or DTL, appeared. Then, DTL underwent a major modification and evolved into Transistor-Transistor Logic—TTL.

TTL remains the most popular family of digital logic because it is fast, low cost, readily available in a large variety of circuits, and easy to use once its characteristics are known. Further, many of the digital logic circuits and techniques developed for TTL devices are used in other logic families such as PMOS, NMOS, and CMOS. These same digital techniques are also used in microprocessors, in complex LSI chips for special jobs, and in custom LSI circuits. Frequently, for complex LSI chips to work properly, some TTL "glue" is used.

The book is meant to serve as a guide to TTL families and as an introduction to many of the techniques used in digital circuits.

A number of [illegible] text have been made. In addi- [illegible] all major families is included [illegible] devices.

[illegible] conductor manufacturers for [illegible] s book. They have helped me [illegible] t during the past few years, [illegible] information and data. I par- [illegible] to thank Texas Instruments Incorporated, Fairchild Semiconductor, Motorola Semiconductor Products Incorporated, National Semiconductor, Signetics Corporation, and Teledyne Semiconductor.

GEORGE FLYNN

Contents

CHAPTER 1

BASIC TRANSISTOR-TRANSISTOR LOGIC 7
Digital Families—Series 54/74 Circuits—The Basic Gate—NOR Gates—Inverters—AND-OR-INVERT Gates—Open-Collector and Wired-OR Circuits—Expandable Gates—Loading Rules—Noise Immunity—AND Gates

CHAPTER 2

FLIP-FLOPS 29
Set-Reset Flip-Flops—NOR-Gate Flip-Flops—Clocked Flip-Flops—TTL Flip-Flops—Other Versions

CHAPTER 3

DECODERS 51
One-of-Four Decoder—One-Out-of-Ten Decoder—Seven-Segment Decoders—Lamp Test and Ripple Blanking

CHAPTER 4

MULTIPLEXERS 67
Data Selectors—Multiple Data Input—Multiple Load Input

CHAPTER 5

SHIFT REGISTERS 71
Eight-Bit Shift Register—Serial-Parallel Shift Register—Left-Shift and Right-Shift Registers

CHAPTER 6

COUNTERS 79
Four-Bit Binary Counters—Divide-by-Twelve Counters—Decade Counter—Up/Down Binary Counter—Up/Down Decade Counter—Variable Modulo Counter

CHAPTER 7

ARITHMETIC CIRCUITS 97
Adders—True/Complement Circuit—Comparator—Exclusive OR and Exclusive NOR

CHAPTER 8

PARITY AND PRIORITY 111
Parity Generator—Priority Encoder

CHAPTER 9

MEMORIES 119
Random-Access Memory (RAM)—Register File—Read-Only Memory (ROM)—Content Addressable Memory

CHAPTER 10

SPECIAL CIRCUITS 134
Interface Driver—One-Shot Multivibrator—Latches—Schmitt Triggers—Zero-Crossing Detector—Line Drivers and Receivers

CHAPTER 11

INCREASING TTL SPEED AND DEVICE DENSITY 149
Propagation Time—High-Speed TTL—Low-Power TTL—Active Bypass TTL—Schottky-Clamped TTL—Low-Power Schottky TTL—PNP Inputs—High-Noise Immunity Logic—Tri-State Logic—TTL Trends—Families of TTL

CHAPTER 12

TTL APPLICATION 164
Up/Down Counting System—Data Transmission System

APPENDIX A

DIGITAL LOGIC CONVENTIONS 173

APPENDIX B

NUMBERING SYSTEMS 177

APPENDIX C

TTL POWER SUPPLY 181

APPENDIX D

GUIDELINES FOR SYSTEM DESIGN 183

APPENDIX E

GLOSSARY 185

APPENDIX F

TTL DEVICES 191

APPENDIX G

PIN ASSIGNMENTS 223

INDEX 283

CHAPTER 1

Basic Transistor-Transistor Logic

If you were told that some day practically everything electronic will be done digitally, you might think you were being kidded, but you can find people who think this will happen. They believe that even your tv set and quadrasonic hi-fi equipment will be digital.

When someone says that hi-fi equipment will go digital, just what is meant? In a simple hypothetical case, it means that your tapes or records would no longer be imprinted with continuous analog waveforms but would consist of only a string of pulses. The pulses and the spaces between them represent the ones and zeros of a digital word, and the digital word in turn represents a voltage level. The second word (string of pulses) on the tape is a little different and represents a slightly different voltage—maybe higher, maybe lower. It is easy to visualize a series of 10 or 20 words that represent selected points on a sine wave of voltage. All right, you have a string of digital words that represent a sine wave of voltage, but what do you do with these words?

Let's take each word as it comes along and put it into a digital-to-analog converter, which converts the string of pulses into the voltage level the word represents. Apply the voltage to a loudspeaker. With only one word and one voltage level, the most you can expect from the speaker is a grunt or a click. Now feed the speaker a whole series of words representing the sine wave. If you do it fast enough, and repeat the series a few hundred or a few thousand times, the speaker starts to respond. While the speaker may try to jump from the voltage level of one word to the voltage level of the next, it cannot move instantaneously. Thus, it acts to smooth out the "jumps" between words. If more filtering is needed, a capacitor connected across the speaker terminals will smooth things out.

If you are going to digitize each sine wave ten times per cycle, and if you want the speaker to produce a 1-kHz tone, you have to supply 1000 cycles per second times 10 words per cycle, or 10,000 words per second. This is no problem with today's electronics. You can, in fact, supply the speaker with millions of words per second—far more than the speaker can respond to. The waveforms, naturally, are not limited to sine waves but can represent anything from the croak of a frog to the singing of a rock music star.

At about this point, cynics will begin to point to the horrible complexity of using digital words compared to the nice simplicity of working with analog or linear circuits. Digital electronics looks and is complex, but it has certain advantages. First, it is a system that allows background noise to be almost completely eliminated. Second, digital systems tend to use the same building blocks (electronic components) in many different ways, and thus the building blocks become cheaper. Third, digital circuits are concerned primarily with the flow of information, not with the transmission of power. Thus, the digital words are manipulated at very low power levels—microwatts or even nanowatts. After the digital processing is completed, and the word is ready to drive a speaker, the power level is boosted to the required level.

If anyone still doubts that digital electronics will move out of the electronic computer and into other aspects of his life, he should consider just two examples. The entertainment and public address systems of the jumbo jets, like the Boeing 747, are multiplexed digital systems. Bell Telephone Company has digitized much of the telephone system and will do a lot more. If you haven't already been digitized by the phone company, just wait; you will be before long. You may never know whether you've been digitized or not because only an expert can tell the difference between a digitized voice and the real thing.

DIGITAL FAMILIES

Techniques for digitizing and dedigitizing information are many. Furthermore, a number of electronic approaches have been developed to solve the various problems that digitizing presents. Three major electronic families (tribes might be more accurate) are currently favored by system designers. The most widely used family of digital functions today is *transistor-transistor logic,* abbreviated TTL or T^2L. TTL is a favorite because it is fast, readily available, and relatively low cost. A second type of logic is called *emitter-coupled logic* or ECL. ECL is the fastest logic known and thus finds favor in the high speed circuits of large computers. The third important class of digital electronics is based on *metal oxide semiconductors* and is called MOS. MOS allows tremendous complexity in circuits and provides low power and low cost systems but, until recently, has been very slow compared to TTL and ECL.

No matter what kind of electronic circuits are used to build digital systems, the basic digital building blocks are very similar from system to system. Any one family is built up around one basic block. In TTL, the so-called NAND gate is basic. In *diode-transistor logic* (DTL), the NOR gate is basic. With the gates, you can build counters, flip-flops, shift registers, etc. These, in turn, are used to build mathematical manipulators, frequency synthesizers, digital-to-analog converters, and other circuits.

SERIES 54/74 CIRCUITS

We will investigate digital electronic systems starting with what is known as standard TTL, specifically the family known as type 5400/7400. The 5400/7400 family, or type 54/74 as it is usually called, was developed by Texas Instruments in the early 1960s and has been used throughout digital circuitry. Today about eight other companies make ICs in the type 54/74 family, and new devices appear every few days or so. In addition, several new families of type 54/74 TTL have been developed that emphasize special features such as high speed or low power. Once we finish examining the standard type 54/74, we'll take a look at the new versions and also some of the other TTL families.

What, you may wonder, does 54/74 stand for? Consider a specific IC, type SN5401; it is a "quad, 2-input positive NAND gate" rated for continuous operation at ambient temperatures from −55° to +125° C, and it has a supply voltage (V_{CC}) range from 4.5 to 5.5 volts. Type SN7401 is identical to type SN5401, except for the temperature and voltage ranges. It should only be used at temperatures between 0°C and +70° C and for a V_{CC} between 4.75 and 5.25 volts.

THE BASIC GATE

TTL is a positive-voltage logic system. This means that a high signal (or a ONE or plain 1) is a positive voltage of approximately 3.6 volts, while a low (or ZERO or 0) signal is as near to zero volts as the basic circuit will allow. ZERO is the saturation voltage of the collector-to-emitter structure of a transistor and is typically about +0.2 volt.

The basic circuit of TTL is shown in Fig. 1-1. Except for the input transistor, the circuit is very straightforward. We will ignore the input transistor for the moment. Refer to the rest

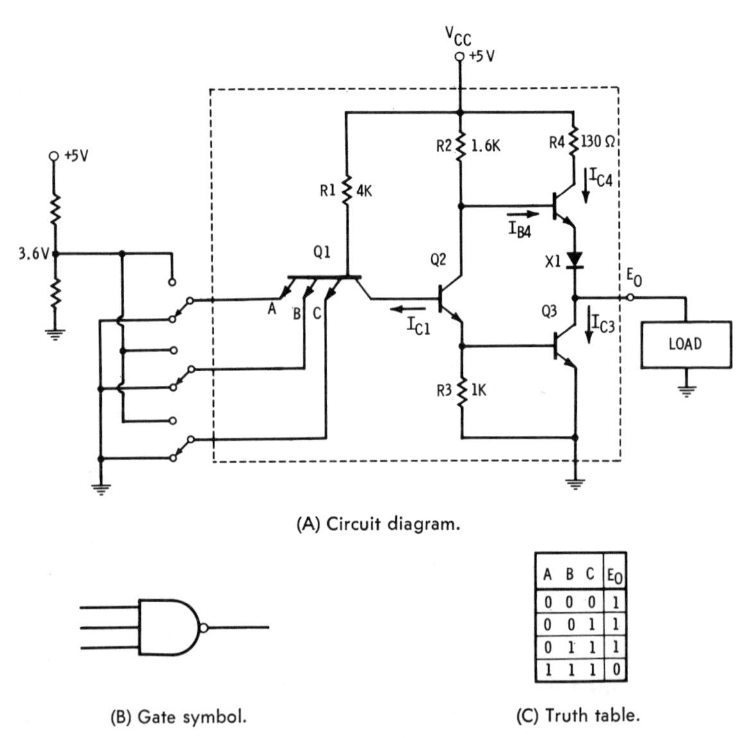

(A) Circuit diagram.

A	B	C	E_O
0	0	0	1
0	0	1	1
0	1	1	1
1	1	1	0

(B) Gate symbol.

(C) Truth table.

Fig. 1-1. Basic NAND gate.

of the NAND gate, the output circuit, shown in Fig. 1-2. Let the base of transistor Q2 be grounded. With the base grounded, Q2 is a very high impedance, and hardly any current flows from the collector to the emitter. The voltage applied to the base of transistor Q3 is close to zero; thus, Q3 is also a very high impedance, or open. The collector of Q2, on the other hand, is close to 5 volts, and thus, transistor Q4 is strongly on

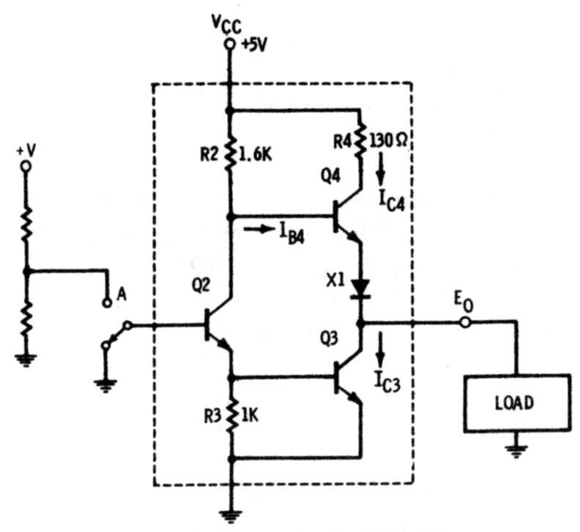

Fig. 1-2. Output circuit of Fig. 1-1.

—Q4 is saturated. The output voltage, E_O, of the circuit is then a function of load current and the series impedance.

The series impedance is the 130-ohm collector resistor of transistor Q4, the collector-to-emitter impedance of transistor Q4, and the forward impedance of the diode (X1). The load is usually the inputs of other gates. With other gates as loads, the output voltage (E_O) will be approximately 3.5 volts—a logical 1 (high).

Turn the switch in Fig. 1-2 to point A so that about +1.6 volts is applied to the base of transistor Q2. This is more than enough voltage to cause transistor Q2 to go into saturation. With Q2 on, the voltage fed to the base of transistor Q3 rises, and Q3 is saturated. At the same time, the voltage at the collector of transistor Q2 drops from its previous value of close to 5 volts. This is the base drive to transistor Q4. For Q4 to conduct, its base must be about 1.8 volts. Impedances R2 and R3 have been selected so that when transistor Q2 is on, the base voltage to transistor Q3 is high enough to saturate Q3, and the base voltage to transistor Q4 is too low to turn Q4 on. Thus, transistor Q4 is cut off.

The output voltage of the circuit is now the saturation voltage of transistor Q3. Again, the load is the input circuits of the following gates. But the output voltage is near zero, and no current can flow out of the circuit through transistor Q4, since this transistor is off. What the output circuit can do, however, is to accept current from other sources, and this is how it is used. It is a *current sink*—a low impedance path to ground—for the input circuits of the succeeding gates.

The Input Circuit

Look at the input circuit of Fig. 1-1. We find an odd transistor with multiple emitters, and it is hooked up wrong. How can transistor Q1 ever have any effect on transistor Q2? First, let all three emitters of Q1 be connected to ground through the toggle switches. The base of Q1 is connected to +5 volts through the 4K resistor; current flows through the base-to-emitter junctions; and transistor Q1 is strongly on—saturated. With transistor Q1 saturated, the voltage at its collector terminal is approximately the same as the voltage of its emitter terminal, which is at ground potential. Thus, the base of transistor Q2 is near ground potential, and the transistor is cut off. Any collector current that flows through Q1 to ground must go through a turned-off transistor (Q2). Current I_{C1} is going to be very small. Since transistor Q2 is off, transistor Q4 is on; the output voltage is high, and the output of the gate is a high (a 1).

Now, change the switch for emitter A of transistor Q1 and feed it a positive voltage. Let emitters B and C stay at ground potential or 0. What happens to transistor Q1? If any emitter of a multiemitter transistor is properly biased (in this case, connected to ground), the transistor acts like a normal single-emitter transistor. Current from the base to emitter A ceases because the emitter voltage is higher than the base voltage; the base-to-emitter junction is reverse biased. Emitters B and C are still grounded, so they still conduct current. Transistor Q2 remains cut off.

Keep emitter A positive and connect emitter B to the positive voltage; leave emitter C grounded. What happens? Transistor Q1 is still turned on by emitter C; transistor Q2 is still cut off so the output stays high.

Now connect emitter C to the positive voltage so that all three inputs are high. No current flows to any emitter of transistor Q1 from the base of Q1. Thus, with all the emitters high, the base-to-collector junction of transistor Q1 becomes forward biased. There is current through the 4K resistor (R1) into the base of transistor Q2. Transistor Q2 is turned on, which causes transistor Q3 to turn on and transistor Q4 to cut off.

Connect any one of the three emitters of transistor Q1 to ground again. Immediately, Q1 goes into saturation, turning transistor Q2 off and driving the output to the high (1) state. To summarize, the output will be a 1, if one or more inputs is a 0 (or if all inputs are 0). Gate operation is summarized by the truth table shown in Fig. 1-1B. Output voltage E_O will be 0 only when all inputs are 1.

What if an input transistor has four or eight emitters, as some have? The same logic holds. If any one input is 0, the output is 1; only if all inputs are a 1 can the output be a 0.

If we try to state the logical operation of the 3-input gate of Fig. 1-1, we have the statement: "When input A is a 1, AND input B is a 1, AND input C is a 1, the output is a 0." (If we had been able to say that the output is a 1 when A AND B AND C are all 1s, we would have had an AND gate.) What we actually have is an AND gate plus a signal inversion—a Negated-AND gate or a NAND gate. The gate shown has three inputs but the same ideas apply to NAND gates with more, and less, inputs.

Totem Pole Output

Before going further, let us take a look at one of the peculiarities of TTL. Since the output of the gate is either a high or a low, either transistor Q3 or transistor Q4 must be on at all times. Because the schematic (Fig. 1-1C) is drawn with transistor Q4 above transistor Q3, the output circuit looks like a totem pole although, in operation, the circuit acts much like a seesaw. We have assumed that when transistor Q3 turns on, transistor Q4 turns off simultaneously, and vice versa. In actuality, both output transistors are on at the same time during the transition. The result is that the output circuit shunts current to ground during the transition.

The "worst case" of current shunting occurs when the circuit is going from a 0 output to a 1 output. It takes transistor Q3 longer to turn off than it takes transistor Q4 to turn on. The result is a spike of excess current, as shown in Fig. 1-3.

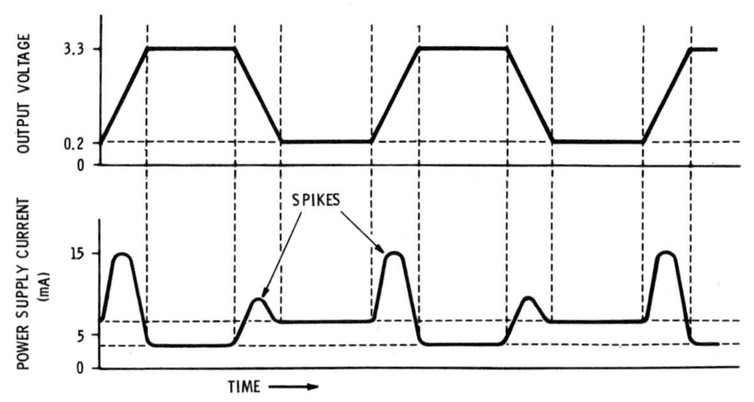

Fig. 1-3. Gate current spikes during changes of gate output.

When the output goes from 1 to 0, excess current is again drawn, but not as much because transistor Q4 is driven into the off state quickly, rather than being allowed to decrease to it naturally (as transistor Q3 does during the transition from 0 to 1).

One result of current spiking is that the system's power consumption increases with the speed of circuit operation—that is, with the clock rate of the system. For type 54/74 logic, the quiescent (clock stopped, nothing happening) dissipation is about 6 mW per gate. With the clock running at

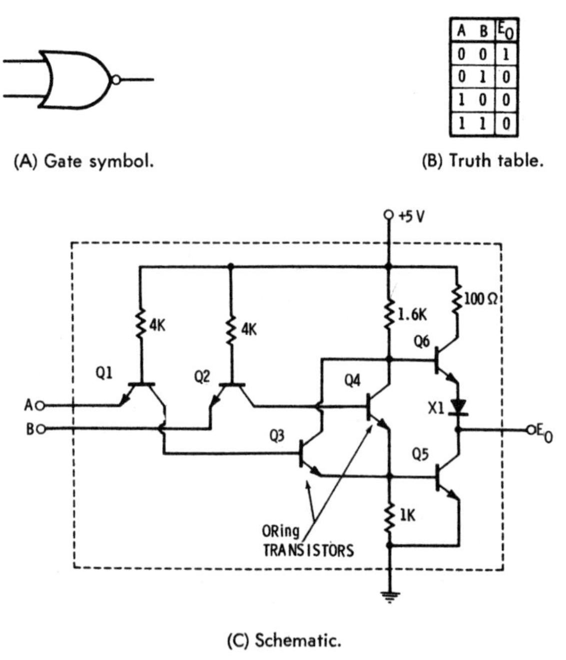

A	B	E_0
0	0	1
0	1	0
1	0	0
1	1	0

(A) Gate symbol.

(B) Truth table.

(C) Schematic.

Fig. 1-4. Basic NOR gate.

10 MHz, the dissipation is about 10 mW per gate; at 20 MHz, it is about 20 mW per gate. Thus the change in power consumption, as a function of operating frequency, is substantial. However, since the clock rate in a given system is usually fixed, changes in power supply requirements do not normally occur when the system is operated with the clock off. But, if many gates in a system *all* have to change simultaneously, a large amount of current may be demanded, with resultant spill-over effects on voltage regulation and transient (noise) characteristics.

NOR GATES

While a logic family is built around one gate, you still have to perform other functions. The two basic functions in all types of digital logic are AND and OR; except that in TTL, these become NAND and NOR.

The development of a NOR gate from the basic NAND gate is straightforward. The circuit is shown in Fig. 1-4. If both input A and input B are high, then transistors Q3 and Q4 are on. Transistor Q5 is also on; thus, the output of the gate is 0. If input A goes low while input B remains high, transistor Q3 turns off, but Q4 stays on and holds Q5 on; the output is 0. Similarly, if input B goes low while input A remains high, the output is still 0. Thus, the output is 0 if either input A *OR* input B is a 1, and the function is a Negated-OR or NOR. If both A and B are 0, then both transistor Q3 and transistor Q4 are off; Q5 is cut off, and transistor Q6 is turned on. The output is a 1. The truth table (Fig. 1-4B) shows the various conditions of the circuit.

INVERTERS

A recurring problem in digital systems is a signal that appears as a high instead of a low, or as a low instead of a high. The problem is easily solved by using an inverter to change a 0 to a 1, or a 1 to a 0. The symbol(s) and truth table for an inverter is shown in Fig. 1-5.

A	Q
0	1
1	0

(A) Symbol. (B) Truth table.

Fig. 1-5. Inverter function.

A simple inverter can be made from a single transistor as shown in Fig. 1-6. When input A is high, the transistor is saturated, and the output voltage E_O is low. When input A is 0 or low, the transistor is essentially an open circuit, and E_O is high (1). The single-transistor inverter is sometimes used in the output circuits of complex ICs to provide buffering and/or inversion. The circuit type 5404/7404, called a Hex Inverter, is more complex. It consists of six identical TTL inverter gates with common V_{CC} and ground connections. The circuit (Fig.

1-7), a 1-input NAND gate, is the schematic of each inverter in the IC.

When an inverter is needed but is not readily available, the two inputs of a NAND gate can be permanently connected together. (Also, one input of a NAND gate can be permanently connected to a 1.) It will then function as a simple inverter. A NOR gate can function as an inverter if both inputs are tied together or one input is connected permanently to ground.

In more complex ICs, inversion may be obtained by any one of the above methods. Regardless of the method used, the inverter symbol(s) shown in Fig. 1-5 is used on the logic diagrams.

A	E_0
LOW	HIGH
HIGH	LOW

(A) Circuit diagram. (B) Truth table.

Fig. 1-6. Simple transistor inverter.

AND-OR-INVERT GATES

One step beyond the NOR gate is the AND-OR-INVERT gate. The circuit, truth table, and symbol are shown in Fig. 1-8. The output is 0 if both A and B are 1s or if C and D are 1s. The circuit is the equivalent of a NOR gate with multiemitter ANDing transistors.

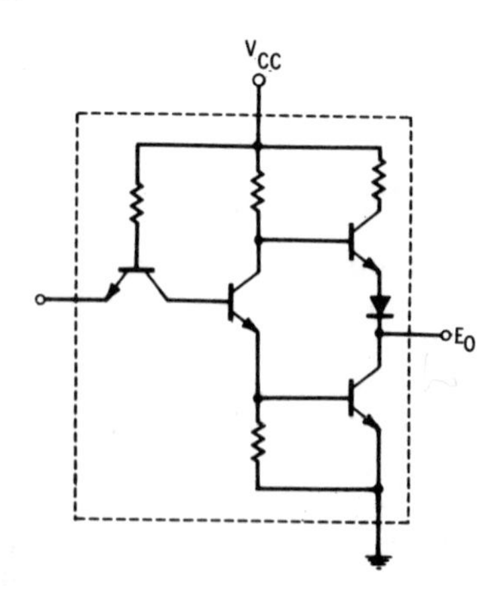

Fig. 1-7. One-input NAND gate inverter.

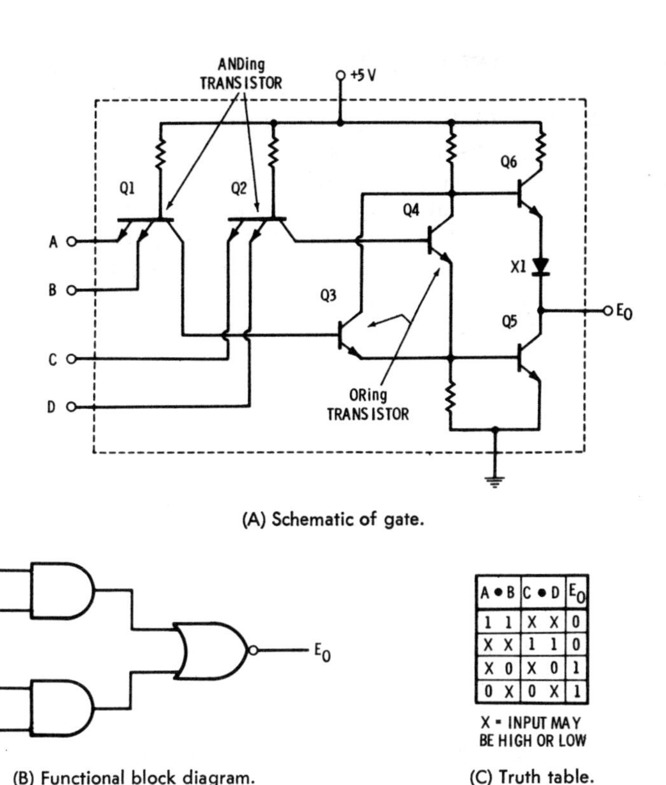

(A) Schematic of gate.

(B) Functional block diagram.

A • B	C • D	E_0
1 1	X X	0
X X	1 1	0
X 0	X 0	1
0 X	0 X	1

(C) Truth table.

Fig. 1-8. An AND-OR-Invert gate.

The function is thus an AND-OR with an inverted output. Naming a function of this kind is tricky. If the convention used with the NAND and NOR gates was followed, you would say you have a negated AND-OR gate, which you might call a NANDOR. But this convention was not followed, and the people who name logic designs used the more precise AND-OR-INVERT.

OPEN-COLLECTOR AND WIRED-OR CIRCUITS

A major disadvantage of the totem pole output is that it prevents the use of the so-called wired-OR circuit that has been widely used in other logic families, particularly in diode-transistor-logic (DTL). When two TTL outputs are tied together, and if one gate has a high output and the other has a low output, the high gate will drive an excessive amount of current into the low gate. Obviously, this is not good.

The lack of the wired-OR connection requires that the output of the basic TTL gate be buffered when the logic so demands.

This means extra circuits. To get around this, manufacturers have developed modified circuits, wherein transistor Q4 in the output circuit is omitted and the collector of transistor Q3 is left open, as shown in Fig. 1-9.

The truth table shows that the circuit functions as a NAND gate, except that transistor Q3 operates much like a toggle switch. When the A and B inputs are high, transistor Q3 is saturated and its series impedance from collector to emitter is very low. When either A or B input is low, transistor Q3 has no base drive and is a very high impedance. A load, such as a

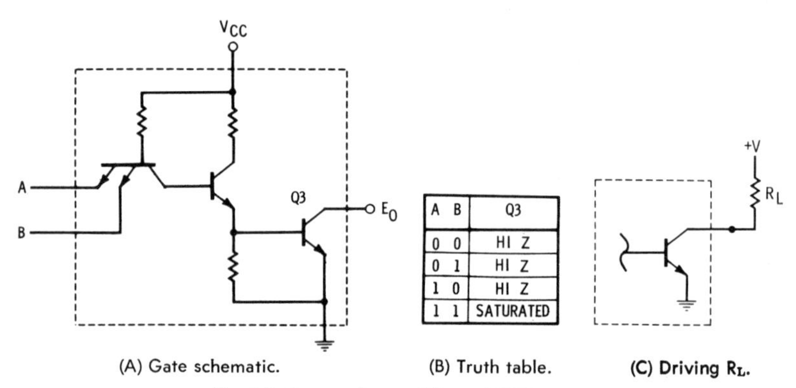

A	B	Q3
0	0	HI Z
0	1	HI Z
1	0	HI Z
1	1	SATURATED

(A) Gate schematic. (B) Truth table. (C) Driving R_L.

Fig. 1-9. Open-collector, 2-input NAND gate.

lamp or R_L (Fig. 1-9C) can be driven by a separate voltage source greater than the normal 5-volts source, as long as the current rating and breakdown voltage of transistor Q3 is not exceeded. In certain IC circuits designed to drive cold-cathode glow tubes, transistors having a high breakdown voltage are provided.

The wired-OR circuit is shown in Fig. 1-10. As long as all three output transistors are off (high Z), the common tie point has a high impedance to ground. If any one of the three transistors is saturated, the point is brought close to ground.

The wired-OR circuit can also be interpreted as a wired-AND. Output impedance will be high only if A is high, AND B is high, AND C is high. Otherwise, the output impedance is low.

When the voltage present at the common tie point is used as an input to a gate, a so-called "pull-up" resistor may be necessary (as shown in Fig. 1-11). When all the transistors are cut off, the pull-up resistor provides a source of positive voltage to the load. The size of the pull-up resistor is determined by how much current the circuit has to supply, both when on and when off.

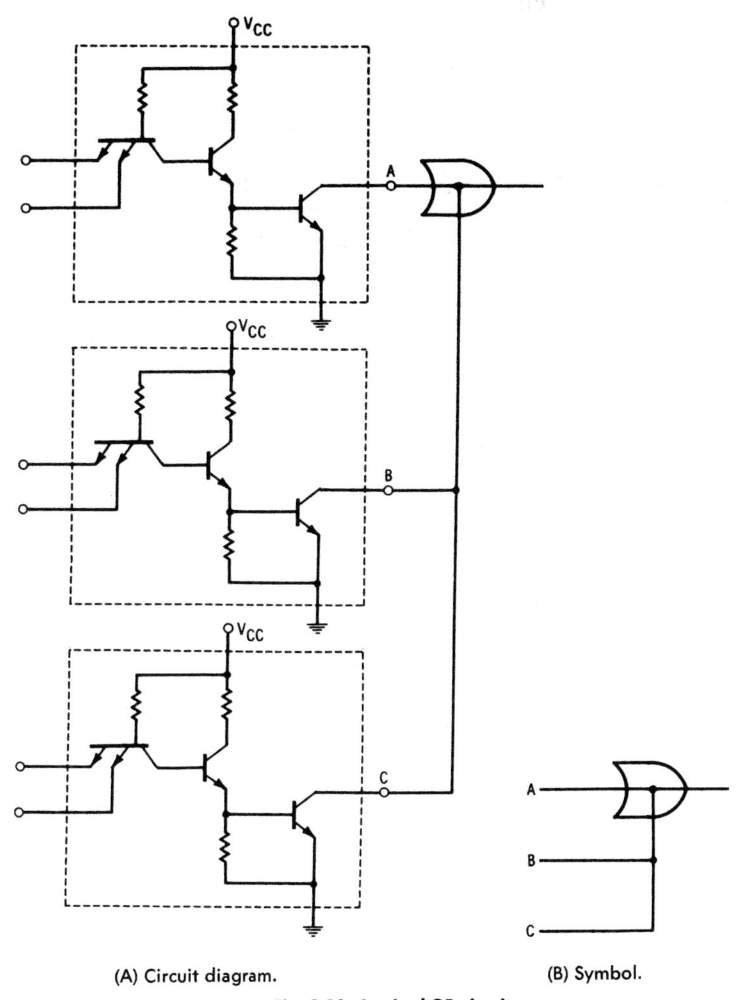

(A) Circuit diagram.

(B) Symbol.

Fig. 1-10. A wired-OR circuit.

EXPANDABLE GATES

In logic circuits, many inputs of the AND-OR type often need to be handled. To meet these needs, integrated circuits having many inputs have been developed. Further, some of these ICs bring certain tie points outside the IC package to allow the logic to be expanded and thus handle more complex jobs. This operation can best be understood by an example.

A typical expandable gate, circuit type 5450/7450, is shown in Fig. 1-12. The device is called an "Expandable Dual 2-Wide,

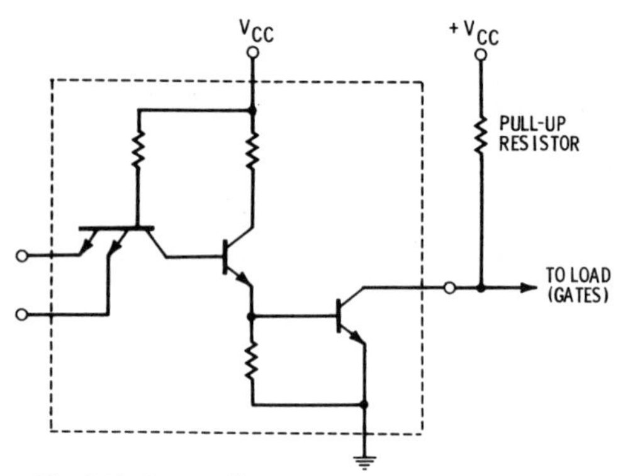

Fig. 1-11. Open-collector gate with pull-up resistor.

2-Input AND-OR-INVERT gate." We have already discussed the AND-OR-INVERT part of the description. The "2-Input" means that each AND gate has two inputs. (Some gates have 3-inputs, some 4, some 8, etc.) The "2-Wide" means that each part of the OR gate is fed by an AND gate. (Thus, two AND gates feed one OR gate). The function of the device is much clearer when shown by logic symbols as in Fig. 1-13. The "Dual" means that the IC contains two complete circuits. The word "Dual" is being used somewhat loosely by the manufacturers as the type 5450/7450 IC package does contain two separate 2-wide 2-input AND-OR-INVERT gate circuits, but only one of the gates is expandable. The other is a plain gate.

The only word left in the description is "Expandable," and this turns out to be straightforward. In the development of

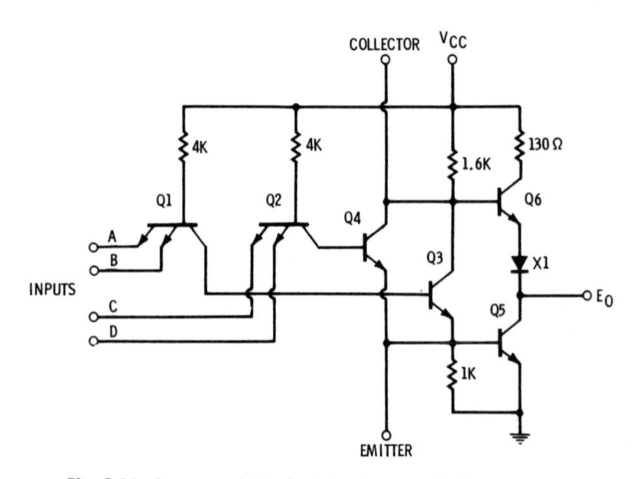

Fig. 1-12. An expandable 2-wide 2-input AND-OR-Invert gate.

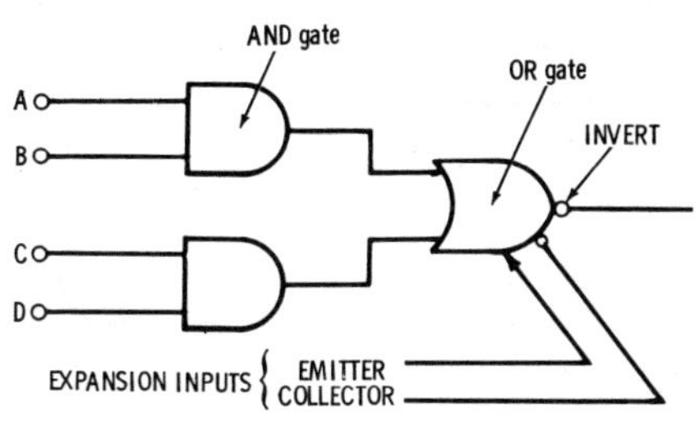

Fig. 1-13. Block diagram for an expandable gate.

the NOR-gate function, we saw how transistors Q3 and Q4 were utilized to form an ORing function. In Fig. 1-12, we see that the common points (the collectors and emitters) of ORing transistors Q3 and Q4 have been brought outside the IC to allow external connections.

The circuit shown in Fig. 1-14A is for a type 54/7460 Dual 4-Input Expander. The logic diagram for the expander is shown in Fig. 1-14B. All you have to do is connect input transistor Q1 to a +5-volts supply voltage and then connect the ORing transistor outputs to the equivalent points of a type 5450 or 7450 expandable gate. Thus, you have expanded the logic function to perform as indicated in Fig. 1-15. That is, you now have 3 AND gates (two with 2 inputs and one with 4 inputs) feeding an OR gate; the OR-gate output is then inverted.

What if you wanted to hang two expanders onto the expandable section of a type 5450 or 7450 circuit? Could you do it? A close look at the basic circuits shows that the input circuits are not affected and neither are the output transistors. Furthermore, if one of the ORing transistors is saturated, then the effect of turning on another ORing transistor will be negligible. But connecting expanders adds capacitance to the circuit (at point A in Fig. 1-12), which slows things down. Ex-

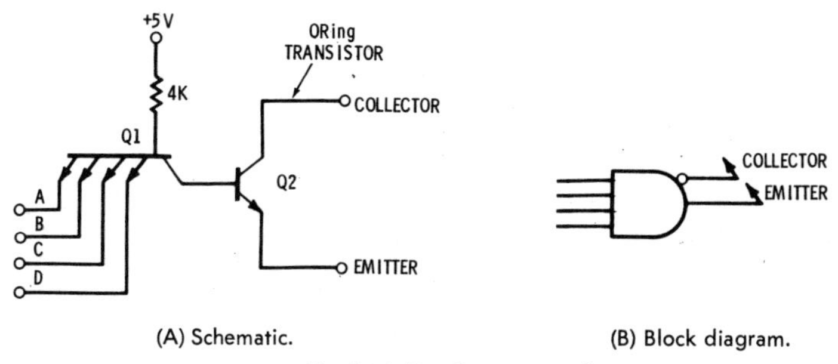

(A) Schematic. (B) Block diagram.

Fig. 1-14. Four-input expander.

pansion is thus usually limited to 4 or 5 expanders. (A total of four expander gates may be connected to the expander inputs of a type 5450 or 7450 gate.)

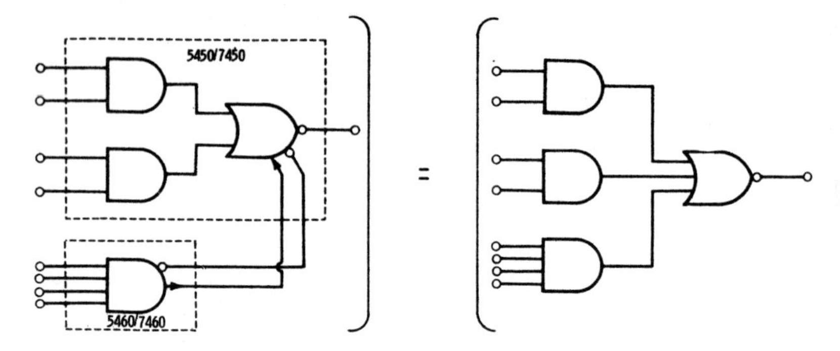

Fig. 1-15. Diagram for expandable gate with expander.

LOADING RULES

Most digital circuits talk to other digital circuits. Only rarely must a gate talk to the outside world, such as operating an indicator light or working into an interface circuit of some kind. Because so much digital conversation is gate to gate, the input and output circuits have been matched as far as possible to make things simple and easy.

The circuit shown in Fig. 1-16 illustrates the loading situation. Gate 1 is high and delivering current, and Gate B is low and is sinking current. Gate 3 has 3 inputs, one of which is permanently connected to a source of +3.5 volts. Input B can be manually connected to either +3.5 volts or to ground. Input C is driven by Gate 1. Since all three inputs of Gate 3 are high, the output of the gate will be low. The toggle switch option on input B allows this input to be driven low when desired, which will drive the gate high. This function is useful if registers, flip-flops, or memories are to be manually loaded.

The current flow into the emitters of Gate 3 is the reverse leakage current of the diode junctions. Since each emitter forms a diode, each draws leakage current, typically about 40 μA.

Input A of Gate 4 is permanently connected to +5 volts through a 1K resistor. This keeps input A high, yet protects it if the supply voltage should rise above its normal maximum level of 5.5 volts. Inputs B and C of Gate 4 are driven by Gate 1, and each draws about 40 μA. Gate 4 is satisfied and its output is low.

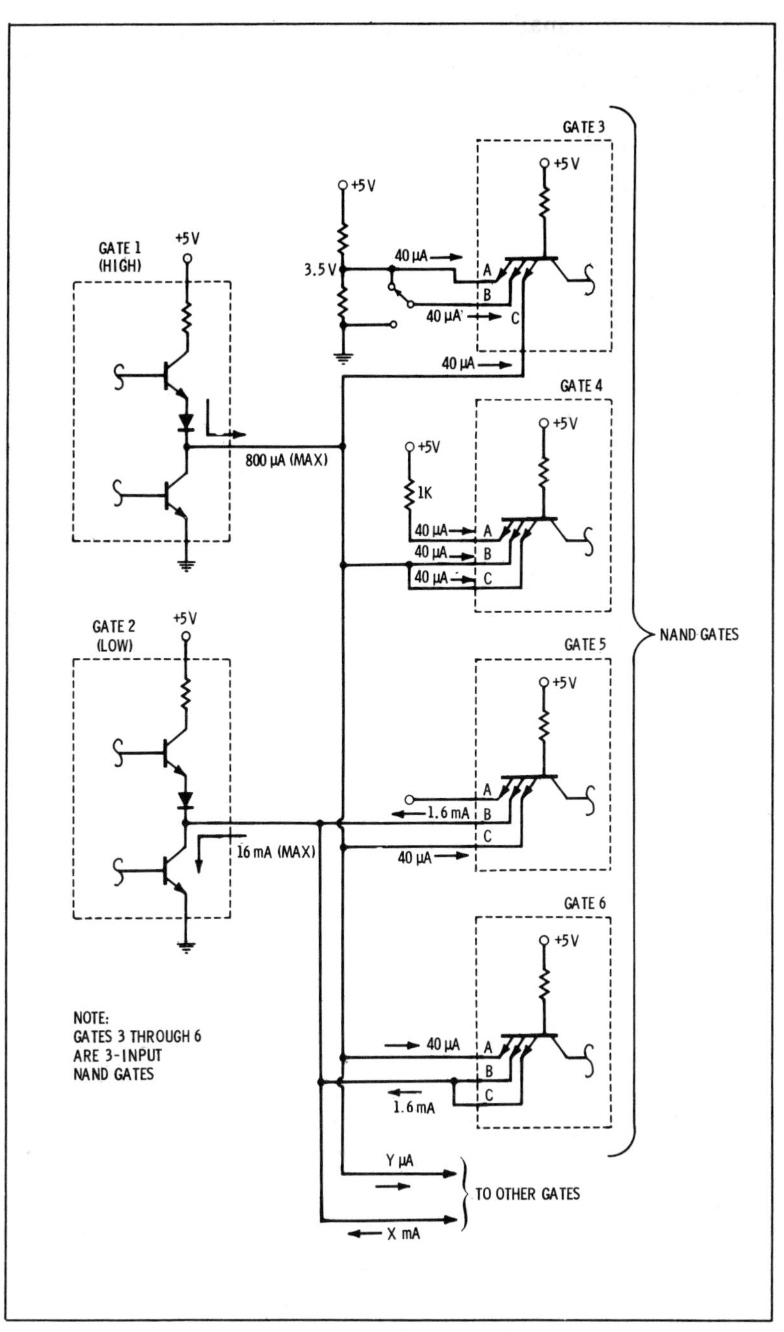

Fig. 1-16. Gate-to-gate loading conditions.

Input A of Gate 5 is open. As a result, no current flows in or out of the emitter, and the input acts as if it were permanently high. When an input is left open, it is subject to noise pickup. Further, the distributed capacitance of the open input slows down the operation of the gate. Thus, open inputs are undesirable. Input B is connected to ground through Gate 2. Approximately 1.6 mA will flow from Gate 5 to Gate 2; Gate 5 is driven high. The 40 μA into input C of Gate 5 is swallowed up by the 1.6 mA out of the same transistor. (The ratio: 1.6 mA/40 μA = 40.)

Gate 6 has 40 μA input into emitter A and 1.6 mA out of emitters B and C combined. (Once any emitter is driven low, the input transistor is driven into saturation and thus cannot supply significantly more current even when other emitters go low.) Thus if Gate 1 should also go low, the 1.6 mA out of Gate 6 would be split up, with ⅓ going to Gate 1 and ⅔ to Gate 2.

For ease in circuit design, the 40 μA into an emitter is defined as a *unit load* for a high gate (Gate 1), and the 1.6 mA out of an input transistor is defined as a *unit load* for a low gate (Gate 2).

The maximum current that can be sunk into a low gate without causing the output voltage to rise above the maximum limit of 0.4 volt is 16 mA. As a result, a low gate can drive 10 inputs; the fan-out is ten.

The maximum current that a high gate can deliver is 800 μA. Thus, the fan-out for a high gate is 800 μA/40 μA = 20 unit loads.

The allowable fan-out, therefore, is 10 when a gate is low and 20 when it is high. The lower fan-out must be observed as long as the gate is allowed to go both low and high. When a gate is going to be permanently high, the higher fan-out can be used.

NOISE IMMUNITY

All electronic circuits have trouble with noise and, although digital circuits are far more resistant to noise than analog circuits, they are not immune. If a large motor starts up near the digital circuit, or a bulldozer is driven through a buried cable connected to the circuitry just as a flip-flop is about to flop, it is possible that the flip-flop will not flop but will stay in the flip state. The resulting error may or may not be serious. If the digital information is being stored in a computer memory, the error may never be found.

Digital designers tend to get edgy if errors occur more than about once in 10 million bits of data. System designers do not like flip-flops that flop when they shouldn't or don't flop when they should. Gates that open when they should close, or vice versa, irritate them. Not much can be done to stop roving, errant bulldozers, but errors from other sources tend to be more manageable. Error prevention is based primarily on the naturally high noise immunity of digital circuits.

The input/output characteristics of the basic TTL gate, shown in Fig. 1-17, indicates how noise immunity is achieved. Let input A of the NAND gate be high, and let input B be driven by voltage E_{in}. Output voltage is then controlled by E_{in}. When E_{in} is 0, E_O will be high and will normally be somewhere between +2.4 and +3.9 volts (Region I of Fig. 1-18). The actual value of E_O is determined by a number of variables. If the gate is operating in a high ambient temperature, then E_O will be on the high side. If the ambient temperature is down around −55° C, E_O will be low.

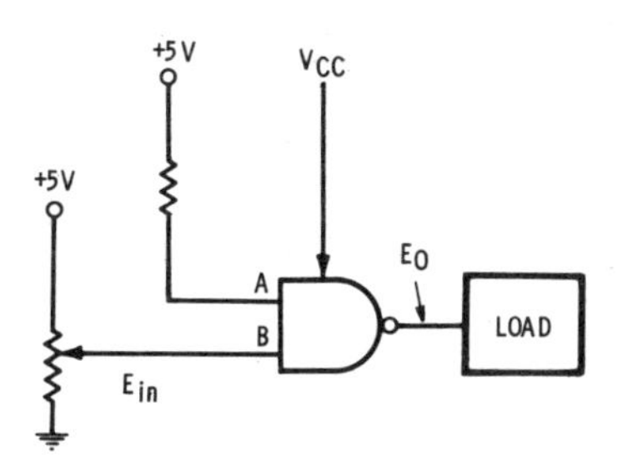

Fig. 1-17. Input/output characteristics of TTL gate.

Another factor affecting E_O is the load, which means the fan-out on the gate. The voltage of the power supply feeding the gate obviously affects E_O. Military versions of TTL allow V_{CC} to be anywhere between 4.5 and 5.5 volts. Commercial versions normally require V_{CC} to be between 4.75 and 5.25 volts. When E_O is in the high state, it tracks V_{CC} fairly closely. When E_O is in the low state, it is not affected much by V_{CC}.

Still another variable is the individual gate itself. Although quality control in the manufacture of ICs is extremely high, differences in materials, mask alignments, dopant purity, furnace temperatures, processing time, etc., cause minute changes from one circuit to the next. One result is minor changes in E_O.

What happens to the output voltage, E_O, as the input voltage, E_{in}, is slowly increased from 0 to maximum? Assuming that E_O is tracking along the *low limit line* in Fig. 1-18, it will be 2.4 volts at $E_{in} = 0$. Then E_O will start to decrease when E_{in}

changes to 0.75 volt. As E_{in} increases from about 0.80 to 1.1 volts, E_O falls rapidly to about 0.2 volt, the saturation voltage of the output transistor. Now, start again with E_{in} at 0 volt and assume E_O tracks along the *high limit line.* Output voltage E_O is more sensitive to the input voltage (E_{in}), but it does not drop below 2.4 volts until E_{in} is about 1.0 volt. When E_{in} reaches 1.4 volts, E_O is minimum and will be less than 0.4 volt.

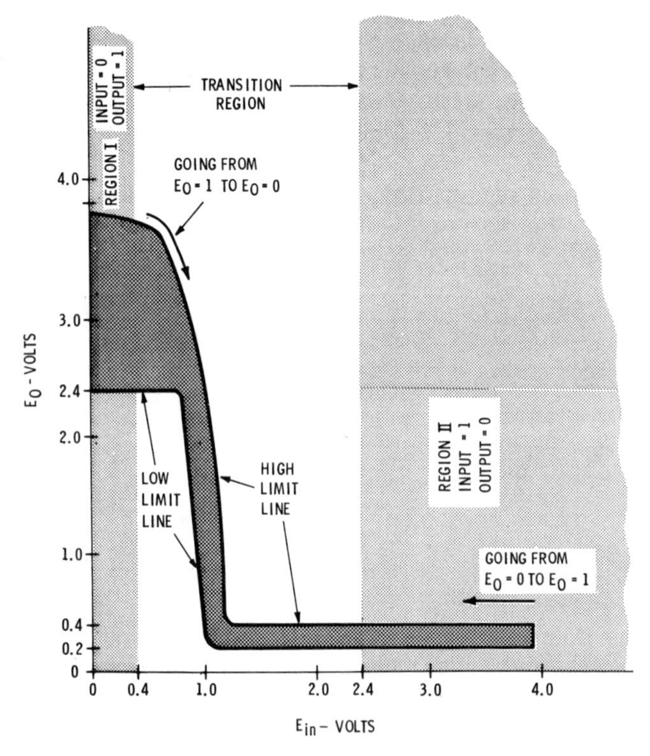

Fig. 1-18. Noise margin.

When a gate is low, its maximum output is 0.4 volt. This is 0.7 volt below the minimum of 1.1 volts needed to cause the next gate to act as if it sees a high. This 0.7 volt is the noise margin. It protects the driven gate from seeing a false 1 (generated by noise spikes on the signal line).

Similar considerations apply when we want to drive a gate high. In this case, the input voltage E_{in} starts out in Region II (Fig. 1-18) and tracks along either the high or the low limit line. In one example, E_O begins to go high when E_{in} falls to 1.3 volts, and in the other example, when E_{in} falls to about 1.1

volts. In either case, E_O is always above 2.4 volts whenever E_{in} is below 0.75 volt. Since the maximum output from a low driving gate is 0.4 volt, the "worst case" noise margin protecting a driven gate from seeing a false 0 (generated by noise) is $0.75 - 0.4 = 0.35$ volt.

In most systems, the noise margins will be better than the values just noted. For operation at typical ambient temperatures around 20° C (68° F), the noise margin for TTL systems is generally stated by manufacturers to be about 1.2 volts.

So far we have considered noise as occurring only on the input or signal line. Noise can also occur on both the power-supply line and the ground wires. Any spikes or transients, up to about 3 volts, occurring on the power supply line will usually not cause false gate operation; neither will any spikes of about 1 volt occurring on the ground line. Further, the spike must last for a period of about 50 nanoseconds before it causes any trouble. (Spikes occurring on the signal line only have to last for a period of about 20 nanoseconds before they start causing errors.)

As noted earlier, TTL is a fast logic, and the gates will change from Region I to Region II (Fig. 1-18) in about 10 ns. When you try to turn gates on and off in that short a time, you are dealing with outputs that are changing at the rate of 1.6 million amps per second (1.6 mA/10 ns) and 2.5 billion volts per second (2.5 V/10 ns). All the noise protection you can possibly get is needed. One of the secrets to obtaining a noise-free TTL system is to have as much bypass capacitance in the V_{CC} line as possible. Also, use a decent size wire in the V_{CC} line—size No. 20 wire or larger is recommended.

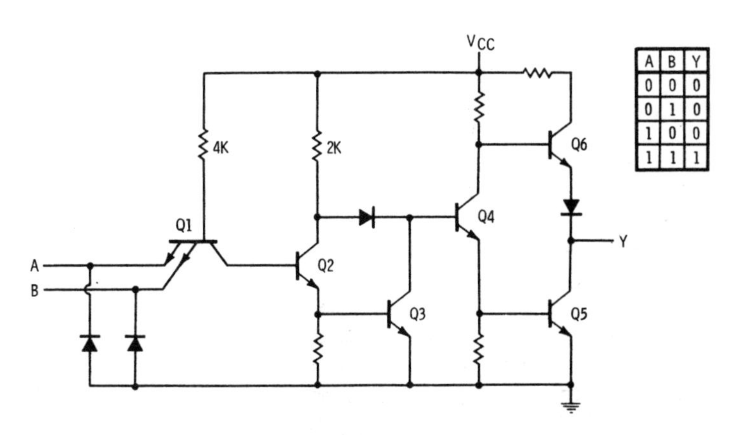

A	B	Y
0	0	0
0	1	0
1	0	0
1	1	1

Fig. 1-19. AND gate.

AND GATES

Often it is desirable to be able to perform the AND function rather than NAND. Type 7408 is a quad, 2-input AND gate and is essentially a NAND with an extra inverter stage built in.

When both inputs (Fig. 1-19) are high, the collector of Q1 is high, Q2 is on, Q3 is on, Q4 is off, Q6 is on and the output Y is high. If either A or B is low, Q2 is off, Q3 is off, Q4 is on, Q5 is on, and Q6 is off; thus, the output is low. AND logic has been performed as shown by the truth table.

Three- and four-input AND gates are also available. Not all manufacturers use exactly the same circuit, but the result is the same.

CHAPTER 2

Flip-Flops

Flip-flops form a class of basic circuits vital in all forms of digital logic. Flip-flops can store digital data, remember information, and they can count. A number of basic types have been developed and they are used in a great variety of ways.

A flip-flop can be formed from just two cross-coupled transistors (method used in memory circuits where simplicity is desired), but most TTL flip-flops are made from NAND or NOR gates. Fig. 2-1 shows two NAND gates connected to operate as a single flip-flop. (V_{CC} and ground connections are not shown on logic diagrams. However, when a circuit is constructed, all the power supplies, grounds, floating inputs, circuit loads, etc., must be considered.)

SET-RESET FLIP-FLOPS

The flip-flop in Fig. 2-1 has two inputs (A and B) and one output (Q). Each input can be a 1 or a 0, and Q can be either 1 or 0. Four combinations of inputs are possible, excluding inputs left open which is the equivalent of being high or 1: (1) $A = 0$, $B = 0$; (2) $A = 0$, $B = 1$; (3) $A = 1$, $B = 0$; and $A = 1$, $B = 1$. What will the output (Q) be for each set of inputs?

First, consider $A = 1$ and $B = 0$, as shown in Fig. 2-2A. From the truth table (Fig. 2-1C) that for a 2-input NAND gate, if either input is 0, the output of the gate must be 1. On the other hand, if only one input to a NAND gate is known and it

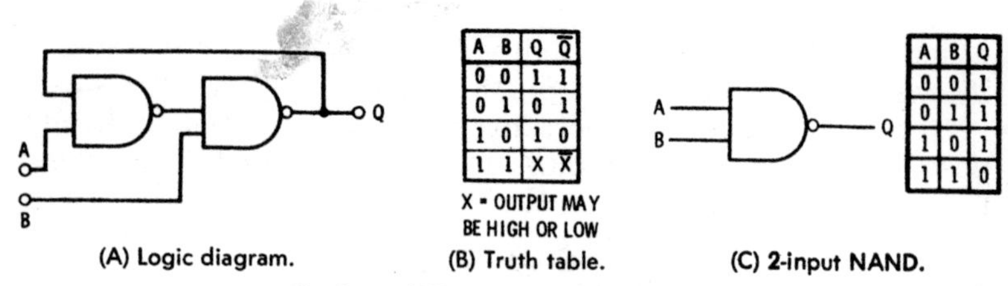

A	B	Q	$\overline{Q}$
0	0	1	1
0	1	0	1
1	0	1	0
1	1	X	$\overline{X}$

A	B	Q
0	0	1
0	1	1
1	0	1
1	1	0

(A) Logic diagram. (B) Truth table. (C) 2-input NAND.

Fig. 2-1. A NAND-gate Set-Reset flip-flop.

is a 1, then the output of the gate is not known. The output can be 0 or 1, depending on the other input.

We see that with inputs as shown in Fig. 2-2A, Gate 2 is driven to an output of Q = 1, because input B is 0. This in turn causes Gate 1 to have a 1 for both inputs, and thus to have an output of 0, as required by the truth table for NAND gates. (Gate 1 output of 0 is the second input for Gate 2. Two low inputs to NAND Gate 2 make Q = 1).

Suppose the inputs are suddenly changed so that A = 0 and B = 1, as shown in Fig. 2-2B; what happens? Gate 1, with at least one of its inputs 0, must have a 1 out. This means both inputs of Gate 2 are a 1, and its output is 0. If we call the state of the gates in Fig. 2-2A the *flip* state, then Fig. 2-2B is the *flop* state.

Two other sets of inputs are possible. A = B = 0 and A = B = 1. Fig. 2-2C shows the state of the circuit when A = B = 0. Both gates are driven to 1 and the output is a 1. In Figs. 2-2A and 2-2C, B = 0 and controls the output; in Fig. 2-2B, A alone is 0 and is in control. In Fig. 2-2D, A = B = 1 and neither is in control. Thus, the output of the circuit in Fig. 2-2D can be 0 or 1.

The circuit of Fig. 2-2D can be considered the quiescent state of the flip-flop. The flip-flop is set to one state or the

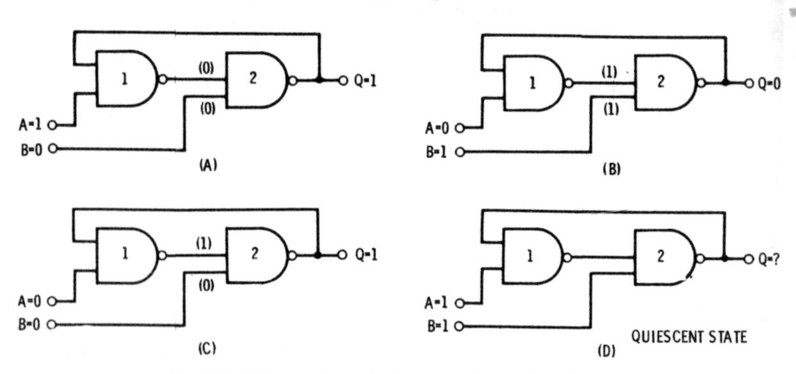

Fig. 2-2. Different input/output conditions for Fig. 2-1A.

other by setting one input to 0 while the other is high. If both inputs are then brought high, the flip-flop will remain as set.

One further state of operation needs to be considered. Suppose all power to the circuit has been off and is suddenly turned on. What state does the flip-flop take when the circuit stabilizes? Only the condition shown by Fig. 2-2D is uncertain and, in this case, the output can be either 1 or 0.

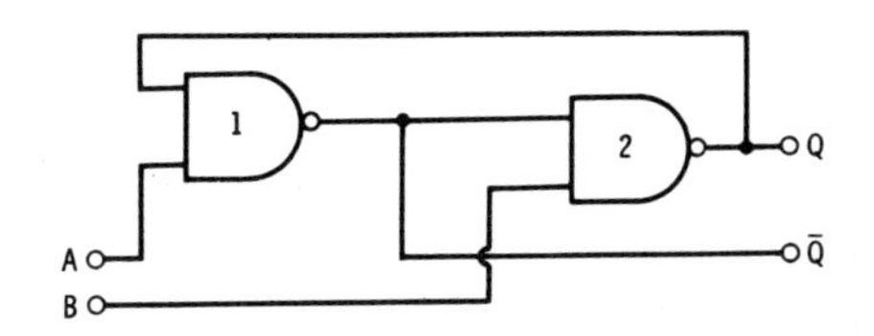

Fig. 2-3. Negative output—$\bar{Q}$.

From the above considerations, the truth table of Fig. 2-1B is constructed. Note that the truth table contains a heading for $\bar{Q}$, and that $\bar{Q}$ is the negative of Q. (A negative of the output Q always exists in a flip-flop, as shown in Fig. 2-3. The $\bar{Q}$ output, however, is not always accessible for use.) The unknown "X" in the truth table indicates that the status of the output is not predictable. The symbol $\bar{X}$ is used to show that $\bar{Q}$ will be the opposite of the output Q.

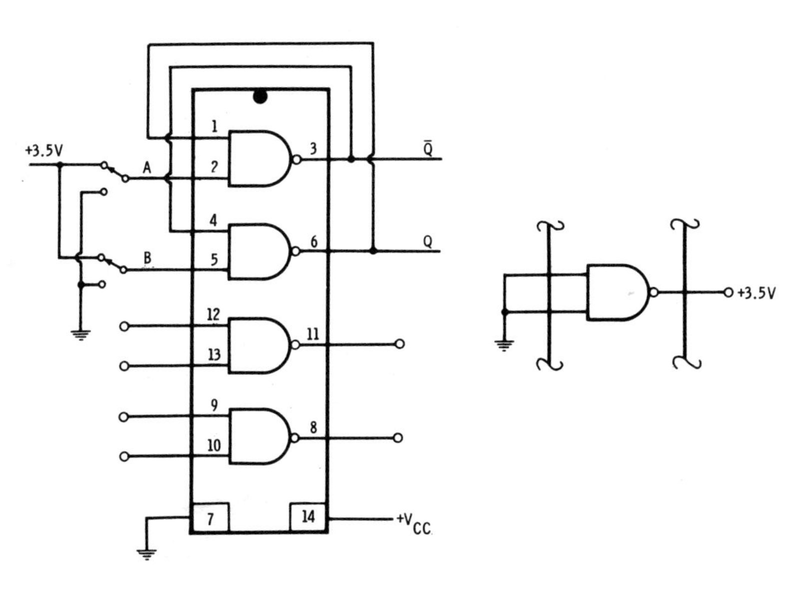

(A) Circuit using a type 7400 IC.

(B) Input signal source using extra gate.

Fig. 2-4. Constructing a Set-Reset flip-flop.

The above flip-flop is known as a Set-Reset type since it can be set to one condition and reset to the other at any time, in accordance with the truth table. A Set-Reset flip-flop can be constructed using one type 7400 IC, as shown in Fig. 2-4. Since the 7400 device contains four NAND gates, you can actually build two complete and independent flip-flops. The simplicity of connecting such building blocks together is one of the major advantages of digital circuits.

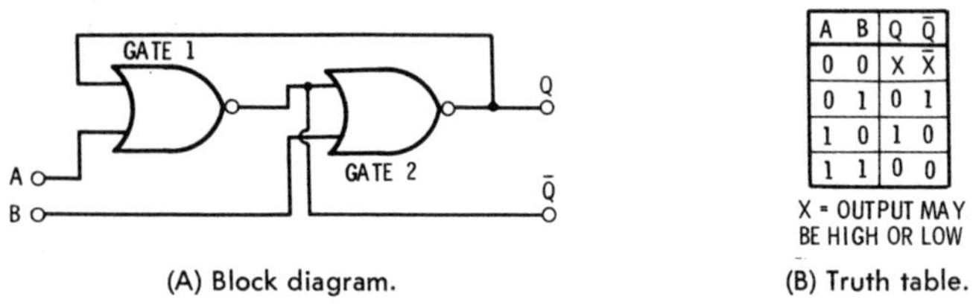

(A) Block diagram.

A	B	Q	$\bar{Q}$
0	0	X	$\bar{X}$
0	1	0	1
1	0	1	0
1	1	0	0

X = OUTPUT MAY BE HIGH OR LOW

(B) Truth table.

Fig. 2-5. A NOR-gate flip-flop.

The circuit shown in Fig. 2-4A includes both Q and $\bar{Q}$ outputs. It uses toggle switches to set the inputs to 1 or 0. A convenient source of input signal is to use one of the unused NAND gates, connected as shown in Fig. 2-4B.

NOR-GATE FLIP-FLOPS

Flip-flops can also be built with NOR gates, as shown in Fig. 2-5. Although the circuit is very similar to the NAND gate flip-flop of Fig. 2-1, it does have a few subtle differences. The truth table for a NOR gate shows that a 1 input is controlling and always drives the gate to 0. From this reasoning, the states indicated in Fig. 2-6 are obtained.

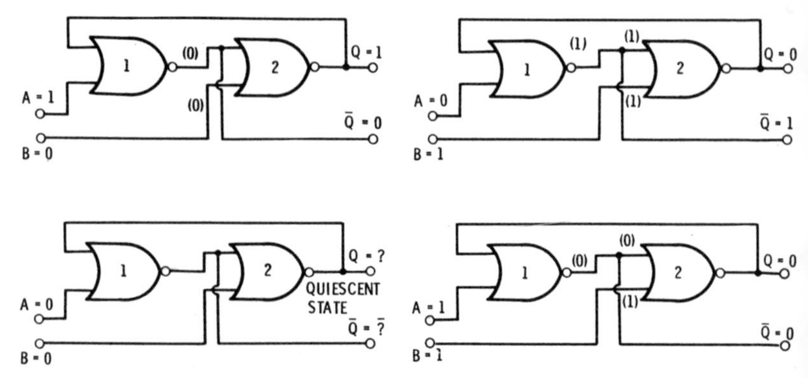

Fig. 2-6. Different input/output conditions for Fig. 2-5A.

In the NOR-gate flip-flop, the input conditions of A = B = 1 give Q = $\bar{Q}$ = 0. The NAND-gate inputs of A = B = 0 gave Q = $\bar{Q}$ = 1. An uncertain output is obtained with a NOR-gate flip-flop when A = B = 0, and in a NAND-gate flip-flop when A = B = 1. In building logic circuits, the designer does not want to be required to declare that a particular flip-flop must be a NAND-gate type, while an identical nearby flip-flop is to be a NOR-gate type. Two of the four possible sets of inputs for both NAND- and NOR-gate flip-flops do give unambiguous results, however. As long as the logic designer ensures that only these two sets of inputs are applied to the inputs, he can use NAND-gate and NOR-gate flip-flops interchangeably. (The two sets of inputs that give unambiguous results with both types are A = 1 with B = 0, and A = 0 with B = 1.)

The labeling of the inputs and the Q and $\bar{Q}$ outputs is entirely arbitrary. Therefore, instead of calling the inputs A and B, we can call one the *Set* input (S) and the other the *Reset* input (R). This leads to the Set-Reset flip-flop symbol shown in Fig. 2-7 and its truth table. The Q and $\bar{Q}$ outputs are labeled to agree with the truth table.

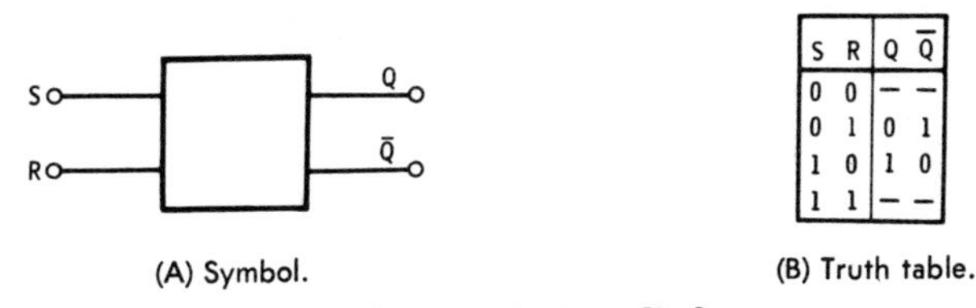

S	R	Q	$\bar{Q}$
0	0	—	—
0	1	0	1
1	0	1	0
1	1	—	—

(A) Symbol. (B) Truth table.

Fig. 2-7. A Set-Reset flip-flop.

A NOR-gate flip-flop can be constructed with a circuit type 7402, as shown in Fig. 2-8A. As with the quadruple NAND device, one of the unused gates can serve as a source of 3.5 volts, a 1 (Fig. 2-8B).

CLOCKED FLIP-FLOPS

While the Set-Reset flip-flop has many uses, it has one characteristic that is a disadvantage in many logic schemes. Whenever the inputs to a Set-Reset flip-flop change, the output changes immediately. It is delayed only by the charge storage characteristics of the semiconductor devices used to make the gates. The delay is only a few nanoseconds and is unpredictable so far as a specific device is concerned.

Assume that the inputs to the flip-flop are measurements being made by the navigation system of an aircraft, and the output of the flip-flop will aid in the control of the autopilot. If the input data changes rapidly, operation of the controls might be erratic, leading to excessive wear of parts and unreliable control. To prevent wild changes in operation, digital systems usually work on a controlled stop-and-go basis. The system is paced by a clock, which is actually an oscillator.

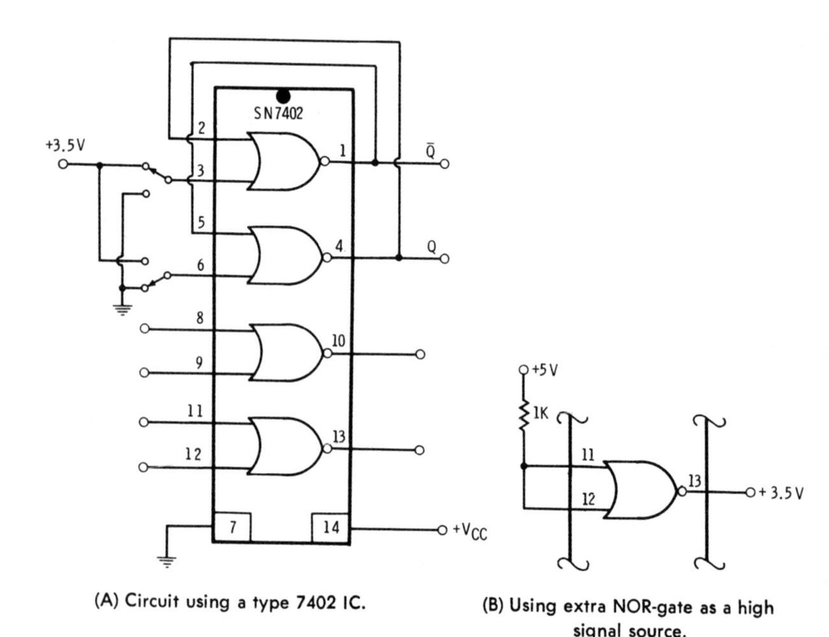

(A) Circuit using a type 7402 IC.

(B) Using extra NOR-gate as a high signal source.

Fig. 2-8. Constructing a NOR-gate flip-flop.

The clock usually acts as a pacing signal, allowing the system to rest most of the time. Then, when all the various subsystems have settled down to a stable condition, it scans all the inputs and outputs to see if something should be changed. In a digital computer, on the other hand, the clock moves the program to the next instruction once the circuits have settled. In a computer, the tendency is to operate at as high a clock rate as possible, so that longer and more complex programs can be handled with as little electronics as possible. In a control system, the clock need only be fast enough to stay ahead of the process or machine being controlled.

The clock signal in a digital system is a square wave of voltage having the same magnitude as the logic signals. The signal must meet certain requirements on rise time, fall time, and duration of being high and low. Many digital circuits are activated when the clock goes high—that is, goes to 1. Some circuits are activated when the clock goes to 0.

Fig. 2-9 shows how an S-R flip-flop can operate in a clocked system. The circuit shows a NAND-gate S-R flip-flop consisting of Gates 1 and 2. Inputs to the flip-flop are A1 and B1. Input A1 is the output of Gate 3, which is a function of input A and the clock pulse CP. When A is 1 and the clock is 1, then A1 is low. Similar action controls input B and Gate 4 output, B1. When the clock is low, both A1 and B1 will be high.

The truth table shows how the flip-flop is controlled. As long as the clock pulse signal is 0, A1 and B1 will both be 1 and the flip-flop will not change state. However, as soon as CP goes high, input signals A and B control the flip-flop. Thus, if $A = 1$ and $B = 0$: A1 is 0, B1 is 1, Q goes to 0, and $\overline{Q}$ goes to 1. If $A = 0$ and $B = 1$, Q goes to 1.

The circuit of Fig. 2-10 shows a NOR-gate flip-flop with AND-gate control. The truth tables in Figs. 2-9 and 2-10 are similar, except that the outputs are different for $A = B = 1$ when CP is 1. We see also that in the NAND-gate circuit, when

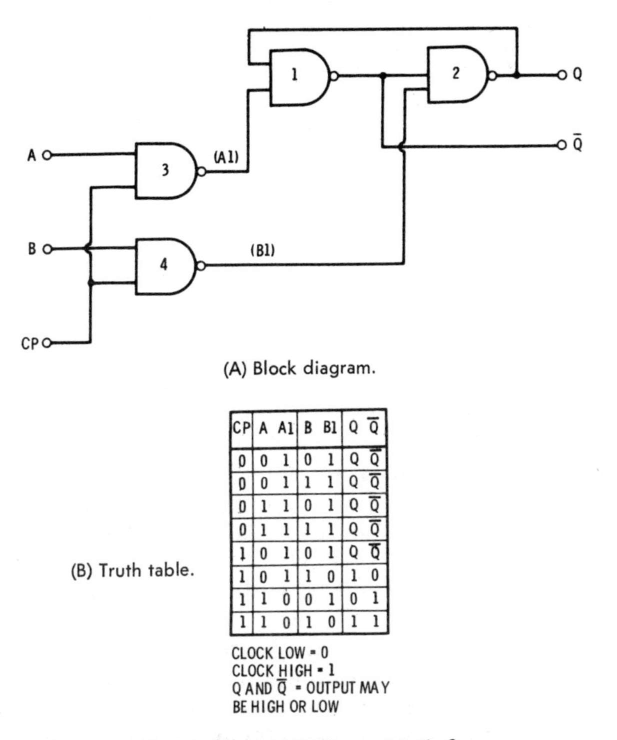

(A) Block diagram.

(B) Truth table.

CP	A	A1	B	B1	Q	$\overline{Q}$
0	0	1	0	1	Q	$\overline{Q}$
0	0	1	1	1	Q	$\overline{Q}$
0	1	1	0	1	Q	$\overline{Q}$
0	1	1	1	1	Q	$\overline{Q}$
1	0	1	0	1	Q	$\overline{Q}$
1	0	1	1	0	1	0
1	1	0	0	1	0	1
1	1	0	1	0	1	1

CLOCK LOW = 0
CLOCK HIGH = 1
Q AND $\overline{Q}$ = OUTPUT MAY BE HIGH OR LOW

Fig. 2-9. Clocked NAND-gate S-R flip-flop.

A = 0 and B = 1, Q goes to 1; while in the NOR-gate circuit, the same inputs give Q = 0.

A NAND-gate flip-flop controlled by AND gates is shown in Fig. 2-11. Whenever CP goes to 0, A1 and B1 go to 0, and Q and $\bar{Q}$ go to a 1. The circuit does not function correctly. Fig. 2-12 shows a NOR-gate flip-flop with NAND-gate control; this circuit does not work correctly either, since Q and $\bar{Q}$ go to 0 when CP goes to 0.

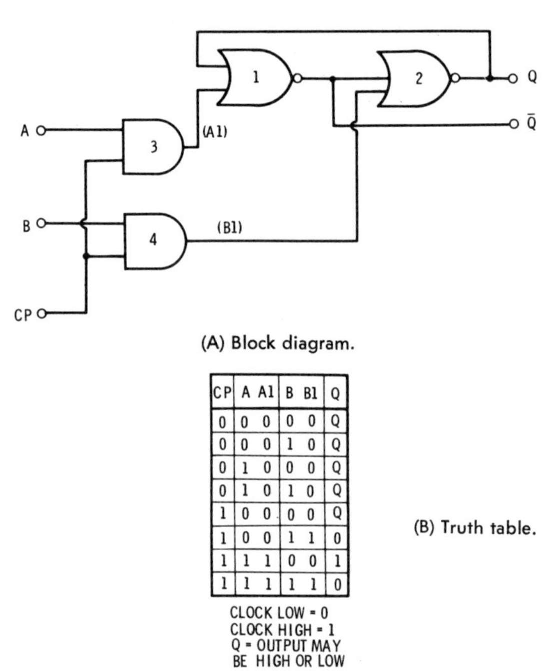

(A) Block diagram.

CP	A	A1	B	B1	Q
0	0	0	0	0	Q
0	0	0	1	0	Q
0	1	0	0	0	Q
0	1	0	1	0	Q
1	0	0	0	0	Q
1	0	0	1	1	0
1	1	1	0	0	1
1	1	1	1	1	0

CLOCK LOW = 0
CLOCK HIGH = 1
Q = OUTPUT MAY
BE HIGH OR LOW

(B) Truth table.

Fig. 2-10. Clocked NOR-gate S-R flip-flop.

Fig. 2-13 shows the equivalent logic circuit of Fig. 2-10. The truth table has been reduced to show only the inputs that are significant. The output column is labeled Q_n. This refers to the state that the clock pulse and the inputs have caused the flip-flop to enter. Excluded inputs are A = B = 0 and A = B = 1. As long as the CP = 0, the inputs will have no effect on the flip-flop. When CP goes high, the flip-flop will take up the state called for.

If A and B should change while CP is high, the flip-flop will follow accordingly. Thus, the inputs are usually required to be stable while the clock is high and data is being entered into the flip-flop. Stability requirements are not difficult to meet

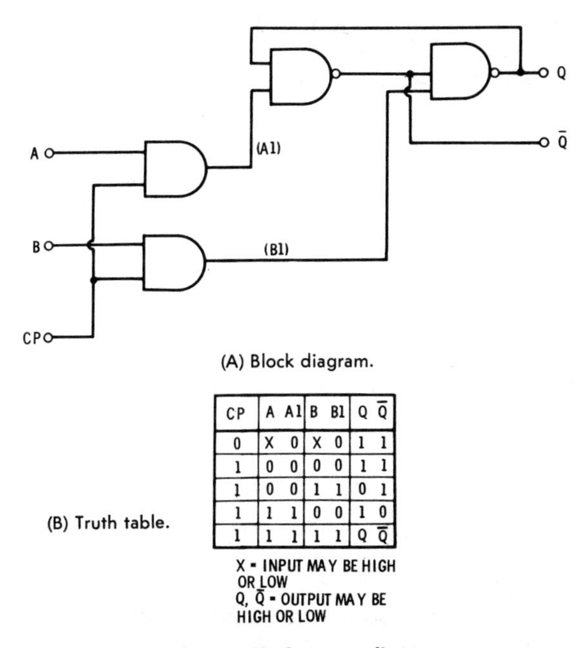

(A) Block diagram.

(B) Truth table.

CP	A	A1	B	B1	Q	$\bar{Q}$
0	X	0	X	0	1	1
1	0	0	0	0	1	1
1	0	0	1	1	0	1
1	1	1	0	0	1	0
1	1	1	1	1	Q	$\bar{Q}$

X = INPUT MAY BE HIGH OR LOW
Q, $\bar{Q}$ = OUTPUT MAY BE HIGH OR LOW

Fig. 2-11. NAND-gate flip-flop controlled by AND gate.

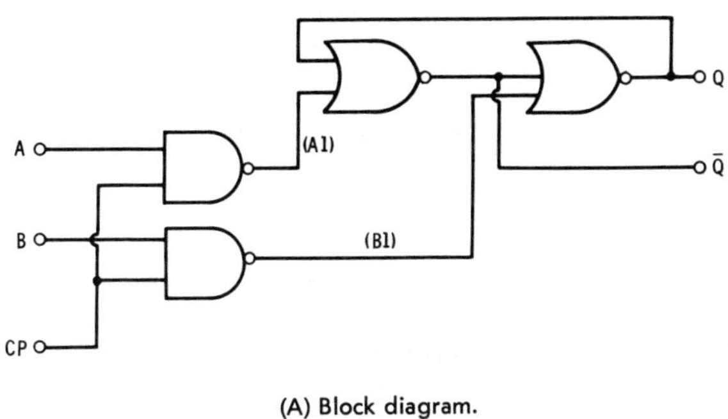

(A) Block diagram.

(B) Truth table.

CP	A	A1	B	B1	Q	$\bar{Q}$
0	X	1	X	1	0	0
1	0	1	0	1	0	0
1	0	1	1	0	1	0
1	1	0	0	1	0	1
1	1	0	1	0	1	1

X = INPUT MAY BE HIGH OR LOW

Fig. 2-12. NOR-gate flip-flop controlled by NAND gate

but must not be ignored. When CP goes low, the flip-flop goes to its quiescent state.

A clocked flip-flop can be easily constructed using a 7400 and a 7402.

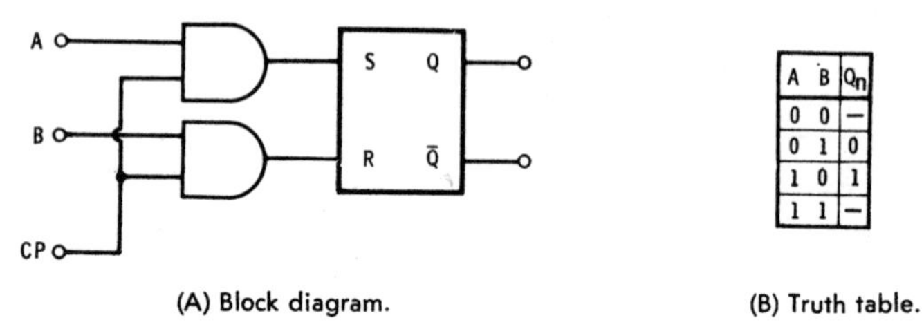

(A) Block diagram.

A	B	Q_n
0	0	—
0	1	0
1	0	1
1	1	—

(B) Truth table.

Fig. 2-13. A clocked S-R flip-flop.

TTL FLIP-FLOPS

In working with digital logic, circuit designers found that certain types of flip-flops were particularly useful. As a result, semiconductor manufacturers started making ICs containing these flip-flops; sometimes one flip-flop to an IC package, sometimes two.

The general-purpose flip-flops available in the type 54/74 family are the D type, the J-K type, and the J-K Master-Slave type. Simpler Set-Reset and clocked Set-Reset flip-flops are used internally in other ICs, such as shift registers and counters, and have recently become available in ICs. Other TTL families do have other types of flip-flops.

D-Type Flip-Flop

The D-type flip-flop is a clocked flip-flop with a very simple truth table. The device has only one input, which is labeled D for Data and which may be either 1 or 0. When the clock pulse occurs, the output of the flip-flop goes to the same state as the D input.

Fig. 2-14 shows the logic diagram of a D-type flip-flop. Two flip-flops are included in the circuit type 5474 or 7474 package. It is called a "Dual D-Type Edge-Triggered Flip-Flop." The circuit has four input terminals: Preset, Clear, Clock, and D. The outputs are Q and $\overline{Q}$. As usual, ground and power connections are not shown on the logic diagram. The flip-flop is shown in the functional block diagram form in Fig. 2-14A and is shown in simplified block form in Fig. 2-14B. Operation of the circuit will be examined using the analysis table in Fig. 2-15.

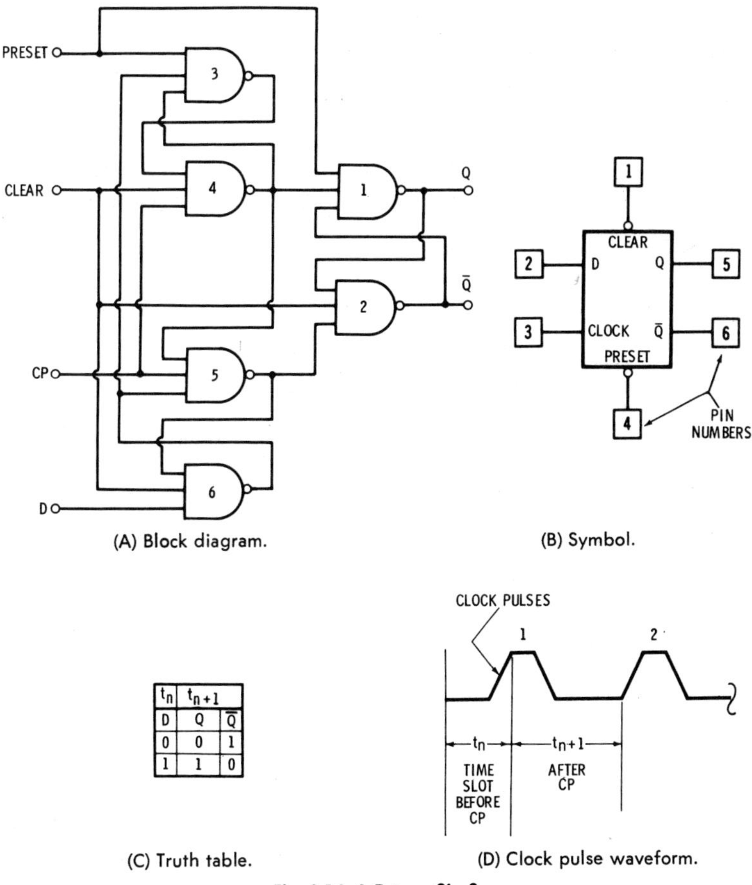

(A) Block diagram.

(B) Symbol.

(C) Truth table.

(D) Clock pulse waveform.

Fig. 2-14. A D-type flip-flop.

The catalog description of the D-type flip-flop states that a low input to the Preset (P) terminal sets output Q to a logical 1, and a low input to Clear (C) terminal sets Q to a logical 0. (The gates have been labeled 1 through 6 to aid the discussion.)

Fig. 2-15. Analysis table for Fig. 2-14.

LINE	INPUTS				INTERNAL GATES						OUTPUTS	
	CP	D	C	P	1	2	3	4	5	6	Q	$\overline{Q}$
1	0	0	1	1			0	1	1	1	Q	$\overline{Q}$
2	0	0	1	0	1	0	1	1	1	1	1	0
3	0	0	0	1	0	1	0	1	1	1	0	1
4	1	0	1	1	0	1	0	1	0	1	0	1
5	0	1	1	1	Q	$\overline{Q}$	1	1	1	0	Q	$\overline{Q}$
6	1	1	1	1	1	0	1	0	1	0	1	0
7	1	1	1	0	1	0	1	0	1	0	1	0

Since the inputs must control the final state of the circuit, we can check circuit operation by varying the inputs one at a time. We are interested in the final condition of Gates 1 and 2, since these provide the outputs Q and $\bar{Q}$.

Try to follow both the logic diagram in Fig. 2-14 and the analysis table in Fig. 2-15. We see that when CP = 0, the outputs of Gates 4 and 5 go to a logical 1, and D = 0 causes Gate 6 to go to a 1. Thus, Gate 3 has all its inputs as 1; its output is 0. Since Gate 4 is already 1, the fact that the output of Gate 3 is 0 does not change anything. We see that Gates 1 and 2 have not been affected by the other gates and, thus, their status is unknown. The outputs of Gates 1 and 2 are Q and $\bar{Q}$ and are stable; whichever output happens to become a 0 will drive the other output to a 1.

The second line of the analysis table shows what happens when the P input goes to 0, with other inputs unchanged. Gates 1 and 3 go to 1, so Q = 1. The Clock is 0 and holds Gate 4 and Gate 5 high, while D = 0 holds Gate 6 at a 1. The input to Gate 2 is a 1 from C, a 1 from Gate 5, and Q = 1; thus, the output of Gate 2 is 0. The flip-flop has been set to Q = 1, $\bar{Q}$ = 0.

Suppose the Clock or D (or both) should become 1 while P is low—will this affect the circuit? We note that as long as P = 0, Q must be 1. From line 7 of the analysis table, we see that Gate 5 will be 1 because Gate 4 or Gate 6 will be 0 if CP or D are high; therefore, Gate 2 is a 0. Thus, when P = 0, it overrides CP and D, regardless of whether they are 1 or 0.

The third line of the analysis table shows how the Clear input resets the circuit. With C = 0 and P = 1, Gate 4 is a 1 and Gate 2 is a 1; Gate 1 has all 1s as inputs and therefore is a 0. Again, the CP and D inputs cannot affect the outputs. If, however, both P and C were 0, the outputs would be driven to a 1 (Q = 1 and $\bar{Q}$ = 1). This is a forbidden or illogical state of affairs, and so this combination of inputs is forbidden.

In normal use, the flip-flop operates with P = C = 1, and data (D) is entered into the flip-flop as the clock goes high. Line 4 of the analysis table shows what occurs when CP = 1 and D = 0. We see that prior to CP = 1 (that is, line 1), Gate 4 was 1 and Gate 3 was 0. When CP goes to 1, Gate 5 has all 1 inputs (output from Gates 6 and 4 and CP), thus its output goes to 0; this is similar for Gate 3, which also goes to 0. Therefore, Gate 5 = 0 makes Gate 2 = $\bar{Q}$ = 1, while Gate 1 has all 1s as inputs (P, Gate 4 and $\bar{Q}$), so Gate 1 = Q = 0. Thus, the Clock has transferred the D = 0 input to the Q = 0 output. When the Clock falls back to zero, line 1 of the truth table applies, and the flip-flop is quiescent at Q = 0 and $\bar{Q}$ = 1.

When D = 1, the flip-flop goes to Q = 1 when CP = 1. Prior to the CP going to 1, but with D = 1, the circuit is as shown in line 5. Because CP = 0, Gates 4 and 5 are high; therefore, Gate 6 has all 1s as inputs and is 0; therefore, Gate 3 has all 1s as inputs and is 0. Gate 1 inputs are P = 1, Gate 4 = 1, and $\bar{Q}$; while Gate 2 inputs are C = 1, Gate 5 = 1 and Q. Thus, Gates 1 and 2 are quiescent.

When CP goes to 1 (line 6), Gate 4 goes to 0, which gives Gate 5 a 1 output. Gate 3 is a 1, Gate 1 is a 1, and Gates 6 and 2 have all 1 inputs and therefore go to 0. Thus Q = 1 and $\bar{Q}$ = 0. When CP falls back to 0, the circuit returns to line 1 or line 5.

Because of the way the circuit operates, it is called edge-triggered, and the data on D is transferred to the flip-flop on the positive-going edge of the clock pulse. Once the circuit has responded to CP, the D input is locked out and a change here has no effect until the next clock pulse.

The truth table for a D-type flip-flop is shown in Fig. 2-14C. Only one input, D, is listed and only one output is needed, although both Q and $\bar{Q}$ are shown. The symbol t_n refers to the time slot (Fig. 2-14D) before the clock pulse. The symbol t_{n+1} means the time slot after the clock pulse. The interpretation, therefore, is that if D = 0 before the clock pulse, Q will be 0 after the pulse; if D = 1 before, Q will be 1 afterwards.

The block symbol (Fig. 2-14B) for the complete flip-flop shows open circles on the Clear and Preset inputs. These open circles mean that when the Clear input is driven to 0, it clears the flip-flop (sets Q to 0); when P = 0, the flip-flop is preset to Q = 1. In some cases, a diagram will show an input with a line above it, such as $\bar{C}$. This means that $\bar{C}$ = 0 is the signal that causes action. In some cases, the line drawn above an input is used together with an open circle on the diagram. This is redundancy or emphasis only, and the line does not negate the open circle, nor does the open circle negate the line.

Note further that the open circle is placed in direct contact with the block diagram outline. When an open circle is drawn some distance away from a block, it usually is meant to show a pin on the IC package; it is not, in this case, a negation symbol.

J-K Master-Slave Flip-Flop

The most popular flip-flop is the so-called J-K flip-flop. The letters J and K have no special meaning and may, in fact, have been merely the label put on the pins (used for inputs) when the circuit was developed. The functional block diagram of a J-K Master-Slave flip-flop type 5473/7473 is shown in Fig.

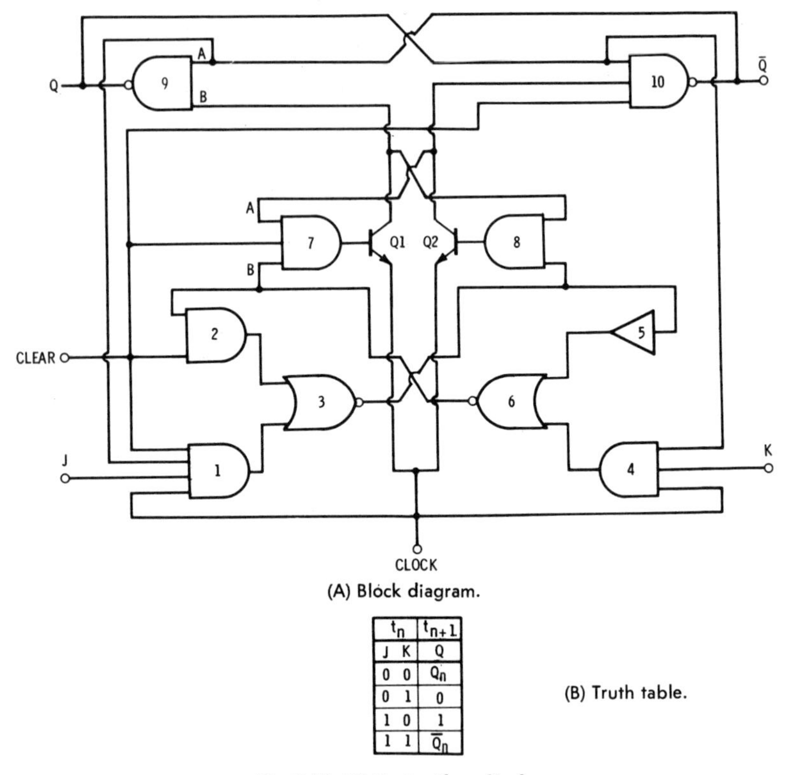

(A) Block diagram.

t_n		t_{n+1}
J	K	Q
0	0	Q_n
0	1	0
1	0	1
1	1	$\overline{Q}_n$

(B) Truth table.

Fig. 2-16. J-K Master-Slave flip-flop.

2-16. Gates 3 and 6 form the master flip-flop, and Gates 9 and 10 form the slave.

The truth table for the circuit shows four types of operation. When inputs J and K are 0, the flip-flop is in the quiescent state and does nothing as clock signals come in. This is shown in the truth table by the notation Q_n, which means that the output Q is the same, in time slot t_{n+1}, as it was in time slot t_n. When $J = 0$ and $K = 1$, the clock drives the output Q to 0; when $J = 1$ and $K = 0$, Q is driven to a 1. Finally, when J and K are both 1, the clock signal causes the flip-flop to change state, or toggle, regardless of whether the previous state was 0 or 1. Thus all four possible inputs are allowed, and each produces its own specific result.

The flip-flop is cleared $(Q = 0)$ as indicated in line 1 of the analysis table (Fig. 2-17). The X notation for inputs J, K, and Clock means that the circuit doesn't care whether these inputs are 1 or 0—they do not affect the output. A low (0) on the Clear input causes Gate 10 to go to high (1). Gate 7 output is

LINE	INPUTS C	J	K	CP	1	2	3	4	5	6	7	8	Q 9	$\overline{Q}$ 10	Q1	Q2
1	0	X	X	X	0	0	1	0	1	0	0	1	0	1	∞	∞
2	1	0	0	0	0	X	X	0	X	X	X	X	1	1	∞	∞
3	1	0	1	0	0		X	0		X						
4	1	0	1		0	0	1	1	1	0	0	1	0	1	∞	LO Z
5	1	0	1		0	0	1	0	1	0	0	1	0	1	∞	LO Z
6	1	1	0		0	1	0	0	0	1	1	0	1	0	LO Z	∞
7	1	1	1		1	1	0	0	0	1	1	0	0	1	LO Z	∞

X = UNKNOWN VALUE

Fig. 2-17. Analysis table for Fig. 2-16.

0 and, thus, transistor Q1 is nonconducting at this point; its collector is "hanging" and both inputs to Gate 9 are high, making Q = 0. (If the Clock should go low while Clear = 0, transistor Q1 still does not conduct, since Gate 7 is 0. Transistor Q2 would conduct, since the output of Gate 8 is 1, and this would cause a second 0 to appear at Gate 10. Thus the state of the Clock is irrelevant.) Also, the states of the J and K inputs are irrelevant.

In line 2, Fig. 2-17, Clear is 1 and J = K = 0. With J = K = 0, Gates 1 and 4 are 0. Gates 3 and 6 are not controlled by Gates 1 and 4 and are indeterminate. Thus, the flip-flop stays locked in whatever state it was in.

Let a clock signal with the waveshape shown in Fig. 2-18 be applied. At point 1 on the waveform, the slave part (Gates 9 and 10) of the circuit is isolated from the master part of the circuit because transistors Q1 and Q2 become open circuits as their emitter voltages are raised toward their collector voltages. With transistors Q1 and Q2 open (infinite impedance), Gate 9 and 10 have these inputs "hanging," which is the equivalent of applying a 1. Since a 0 is the controlling function in a NAND gate, Gates 9 and 10 are no longer affected by what happens in the master part of the circuit, as long as the clock voltage remains above point 1.

At point 2 on the waveform, the clock voltage has risen far enough to remove its inhibiting effect on Gates 1 and 4. However, with J = K = 0 (line 2), Gates 1 and 4 remain a 0, and the flip-flop remains in its previous state. As long as the clock

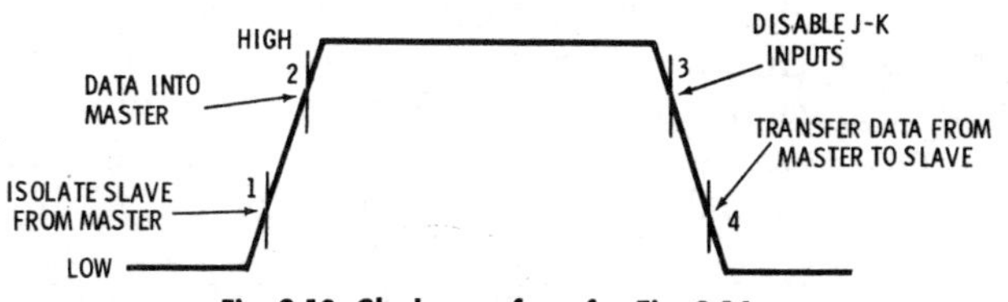

Fig. 2-18. Clock waveform for Fig. 2-16.

voltage stays above point 2, the circuit is susceptible to changes in J and K inputs; normally the J and K inputs will not be changed during this period. As clock voltage falls below point 3, Gates 1 and 4 are again inhibited, thereby disabling the J and K inputs. At point 4 on the waveform, transistors Q1 and Q2 are again enabled; if Gate 7 is high, transistor Q1 will conduct and put a 0 on Gate 9. If Gate 8 is high, transistor Q2 will conduct and put a 0 on Gate 10. In the case just considered, no change has occurred in the master flip-flop, so transistors Q1 and Q2 resume their previous state—one conducting and one open.

In line 3, let $J = 0$ and $K = 1$. With the clock $= 0$, Gates 3 and 6 are not affected. The clock waveform is applied, and at point 1 the slave is isolated from the master. At point 2 (line 4), the inputs are enabled, and since $J = 0$, Gate $1 = 0$ but Gate 3 is still indeterminate—that is, not controlled by input J alone. Gate 4 has the clock and K inputs of a 1 and, thus, its output will depend on the state of its third input (which is the Q output of the slave flip-flop). If Q happens to be a 1, Gate 4 will be a 1, and this will drive Gate 6 to a 0. Gate 2 has a 0 and a 1 for inputs and goes to a 0, causing Gate 3 to have two 0 inputs and go to a 1. Gate 7 is driven to 0 by Gate 6. Gate 8 has one input 1, with the second connected to the collector of transistor Q1. Since transistor Q1 is open at point 2 and above on the waveform, Gate 8 has both inputs a 1 and thus is a 1.

At point 3 on the waveform shown in Fig. 2-18, the J and K inputs are disabled, but this does not affect Gates 2, 3, 5, 6, 7, and 8.

At point 4 on the waveform, the transistors are enabled. Since Gate $8 = 1$, transistor Q2 conducts, thus putting a 0 on one input of Gate 10. With one 0 input, Gate 10 goes to 1, (making $\bar{Q} = 1$), which in turn gives Gates 9 one input $= 1$ and one "hanging" input, so Gate 9 goes to 0. Thus, Q goes to 0 in agreement with the truth table.

In the discussion above, we assumed that Q was a 1. What happens if it is 0? Line 5 shows that the result is exactly the same. At point 1 on the waveform shown in Fig. 2-18, the slave is isolated. At point 2, data is entered into the master. Gate 1 with $J = 0$, stays at 0. With $Q = 0$, Gate 4 has one input 0 and thus is 0. However, for Q to be a 0, both inputs to Gate 9 must be a 1. Thus, input B to Gate 9 must be a 1, which in turn requires that Gate 7 be a 0. (With its base voltage 0, transistor Q1 will be cut off, making input 9B =1.) For Gate 7 to be a 0, its B input must be 0, which in turn requires that Gate 6 be 0. If Gate 6 is 0, Gate $3 = 1$. Thus, when $J = 0$ and $K = 1$, the circuit goes into the $Q = 0$ state, regardless of its previous condition.

The next condition is when $J = 1$ and $K = 0$. The circuit is symmetrical except for Gates 2 and 5. Since the Clear input to Gate 2 is a 1 in normal operation, Gate 2 acts exactly like Gate 5. The circuit will thus perform as described previously, except $\bar{Q}$ always ends up as 0, and Q ends up as 1.

The final case is when $J = K = 1$. Consider the circuit when $Q = 1$. At point 2 on the waveform, Gate 4 is 1 and Gate 1 is 0 (since $\bar{Q} = 0$). Gate 6 is driven to 0 and Gate 3 is driven to 1. When Gate $3 = 1$ and Gate $6 = 0$, the circuit will, as we have seen previously in lines 4 and 5, end up in the $Q = 0$ state at the end of the clock pulse.

Consider circuit operation when $Q = 0$ (line 7). Now at point 2, Gate 4 goes to 0 and Gate 1 goes to 1. Gate 3 goes to a 0 and Gate 6 to a 1. This set of conditions drives Q to a 1 at point 4 of the waveform. Thus we see that the circuit toggles every time a clock pulse enters.

OTHER VERSIONS

The logic diagram shown in Fig. 2-16 is for the circuit type SN5473/SN7473 manufactured by Texas Instruments. The same part, as manufactured by Motorola, does not use Gates 5, 7 or 8. Gates 3 and 6 are allowed to switch transistors Q1 and Q2 directly, rather than being buffered by Gates 7 and 8. The buffering and circuit symmetry provided by Gate 5 is dispensed with in the Motorola version. The circuits function identically, of course, and are interchangeable; otherwise they would have different part numbers.

In many digital circuits, the J and K inputs to be applied to a flip-flop are not single inputs but are functions of several variables. This gives rise to the so-called ANDed J-K flip-flops. The Motorola version of circuit type SN5472/SN7472, an

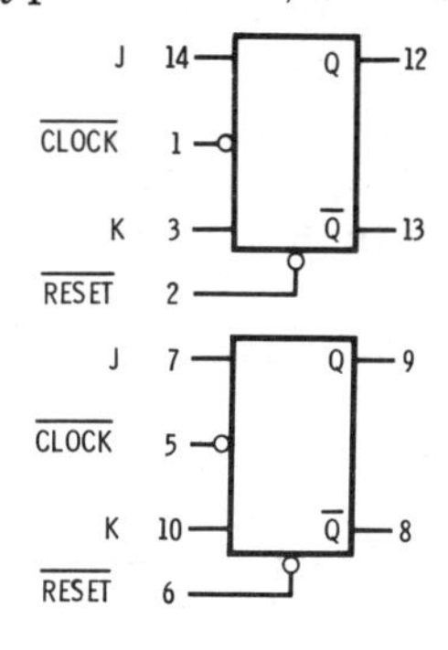

Fig. 2-19. Block symbol for SN5473/SN7473.

ANDed J-K Master-Slave flip-flop with direct Set and Reset, is shown in Fig. 2-20A. Comparing the circuit with Fig. 2-16A (note the interchange of lettering), we see that Gates 7 and 8 are gone, and Gate 5 is symmetrical with Gate 2, thus giving direct Set. For J to be a 1, J1, J2, and J3 must all be 1; this is similar for K.

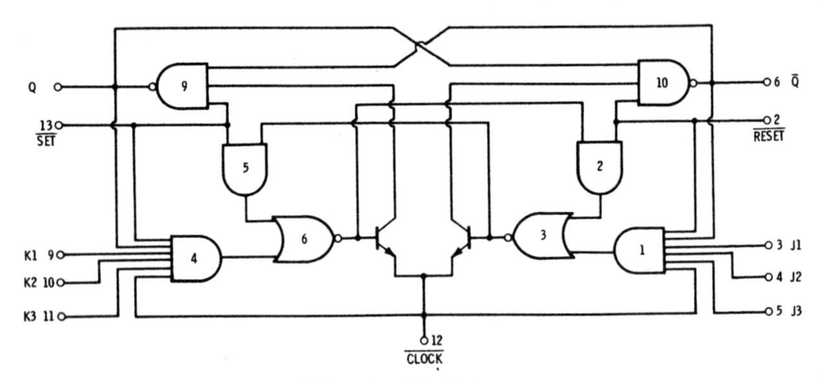

(A) Functional block diagram.

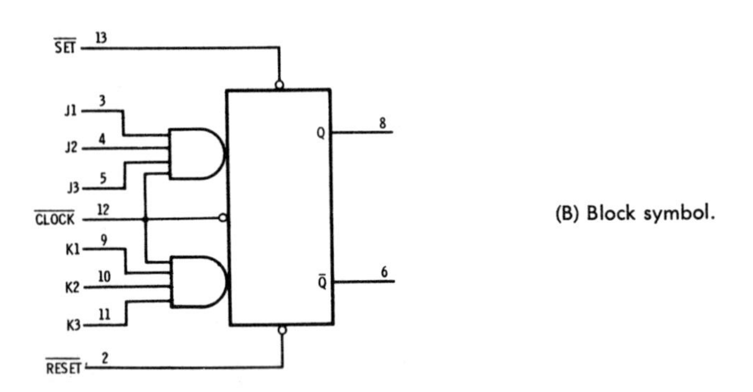

(B) Block symbol.

Fig. 2-20. ANDed J-K Master-Slave flip-flop.

The block symbol drawing for the circuit is shown in Fig. 2-20B. The symbol drawing includes the pin numbers of the IC package. Because of the extra pins needed to handle the extra J and K inputs, only one flip-flop goes into a standard package. The block symbol drawing shown in Fig. 2-19 includes two flip-flops, since the SN5473/SN7473 contains two circuits.

Fig. 2-21 shows the block symbol drawing for circuit type 5470/7470. The J* and K* inputs are true when 0. Thus, K = 1 when K1 is 1, K2 is 1, and K* is 0. Inputs J* and K* must be

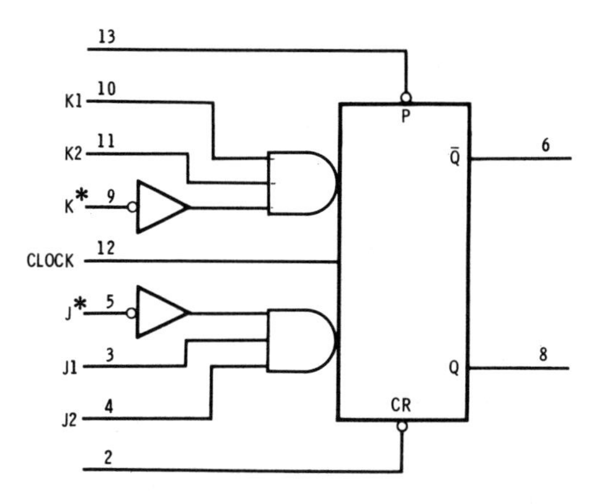

Fig. 2-21. Edge-triggered J-K Master-Slave flip-flop with inverted inputs.

grounded when not used; otherwise they will present a 0 at the AND gate and lock up the circuit accordingly.

High-Speed J-K Flip-Flop

A J-K flip-flop with a somewhat different operation than has been previously considered is shown in Fig. 2-22. This flip-flop is a member of the high speed type 54H/74H family of

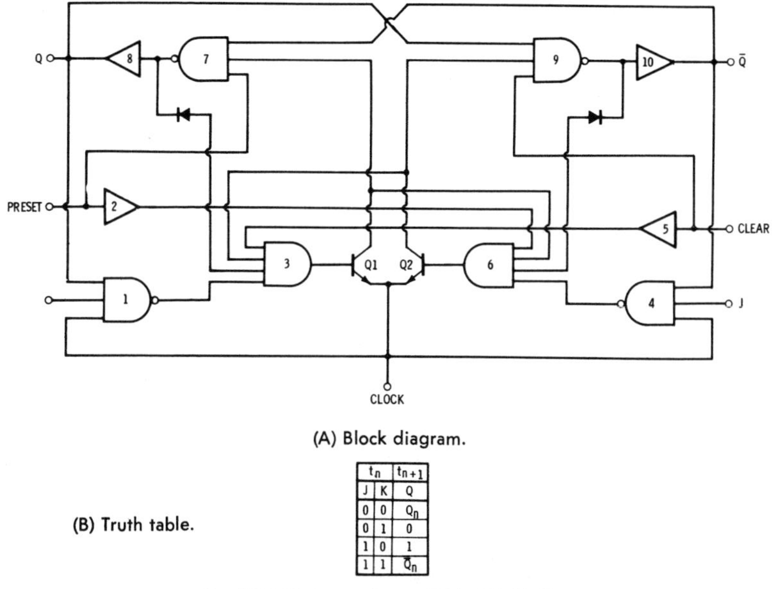

(A) Block diagram.

(B) Truth table.

t_n		t_{n+1}
J	K	Q
0	0	Q_n
0	1	0
1	0	1
1	1	$\bar{Q}_n$

Fig. 2-22. High-speed monolithic J-K flip-flop.

circuits and operates at up to 50 MHz. The truth table, however, is the same as for other J-K flip-flops.

Applying a 0 input to the Preset drives Gate 7, and thus Q, to a 1. (Gate 8 is a buffer amplifier.) With Clear having an input of 1 and the clock low, Gate 9 has all inputs = 1 and, therefore, goes to 0; thus, $\bar{Q} = 0$. Applying an input of 0 to Clear sets Q to 0 and, with Preset = 1, $\bar{Q}$ goes to 1.

LINE	INPUTS					GATES											
												Q		$\bar{Q}$		t_{n+1}	
	P	C	CP	J	K	1	2	3	4	5	6	7	8	9	10	Q	$\bar{Q}$
1	1	1	0	0	0	1	1	1	1	1	0	1	1	0	0	1	0
2	1	1	0	0	1	1	1	1	1	1	0	1	1	0	0	1	0
3				0	1	0	1	0	1	1	1	1	1	0	0	0	1
4	1	1	1	1	0	1	1	1	1	1	0	1	1	0	0	1	0
5	1	1	1	1	1	0	1	0	1	1	1	1	1	0	0	0	1
6	1	1	1	1	1	1	1	0	0	1	0	0	0	1	1	1	0

Fig. 2-23. Analysis table for Fig. 2-22.

Let's examine the circuit using the analysis table shown in Fig. 2-23. While the clock is low, let J = K = 0 (line 1) be applied (Clear and Preset = 1). Gates 1 and 4 will be driven to a 1 regardless of the value of Q and $\bar{Q}$. If Gate 9 = 0, then the input of Gate 6 (that has the diode connected to the junction of Gates 9 and 10) will see a ground and Gate 6 will be a 0. From similar considerations, Gate 3 = 1. When the clock goes high (above point 1 on the waveform in Fig. 2-24), Gates 1 and 4 stay the same; thus, the circuit does not change when J = K = 0.

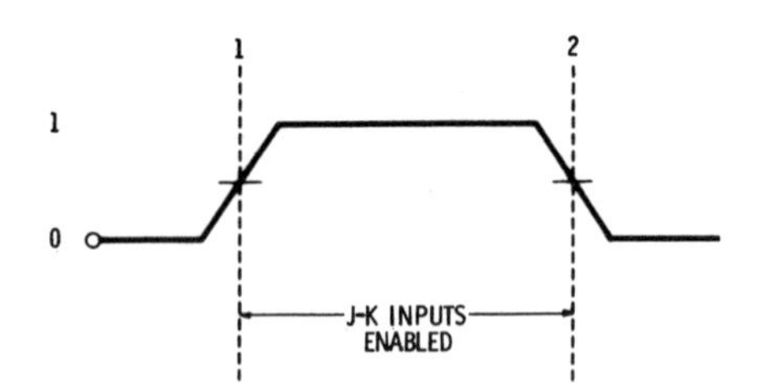

Fig. 2-24. Clock waveform for Fig. 2-22.

With J = 0 and K = 1, Gate 4 will be 1 (line 2 of the table). Assume Q = 1 and $\bar{Q} = 0$. For $\bar{Q}$ to be a 0, Gate 9 must have all inputs = 1. This requires that transistor Q2 be open or cut off; therefore, Gate 6 must be low. For Gate 6 to be low, transistor Q1 must be on. This puts a 0 into both Gate 6 and Gate 7. Gate 1 is high because the clock is low; so Gate 3 has all inputs = 1.

Now, let the clock begin to go high. At point 1 on the clock waveform (Fig. 2-24), the emitter voltages of transistors Q1 and Q2 has risen sufficiently to cut off these transistors; thus, the inputs to which their collectors are connected see a 1. Gates 7 and 9 are thereby isolated from the input section of the flip-flop. At this point Gate 1 will have a 1 on each of its inputs and will go to 0; Gate 3 will go to 0; Gate 4 still has its J input = 0 and will go to 1. Gate 6 will go to 1 because each input is a 1.

Now let the clock go low. As the clock waveform passes below point 2, transistors Q1 and Q2 are enabled. The output

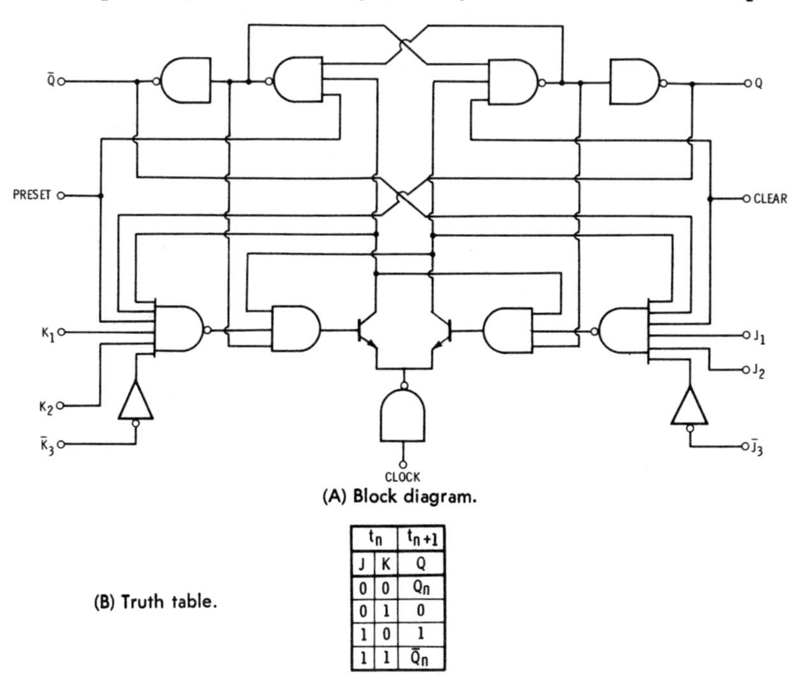

(A) Block diagram.

(B) Truth table.

t_n		t_{n+1}
J	K	Q
0	0	Q_n
0	1	0
1	0	1
1	1	$\bar{Q}_n$

Fig. 2-25. Positive edge-triggered flip-flop.

of Gate 6 is a 1; therefore, transistor Q2 is driven into saturation, which puts a 0 on an input of Gate 9 and $\bar{Q}$ goes to a 1. Gate 3 is 0; therefore, transistor Q1 is cut off and Gate 7 sees a 1 on this input. Gate 7 has all 1s as inputs and goes to 0.

Because the slave flip-flop changes state when the clock goes low, the circuit is called a negative edge-triggered flip-flop.

The final mode of operation is for J = K = 1. With the clock high, the gates are as shown in line 5. When the clock goes low, transistor Q2 turns on and $\bar{Q}$ is driven from 0 to 1. In line 6,

J and K are 1, but now $\bar{Q} = 1$, setting up the gates as shown. When the clock goes low, transistor Q1 turns on driving Q to a 1 and $\bar{Q}$ to a 0. Thus, the circuit toggles on the negative edge of the clock pulse when J = K = 1.

Positive Edge-Triggered Flip-Flop

Both the J-K Master-Slave circuit and the high-speed J-K type 74H106 circuit are negative edge-triggered circuits. Type-D flip-flops, however, trigger on the positive edge of the clock pulse and so does type 7470, shown in Fig. 2-25.

The key to positive-edge triggering in this circuit is the inverter or NAND gate in the clock input. When the external clock pulse goes high, the switching transistors see a signal going low, and the circuit responds accordingly. Circuit operation otherwise is identical to J-K flip-flops.

Note the inverters of the $\bar{J}3$ and $\bar{K}3$ inputs. For clocked operation, these two inputs can be connected to the clock input. If inputs $\bar{J}3$ and $\bar{K}3$ are not used, they should be connected to ground, which will put a 1 on their respective input gate. These 1s free the gates to follow the other inputs.

CHAPTER 3

Decoders

Machine-to-machine communications are accomplished primarily with binary numbers (radix 2), and, since man is most at ease with decimal or radix ten numbers, the need to translate information from one number system to the other occurs constantly. The task of converting a radix ten number (any number from 0 through 9) to a radix 2 number (0 or 1) is usually called encoding; going from radix 2 to radix 10 is usually called decoding.

Encoding devices are usually found at the input terminals of digital systems. They usually are not complicated in their logical structure. To encode a number 9, for example, we only need to set four toggle switches to either a high voltage or ground, in such an order that they permit an output corresponding to the code 1001. Decoding, on the other hand, requires the logical analysis of a number of inputs to determine which output is correct.

Digital circuits are constantly required to decode a set of input signals and generate a specific output. If a circuit is driving a set of signal lights, then each light must have its own specific address. If a circuit is driving a seven-segment readout device, the circuit must be able to choose which segments to light and which to leave dark. If a circuit is operating with a magnetic core memory, some means must be provided to address each specific word location in the memory, both for reading in and reading out. This chapter will discuss some TTL decoders.

ONE-OF-FOUR DECODER

One of the simplest TTL decoders is the Fairchild TTL/MSI 9321, a "Dual One-of-Four Decoder." The functional block diagram is shown in Fig. 3-1A. (The TTL/MSI 9321 is a member of a TTL family very similar to and compatible with type 54/74 circuits. A similar decoder, but a little more complicated, is circuit type SN54155/SN74155.) The circuit has two data inputs, A_0 and A_1, and an enable input $\overline{E}$. The enable input is a

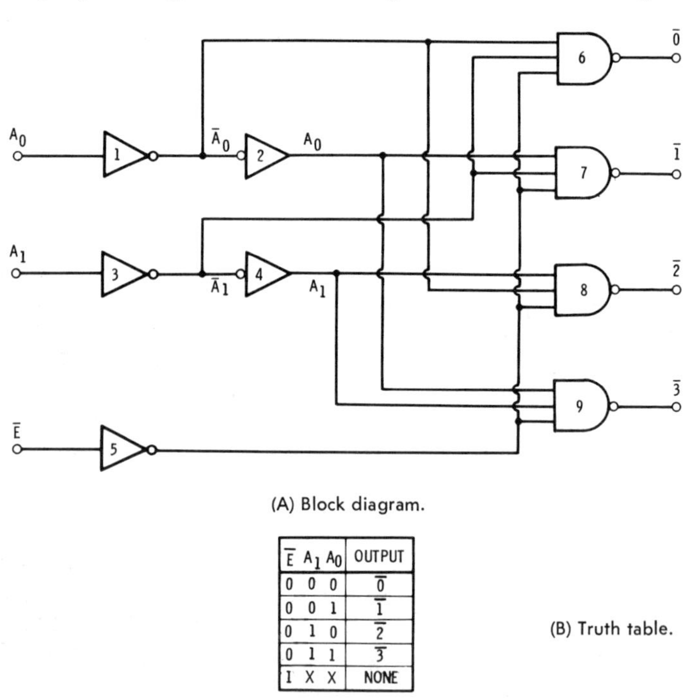

(A) Block diagram.

$\overline{E}$	A_1	A_0	OUTPUT
0	0	0	$\overline{0}$
0	0	1	$\overline{1}$
0	1	0	$\overline{2}$
0	1	1	$\overline{3}$
1	X	X	NONE

(B) Truth table.

Fig. 3-1. Dual one-of-four decoder.

control input and allows the circuit to be synchronized by a clock signal. Inputs A_0 and A_1 are the inputs to be decoded, and together they form the digital word A_1 A_0, as shown in the truth table in Fig. 3-1B. The word A_1 A_0 can be any one of four combinations, and the decoding circuit must determine which of the four outputs to choose for each input word. The outputs are labeled: $\overline{0}$, $\overline{1}$, $\overline{2}$, and $\overline{3}$. The selected output goes to 0 while the others stay high.

The circuit can be considered to consist of four major sections as shown in Fig. 3-2—input address, control, logic, and

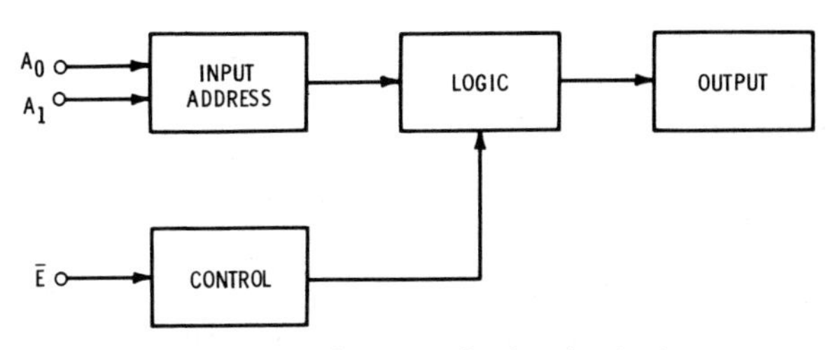

Fig. 3-2. Basic functions of a decoder circuit.

output. When convenient, these various sections in other ICs are allowed to merge into one another and thus cannot always be clearly identified. In the 9321, Gates 1 through 4 (Fig. 3-1A) form the address section, Gate 5 forms the control, and Gates 6 through 8 form the logic. The output section in this device is simply the outputs of Gates 6 through 8, each of which goes to a separate pin of the IC package and can drive a specific load.

In the input section, A_0 drives Gate 1, an inverter. Gate 1 drives Gates 2, 6, and 8. Without Gate 1, any circuit trying to drive input A_0 would have to supply three input circuits; with Gate 1, the device presents an ordinary unit load to the driving circuit.

Gate 1 is followed by Gate 2, which is another inverter. Gate 1 gave buffering and $\overline{A_0}$; Gate 2 gives back A_0. Both A_0 and $\overline{A_0}$ are needed to drive the logic section.

The control section consists only of an inverter. Note that when the enable signal = 1, the output of Gate 5 is 0, and the outputs of Gates 6 through 9 are all 1s; this is the quiescent state of the decoder. When $\overline{E} = 0$, then Gate 5 = 1, and Gates 6 through 9 are controlled by A_0 and A_1. The state of the circuit for $\overline{E} = 1$ is given by line 1 of the analysis table in Fig. 3-3—all outputs are high.

Lines 2 through 5 show the status of the circuit for the four combinations of A_1 A_0. With $A_0 = A_1 = 0$ and $\overline{E} = 0$ (line 2),

LINE	INPUTS			INTERNAL GATES									OUTPUTS			
NBR	$\overline{E}$	A_1	A_0	1	2	3	4	5	6	7	8	9	$\overline{0}$	$\overline{1}$	$\overline{2}$	$\overline{3}$
1	1							0	1	1	1	1	1	1	1	1
2	0	0	0	1	0	1	0	1	0	1	1	1	0	1	1	1
3	0	0	1	0	1	1	0	1	1	0	1	1	1	0	1	1
4	0	1	0	1	0	0	1	1	1	1	0	1	1	1	0	1
5	0	1	1	0	1	0	1	1	1	1	1	0	1	1	1	0

Fig. 3-3. Analysis table for Fig. 3-1.

Gate 6 has a 1 on each input, and thus has an output of 0; output $\overline{0}$ is low. Gate 8 has one input low (A_1 through inverter Gates 3 and 4) and is therefore high; Gate 9 has two inputs low (the outputs of Gates 2 and 4) and is high. Gate 7 is driven high by the input from Gate 2. Thus, all output gates except 6 are high.

Line 3 shows the condition of the gates for $A_0 = 1$ and $A_1 = 0$. The logic function of the device causes all output gates to go high except Gate 7, thereby selecting $\overline{1}$ as the output line. The other two input code combinations (shown on lines 4 and 5) operate similarly to select output $\overline{2}$ or output $\overline{3}$.

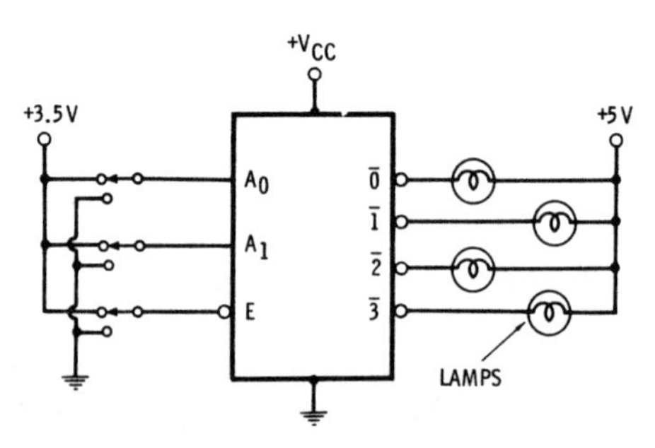

Fig. 3-4. Typical decoder circuit configuration.

Fig. 3-4 shows how the device can be used to light any one of four lamps, depending on the input word A_1 A_0 and control $\overline{E}$. When an output is low, current will flow from +5-volt source through the lamp to ground causing the lamp to light. Again, open circles on the block symbol indicate that a low signal is required for circuit operation (or that the selected output goes low).

ONE-OUT-OF-TEN DECODER

Three different ICs have been developed in the type 54/74 family to decode three different number codes. These are known as the Binary-Coded-Decimal code (BCD), the Excess-3 code, and the Excess-3 Gray code. The three devices are very similar in logical structure and use the same decoding concept as the previously discussed one-out-of-four decoder.

The functional block diagrams for the decoders are shown in Figs. 3-5, 3-6, and 3-7. The decoders do not have an enabling input. Their truth tables are shown in Fig. 3-8.

Decimal numbers from 0 through 15 are shown at the left of the truth tables. Truth table A shows the BCD code for the decimal numbers. The binary number 0000 represents decimal number 0; binary number 0001 represents decimal number 1; binary number 0010 represents decimal 2; etc.

Truth table B shows the Excess-3 binary code, where binary number 0011 represents decimal 0, binary 0100 represents decimal 1, etc. The Excess-3 code is obtained by giving decimal 0 the binary number 0011, which is the same as decimal 3 in BCD. Thus, in Excess-3, the count starts at the equivalent of decimal 3 and ends at decimal 12.

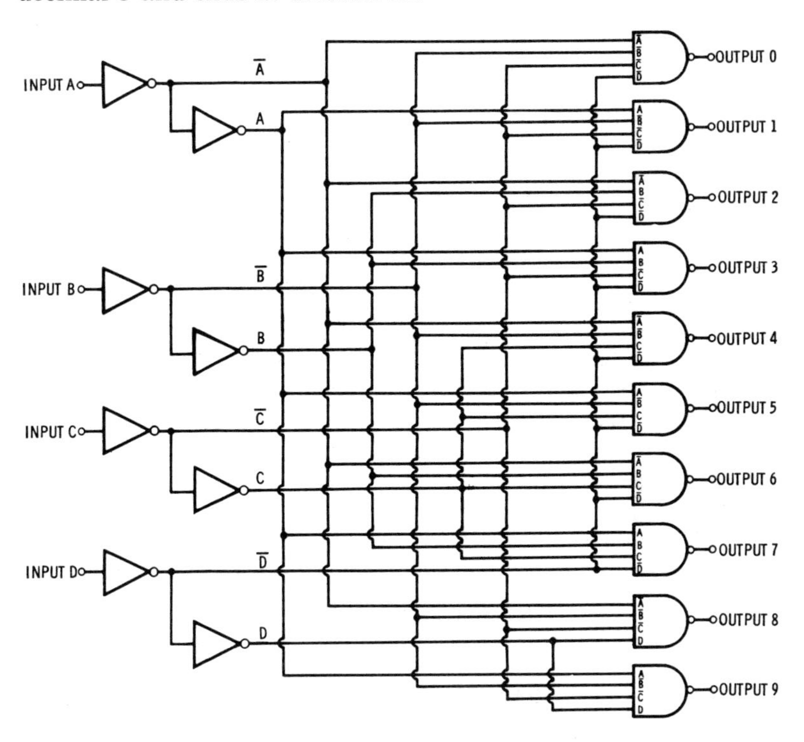

Fig. 3-5. Functional block diagram for a BCD-to-decimal decoder.

Truth table C shows Excess-3 Gray binary code, where binary number 0010 represents decimal 0, etc. The Gray code was originally set up so that no more than 1 bit would change, when counting in sequence from one number to the next higher or lower number. Truth table C shows the Excess-3 version of the Gray code.

Assume you are decoding a BCD signal, and the binary word 0000 is presented to the decoder. The gate controlling output 0 will have as inputs $\overline{A}$, $\overline{B}$, $\overline{C}$, and $\overline{D}$, which are all 1s, and the

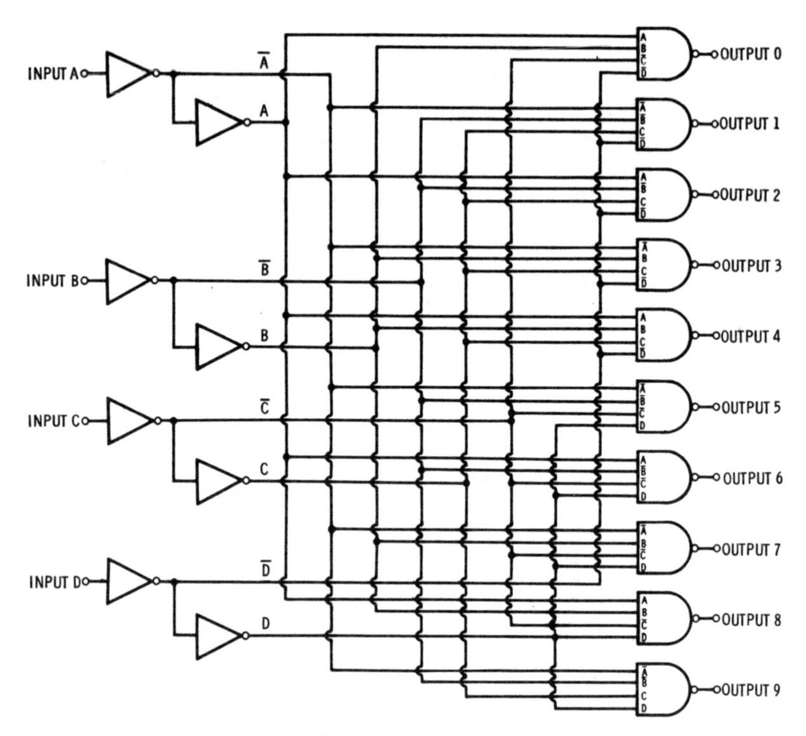

Fig. 3-6. Excess-3-to-decimal decoder functional block diagram.

gate will go to 0. This is shown by the output truth table D in Fig. 3-8. Examination of the logic diagram will show that all the other output gates have at least one input at 0, and thus they will be high. If the input code changes to 0001, the 1 output goes low and the others all go high.

If the signal to be decoded is in Excess-3, we use circuit type 5443/7443, shown in Fig. 3-6. For an input of 0011, the logic again drives output 0 low and all the other outputs high. Circuit type 5444/7444 decodes (Fig. 3-7) Excess-3-Gray signals.

In all three ICs, four inputs are required. Note that with four inputs, there are 16 possible input combinations. Since only 10 outputs are needed, six of the input combinations are meaningless so far as selecting an output is concerned, and so all outputs are high for these inputs. (Remember from Fig. 3-4 that a low output is necessary for circuit operation.)

The three ICs do not have a control section, and thus clocking or enabling is not possible or required. The outputs tend to follow the inputs instantaneously, subject only to the propagation delays of each block in a given chain or path. The shortest

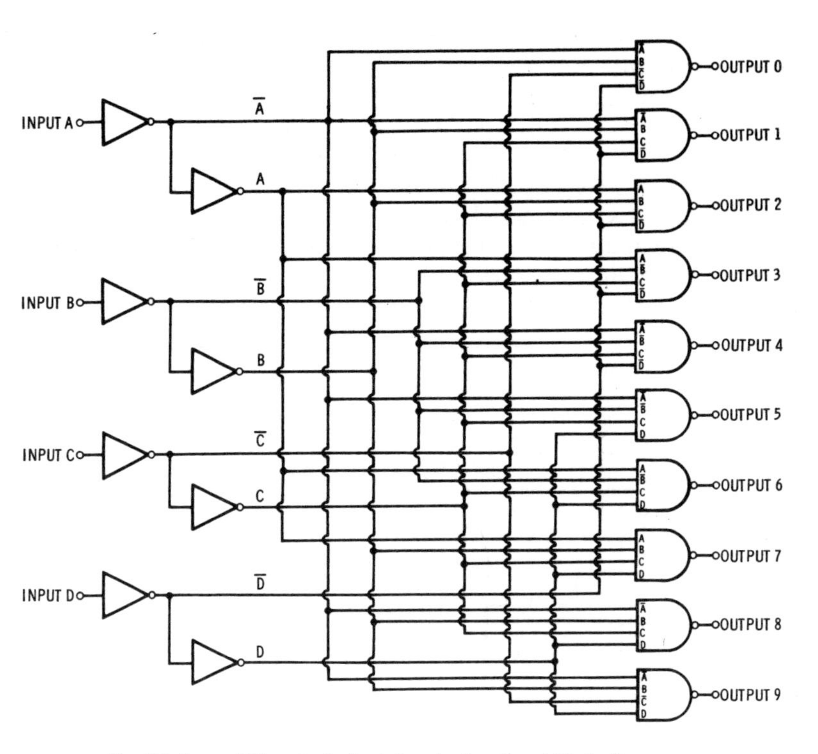

Fig. 3-7. Excess-3-Gray-to-decimal decoder functional block diagram.

DECIMAL NUMBER	A BCD INPUT				B EXCESS 3 INPUT				C EXCESS 3 GRAY INPUT				D OUTPUT (ALL TYPES)									
	D	C	B	A	D	C	B	A	D	C	B	A	0	1	2	3	4	5	6	7	8	9
0	0	0	0	0	0	0	1	1	0	0	1	0	0	1	1	1	1	1	1	1	1	1
1	0	0	0	1	0	1	0	0	0	1	1	0	1	0	1	1	1	1	1	1	1	1
2	0	0	1	0	0	1	0	1	0	1	1	1	1	1	0	1	1	1	1	1	1	1
3	0	0	1	1	0	1	1	0	0	1	0	1	1	1	1	0	1	1	1	1	1	1
4	0	1	0	0	0	1	1	1	0	1	0	0	1	1	1	1	0	1	1	1	1	1
5	0	1	0	1	1	0	0	0	1	1	0	0	1	1	1	1	1	0	1	1	1	1
6	0	1	1	0	1	0	0	1	1	1	0	1	1	1	1	1	1	1	0	1	1	1
7	0	1	1	1	1	0	1	0	1	1	1	1	1	1	1	1	1	1	1	0	1	1
8	1	0	0	0	1	0	1	1	1	1	1	0	1	1	1	1	1	1	1	1	0	1
9	1	0	0	1	1	1	0	0	1	0	1	0	1	1	1	1	1	1	1	1	1	0
10	1	0	1	0	1	1	0	1	1	0	1	1	1	1	1	1	1	1	1	1	1	1
11	1	0	1	1	1	1	1	0	1	0	0	1	1	1	1	1	1	1	1	1	1	1
12	1	1	0	0	1	1	1	1	1	0	0	0	1	1	1	1	1	1	1	1	1	1
13	1	1	0	1	0	0	0	0	0	0	0	0	1	1	1	1	1	1	1	1	1	1
14	1	1	1	0	0	0	0	1	0	0	0	1	1	1	1	1	1	1	1	1	1	1
15	1	1	1	1	0	0	1	0	0	0	1	1	1	1	1	1	1	1	1	1	1	1

Fig. 3-8. Truth tables for Figs. 3-5, 3-6, and 3-7.

signal path is through two blocks consisting of an input inverter and the output NAND gate; the longest path is through two inverters and the output gate.

Many times, a 1-of-10 decoder will be required to decode signals for driving a Nixie tube. Since Nixie tubes require about 170 to 180 volts for operation, the typical TTL IC cannot be directly connected but has to drive buffer transistors having adequate voltage ratings. In the type 7441 BCD-to-decimal decoder/driver shown in Fig. 3-9, the buffer transistors are built in, and the IC can drive a Nixie tube direct.

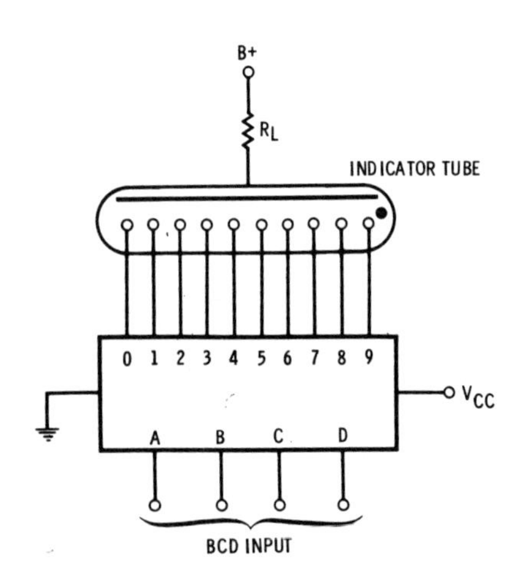

Fig. 3-9. Block symbol for a BCD decoder with direct-drive capability.

Several other decoding ICs have built-in buffer transistors for driving relatively heavy loads. Circuit type 5445/7445 has buffer output transistors rated at 30 volts, and circuit type 54145/74145 has output transistors rated at 15 volts. The output transistors are open-collector type and can sink 80 mA. These devices can drive relays and low-voltage lamps, but not Nixie tubes. The truth table shown in Fig. 3-8A and the functional block diagram (Fig. 3-5) apply also to these two devices.

SEVEN-SEGMENT DECODERS

Fig. 3-10 shows how an indicator tube consisting of seven individual straight-line elements can be used to form numerals from 0 through 9. To form a 7, for example, we light sections a, b, and c and leave the others dark.

When using 7-segment tubes as display elements, special decoders are needed to interpret the input signals and to light up the correct segments of the display tube. The problem is similar to choosing one input out of ten possible inputs, except that now multiple outputs are needed for each input code—from 2 outputs for numeral 1 to 7 outputs for numeral 8.

Several types of ICs have been developed for decoding inputs and driving 7-segment indicators. The basic decoding logic block diagram is shown in Fig. 3-11. The truth table is shown in Fig. 3-12. The control section of the circuit consists of the Blanking Input (BI). When BI = 1, Gate 1 is also a 1. The

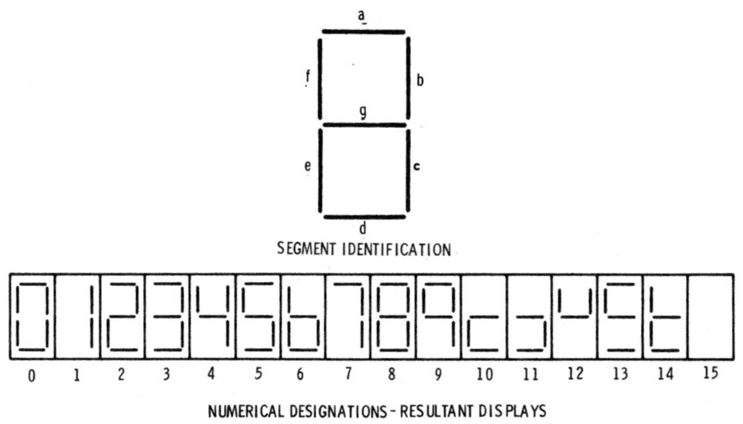

Fig. 3-10. Seven-segment indicator tube.

NAND gates driven by Gate 1 are responsive to inputs A, B, C, and D, and act as the inverters did in previously discussed decoders. To obtain output numeral 1, we need to light segments b and c (Fig. 3-10). The truth table shows that the inputs must be A = 1 and B = C = D = 0.

Looking at the output section, note that each segment is controlled by an AND gate but operates with inverted inputs. Fig. 3-13 shows the logic symbol and truth table for a two-input AND gate of this type; for a true output (1) from this gate, all inputs must be low (0).

For segment a, in Fig. 3-11, one input to the output gate is B and D; this output is obtained from an AND gate, and since B = D = 0, this signal is a 0. The next input to the a-segment gate is $\bar{A} \cdot C$. Since A = 1, $\bar{A} = 0$ and C = 0, this input to the output gate = 0. The last input is $A \cdot \bar{B} \cdot \bar{C} \cdot \bar{D}$. Since A = 1 and $\bar{B} = \bar{C} = \bar{D} = 1$, the output of the AND gate is 1 and, thus, the third input to the a-segment output gate is high; the output signal is 0. In this IC, a selected output must go high; thus, segment a is rejected.

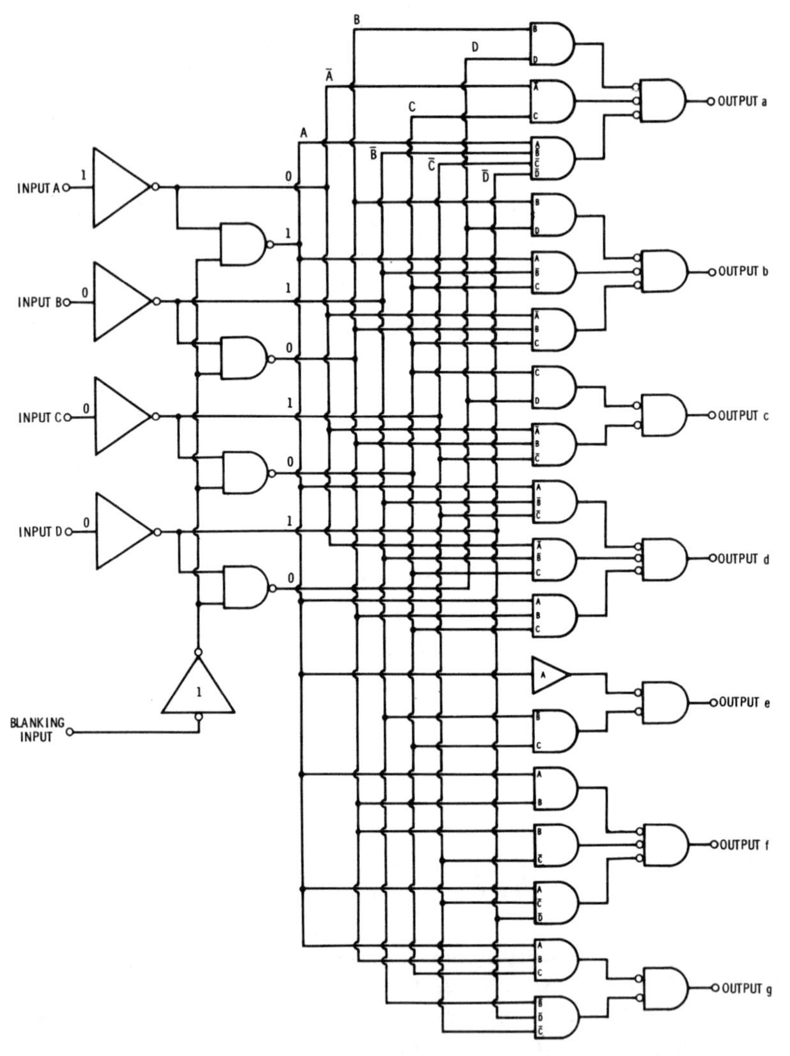

Fig. 3-11. Block diagram for typical IC used to drive indicator tubes.

Similar analysis for segment b shows that the three inputs to its output gate are:

$$B \cdot D = 0 \cdot 0 = 0$$
$$A \cdot \overline{B} \cdot C = 0 \cdot 1 \cdot 0 = 0$$
$$\overline{A} \cdot B \cdot C = 0 \cdot 0 \cdot 0 = 0$$

The b-segment gate is satisfied with three low inputs, and its output is high. Segment b is selected.

	INPUTS					OUTPUTS						
DECIMAL OR FUNCTION	D	C	B	A	Bl	a	b	c	d	e	f	g
0	0	0	0	0	1	1	1	1	1	1	1	0
1	0	0	0	1	1	0	1	1	0	0	0	0
2	0	0	1	0	1	1	1	0	1	1	0	1
3	0	0	1	1	1	1	1	1	1	0	0	1
4	0	1	0	0	1	0	1	1	0	0	1	1
5	0	1	0	1	1	1	0	1	1	0	1	1
6	0	1	1	0	1	0	0	1	1	1	1	1
7	0	1	1	1	1	1	1	1	0	0	0	0
8	1	0	0	0	1	1	1	1	1	1	1	1
9	1	0	0	1	1	1	1	1	0	0	1	1
10	1	0	1	0	1	0	0	0	1	1	0	1
11	1	0	1	1	1	0	0	1	1	0	0	1
12	1	1	0	0	1	0	1	0	0	0	1	1
13	1	1	0	1	1	1	0	0	1	0	1	1
14	1	1	1	0	1	0	0	0	1	1	1	1
15	1	1	1	1	1	0	0	0	0	0	0	0
BI	X	X	X	X	0	0	0	0	0	0	0	0

X = INPUT MAY BE HIGH OR LOW

Fig. 3-12. Truth table for Fig. 3-11.

For the c-segment gate, inputs are:

$$C \cdot D = 0 \cdot 0 = 0$$
$$\bar{A} \cdot B \cdot \bar{C} = 0 \cdot 0 \cdot 1 = 0$$

Thus, the output is high and C is selected.

For the d-segment gate, inputs are:

$$A \cdot \bar{B} \cdot \bar{C} = 1 \cdot 1 \cdot 1 = 1$$
$$\bar{A} \cdot \bar{B} \cdot C = 0 \cdot 1 \cdot 0 = 0$$
$$A \cdot B \cdot C = 1 \cdot 0 \cdot 0 = 0$$

Since the d-segment gate is not satisfied, its output is low.

Similar analysis for segments e, f, and g will show them to be low for the input code being considered. As the inputs are changed, the segment gates go high or low in accordance with the truth table.

The outputs follow the input code without delay or clocking. When the blanking input goes low, it causes the gates it drives

A	B	Q
0	0	1
0	1	0
1	0	0
1	1	0

(A) Logic symbol.

(B) Truth table.

Fig. 3-13. Two-input AND gate with inverted inputs.

to go low regardless of the input signals. This gives as inputs to the decoding logic the inverted input signals A, B, C, and D, plus the internally generated signals A = B = C = D = 1. Thus, for inputs to the a-segment gate (? = unknown), we have:

$$B \cdot D = 1 \cdot 1 = 1$$

$$\bar{A} \cdot C = ? \cdot 1 = ?$$

$$A \cdot \bar{B} \cdot \bar{C} \cdot \bar{D} = 1 \cdot ? \cdot ? \cdot ? = ?$$

Since the gate has at least one input = 1, its output = 0. Examination of the other output gates shows that all have at least one input high; thus, all outputs are low. Since the segments are energized only when BI = 1, this input can be used to turn the segments on and off on a regular basis. Leaving the indicators off part of the time saves operating power and gives control over the brightness of the resulting display. The on/off cycle should be short—30 cycles per second or so—to prevent the display from flickering.

LAMP TEST AND RIPPLE BLANKING

When circuits have a number of lamps that show output or internal conditions, the possibility always exists that one or more of the lights may become defective—burned out, loose in its socket, etc. A lamp-test provision allows an operator to close one push button or switch causing all lamps, or all lamp segments in a seven-segment display, to turn on, regardless of the state of its normal inputs. Any lamp or segment that fails to turn on, in this test, can be assumed to be defective and require maintenance.

Fig. 3-14 shows the basic 7-segment decoding logic diagram of Fig. 3-11, but with several additions. First, all the outputs have inverters, which generally use relatively high-voltage (30 V or 15 V) transistors to boost the power-handling capability of the IC. Signal inversion produces active low outputs instead of active high; thus, the output section of the truth table is the negative (reverse) of the previous circuit.

Three other inputs must be accounted for. These are (1) the "Blanking Input/Ripple-Blanking Output"; (2) "Lamp Test"; and (3) "Ripple-Blanking Input." The connection BI/RBO uses wired-OR (or wired-AND) logic, which is discussed in Chapter 1.

Consider first the lamp-test input (LT). This signal passes through a negated input inverter which acts as a buffer amplifier. Thus, when LT = 1, it does not affect Gates 1, 2, 3, 4, or 5.

When LT = 0, Gates 1, 2, and 3 are driven high. Also, the wired connection between Gates 4 and 5 requires that when LT = 0, BI/RBO must be open or high. With LT = 0, Gate 5 is driven high, which drives Gate 4 high; with Gates 1, 2, and 3 also driven high by LT = 0, and Gate 4 high, Gates 6, 7, and 8 are driven low. The logic diagram has been marked to show the state of Gates 1 through 10 when LT = 0. Further examination of the logic diagram shows that all the output inverters will have a 1 input except output g, which could be on or off depending on input D. Therefore, the LT signal is brought to the g-segment to insure complete testing.

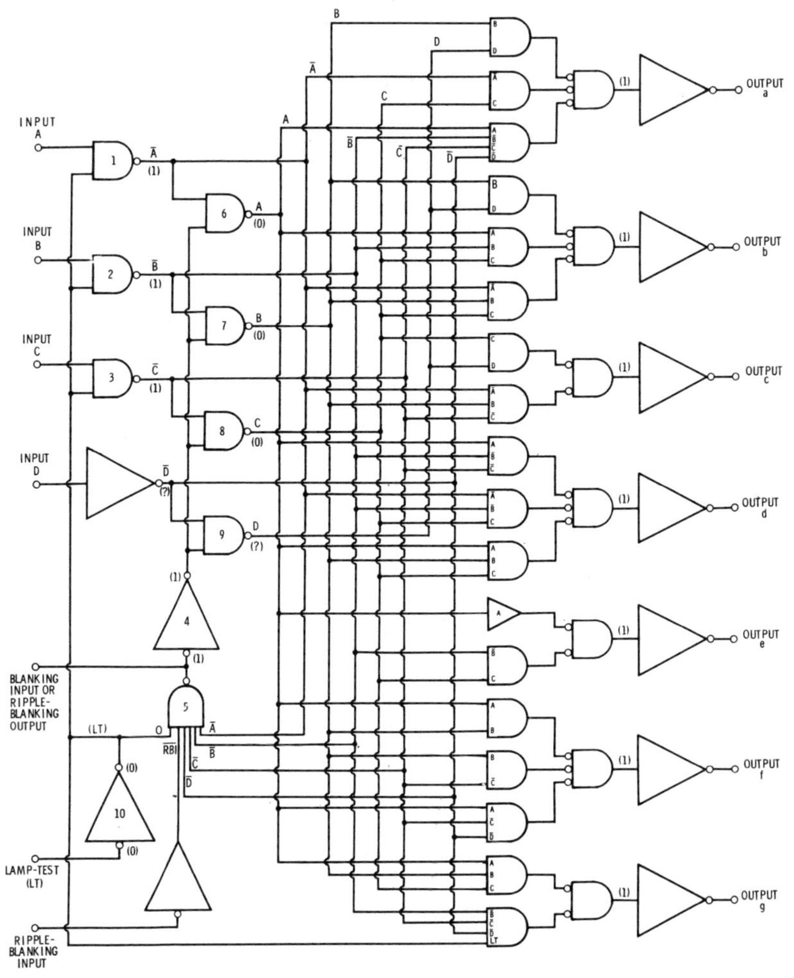

Fig. 3-14. Block diagram of circuitry having provision to test for indicator lamp failure.

Next, consider the Ripple-Blanking Input. Ripple blanking is used to turn off indicators that are not required in a display. If you have a six-digit display running from 000000 to 999999, but want to show only the number 387, you can show it as 000387 or you can blank out the three leading zeros. Blanking out the leading and trailing zeros makes the display easier to read.

When RBI = 1, Gate 5 will have a 0 input and will be high. With Gate 5 high, the decoding circuitry is free to follow inputs A, B, C, and D. All numerals will be decoded and displayed, including ZERO.

	INPUTS							OUTPUTS						
DECIMAL OR FUNCTION	LT	RBI	D	C	B	A	BI/RBO	a	b	c	d	e	f	g
0	1	1	0	0	0	0	1	0	0	0	0	0	0	1
1	1	X	0	0	0	1	1	1	0	0	1	1	1	1
2	1	X	0	0	1	0	1	0	0	1	0	0	1	0
3	1	X	0	0	1	1	1	0	0	0	0	1	1	0
4	1	X	0	1	0	0	1	1	0	0	1	1	0	0
5	1	X	0	1	0	1	1	0	1	0	0	1	0	0
6	1	X	0	1	1	0	1	1	1	0	0	0	0	0
7	1	X	0	1	1	1	1	0	0	0	1	1	1	1
8	1	X	1	0	0	0	1	0	0	0	0	0	0	0
9	1	X	1	0	0	1	1	0	0	0	1	1	0	0
10	1	X	1	0	1	0	1	1	1	1	0	0	1	0
11	1	X	1	0	1	1	1	1	1	0	0	1	1	0
12	1	X	1	1	0	0	1	1	0	1	1	1	0	0
13	1	X	1	1	0	1	1	0	1	1	0	1	0	0
14	1	X	1	1	1	0	1	1	1	1	0	0	0	0
15	1	X	1	1	1	1	1	1	1	1	1	1	1	1
BI	X	X	X	X	X	X	0	1	1	1	1	1	1	1
RBI	1	0	0	0	0	0	0	1	1	1	1	1	1	1
LT	0	X	X	X	X	X	1	0	0	0	0	0	0	0

Fig. 3-15. Truth table for Fig. 3-14.

However, when RBI = 0, the output of Gate 5 depends on inputs $\bar{A}$, $\bar{B}$, $\bar{C}$, and $\bar{D}$ (LT must be high for normal circuit operation). If inputs $A = B = C = D = 0$, then $\bar{A} = \bar{B} = \bar{C} = \bar{D} = 1$, and Gate 5 has all 1s for inputs. Gate 5 is satisfied and goes to 0. With Gate 5 = 0, all segments go high, which is the off condition. Thus, the numeral ZERO is not lighted—it is blanked out. All other numerals from 1 through 9 are displayed normally.

At the same time that ZERO is blanked, the input/output pin BI/RBO is driven to 0. Fig. 3-16 shows how this operating mode can be used for ZERO blanking in a six-numeral display. In this application, the decimal point location is fixed, and the

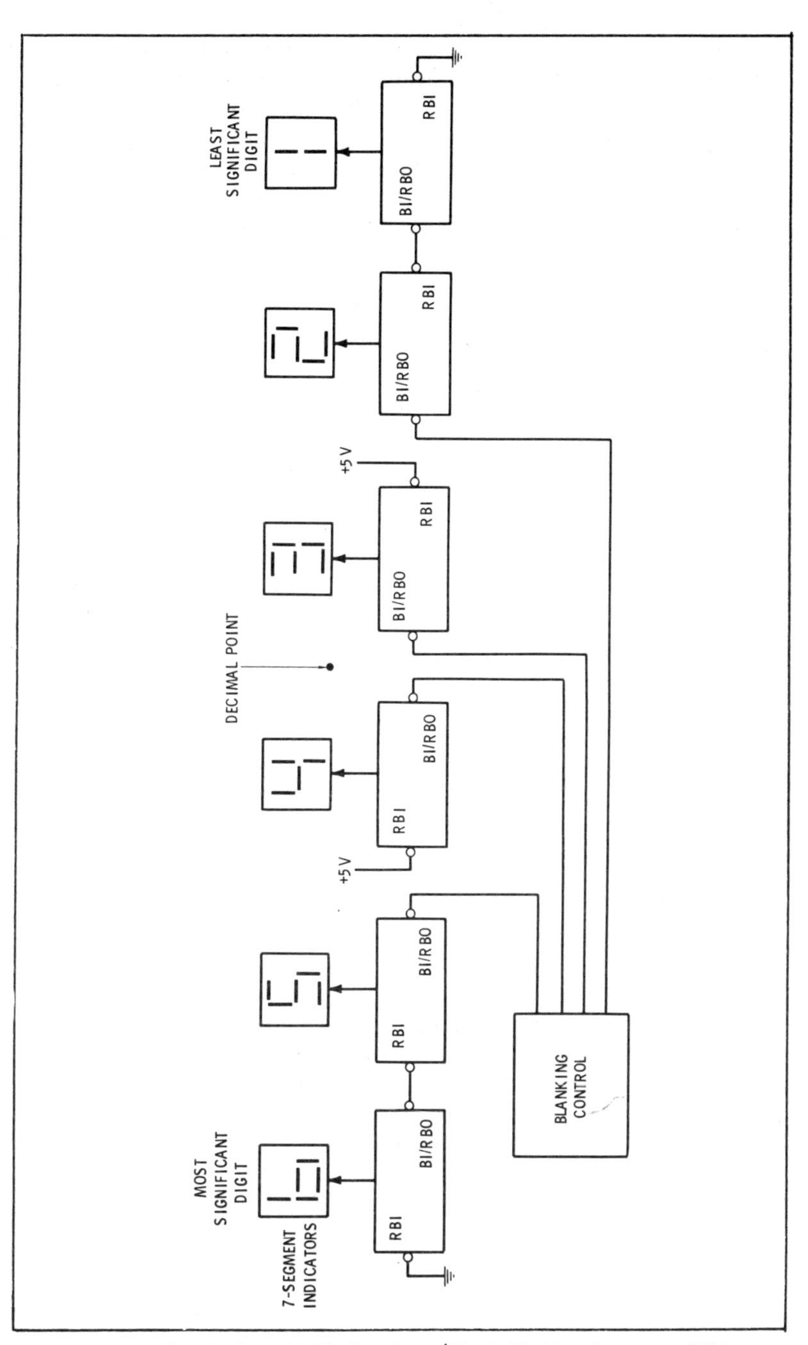

Fig. 3-16. Readout display with Blanking Input/Ripple-Blanking Output capabilities.

decoders on each side of it have their RBI terminals permanently connected to highs. These connections prevent these two digits from blanking out when they are asked to display a ZERO. This type operation helps prevent errors in placing the decimal point when reading the display.

The digits farthest removed from the decimal point have the RBI terminal grounded. This causes the logic to blank out ZEROs in these positions.

The digits in the intermediate positions must respond a little differently. If the Most Significant Digit (extreme left-hand digit) is not a ZERO, then the numeral for the next most significant digit must be lighted, even if it is a ZERO. Considering digit 6, we note from Fig. 3-16 that its RBI terminal is grounded (that is, $= 0$). Thus, when $A = B = C = D = 0$ for this digit, the ZERO is blanked and its Ripple Blanking Output is driven to 0. Since this signal acts as the RBI for digit 5, digit 5 will react similarly to digit 6. If the BI/RBO signal from digit 6 is 0, digit 5 will also blank out a ZERO (when its input $A = B = C = D = 0$). If the BI/RBO signal from digit 6 is a 1, digit 5 will display an output, even if it is a ZERO.

TYPE	OUTPUT LOGIC	LT INPUT	BLANKING INPUT	RBI INPUT	BI/RBO INPUT	OUTPUTS
54/7446	ACTIVE LOW	YES	NO	YES	YES	OPEN COLLECTOR INVERTER, WITHSTAND 30V, MAX REVERSE CURRENT .25mA
54/7447	ACTIVE LOW	YES	NO	YES	YES	OPEN COLLECTOR INVERTER, WITHSTAND 15V, MAX REVERSE CURRENT .25mA
54/7448	ACTIVE HIGH	YES	NO	YES	YES	PASSIVE PULL-UP
54/7449	ACTIVE HIGH	NO	YES	NO	NO	OPEN COLLECTOR

Fig. 3-17. Major characteristics for BCD-to-seven-segment decoder/driver.

Digit 1 acts similarly to digit 6; digit 2 acts similarly to digit 5. Digits 3 and 4 always present a display, even when the numeral is ZERO.

If the intensity of the display is to be controlled, the blanking input can be modulated with a multivibrator. Best results are obtained using a modulation source that allows the duty cycle to be varied.

Major characteristics of various BCD-to-seven-segment ICs are shown in Fig. 3-17.

CHAPTER 4

Multiplexers

Suppose a computer was being fed information (digital words) from a number of different sources. The sources might be manually operated teletypewriters, transducers that are monitoring a chemical process, an electronic counter measuring the frequency of an oscillator circuit, etc. The computer can deal with these various inputs one at a time only. Thus, there must be a way to select each input and exclude all others. The process is called data selection and in manual systems would probably be performed by a selector switch. The data appears first from one source and then from another. Since the information is entering into the computer in a more or less continuous stream of data, the process is also called multiplexing. The opposite problem, that of sorting a stream of digital words and routing each to its correct destination, is called demultiplexing.

DATA SELECTORS

Fig. 4-1 shows a 16-channel data selector/multiplexer, type 54150/74150. Its circuit operation is similar to the previously discussed one-out-of-four decoder. To select the data appearing at input E_0, for example, we address the circuit with the data select input, $A = B = C = D = 0$. To allow the data to appear at output W, an enable signal also has to be provided at the input marked Strobe. The control circuit (Strobe) has an inverted-buffer input and a logical 0 is needed for enabling. With $S = 0$, and $A = B = C = D = 0$, Gate 0 will follow E_0; if $E_0 = 1$, Gate $0 = 1$. Gate W has all inputs 0 except for the input

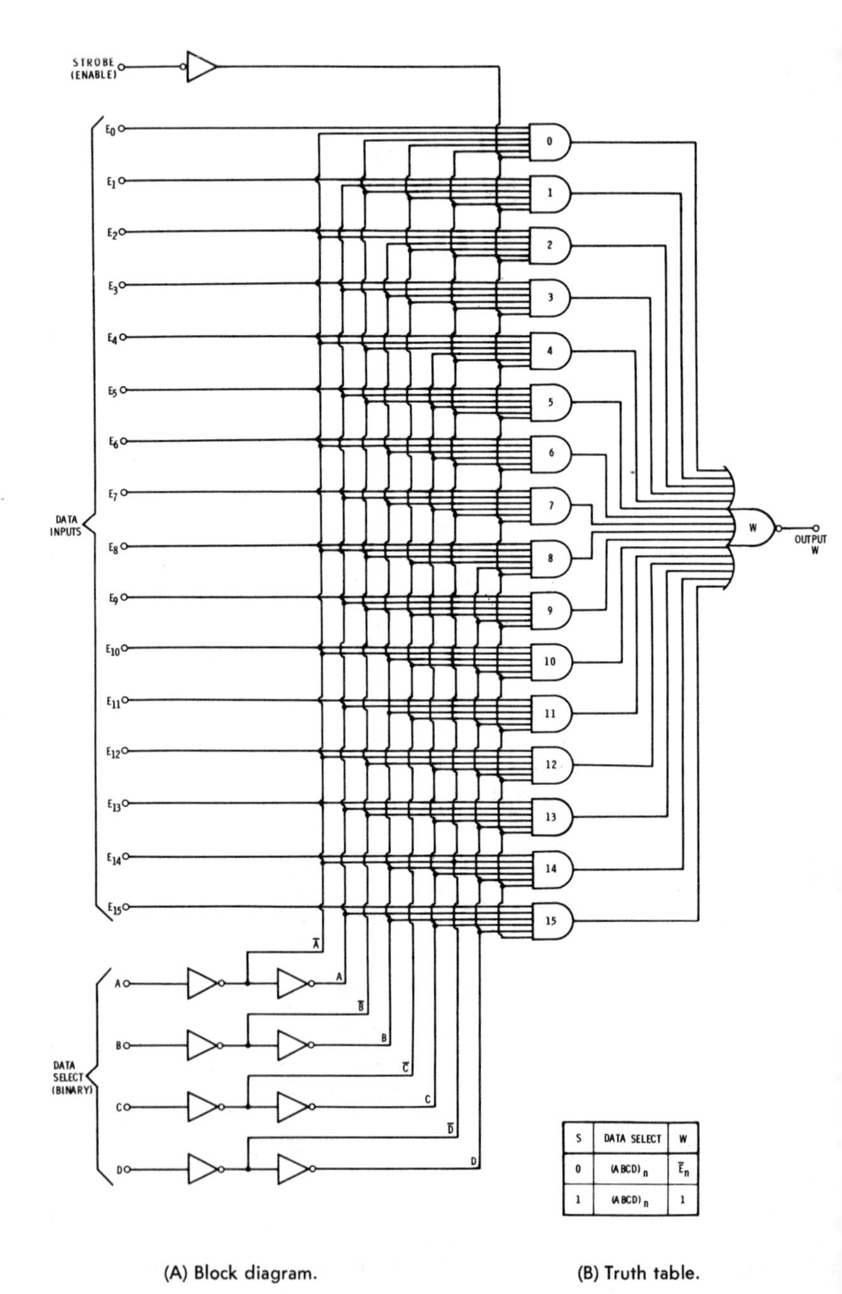

S	DATA SELECT	W
0	$(ABCD)_n$	$\overline{E}_n$
1	$(ABCD)_n$	1

(A) Block diagram. (B) Truth table.

Fig. 4-1. Sixteen-channel data selector/multiplexer.

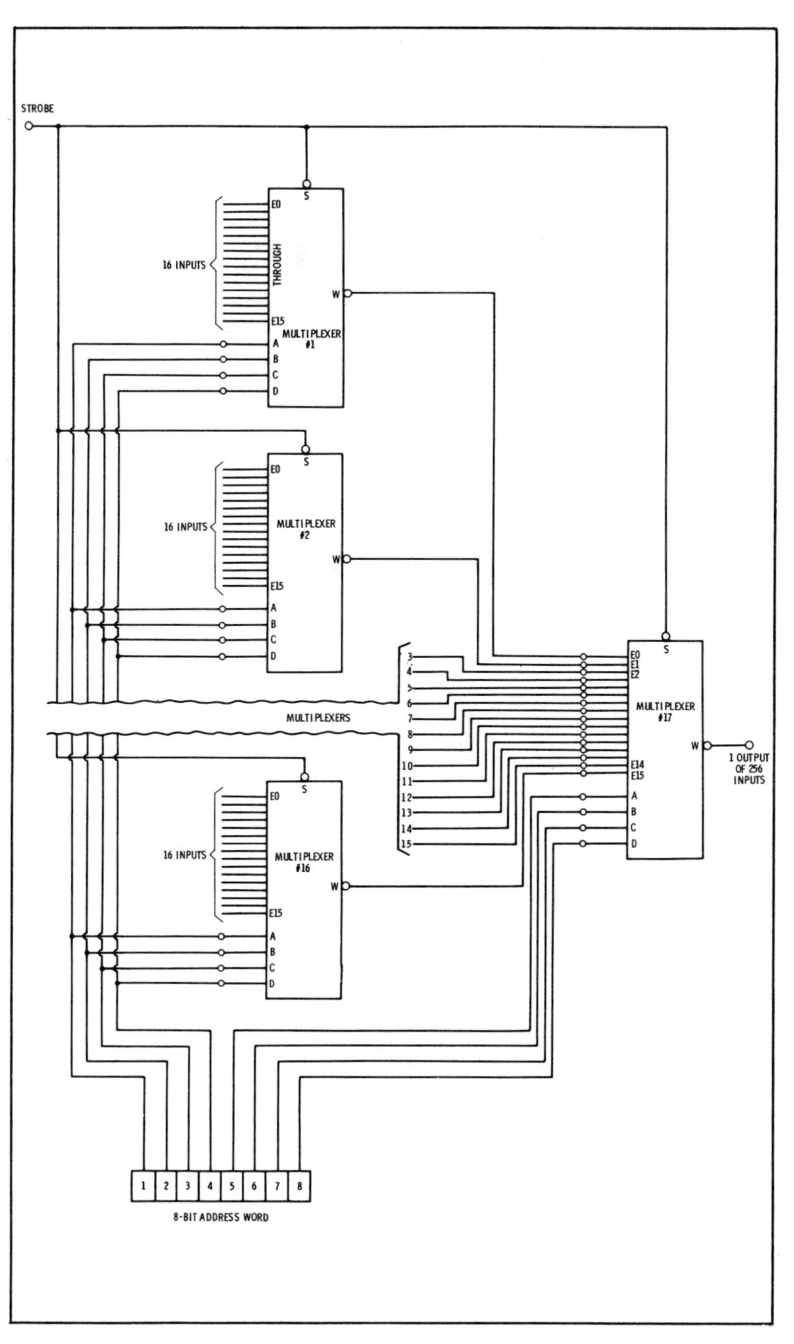

Fig. 4-2. Using multiple devices to increase input capability.

from Gate 0. Therefore, Gate W will follow Gate 0, going to a 1 if Gate 0 is a 0 and going to 0 when it is 1. Thus, Gate W presents the negative of E_0. Other outputs are selected similarly.

Circuit operation is summarized by the truth table, where $(ABCD)_n$ is the address for any specific input E_n.

MULTIPLE DATA INPUT

What if the signal appearing at E is not just a single bit, but is a digital word consisting of 8, 16 or more bits How is this handled? One can see that, as long as S is 0, any data changes occurring at a selected input will be immediately transferred to the output. If the system is designed to function this way, no problem arises. In many cases, however, the Strobe signal will be a pulse train, with the enabling signals arriving in step (maybe slightly ahead or behind but always in the same relationship) with the data signals. In this case, the output W would go to 1 whenever S is 1. If the system is designed this way, the Strobe signal will probably be used as an enabling signal in the circuit being fed by output W. Thus, the Strobe signal controls both the data selection and data input to the following section.

The circuit shown in Fig. 4-1 applies directly to circuit type 54150/74150. Circuit type 54151/74151 is similar but has only 8 inputs for data and 3 inputs for address; thus, it can only multiplex 8 sources. The type 54151/74151 has an extra inverted output to give $\overline{W}$; this output is labeled Y. Another 8-input, 3-address multiplexer, but without the Strobe circuit or the Y output, is circuit type 54152/74152.

MULTIPLE LOAD INPUT

Sometimes it is necessary to multiplex more than 16 signals. This can be accomplished by using a tier or tree of devices as shown in Fig. 4-2, where 17 devices are used to select one input signal out of 256. Note that to address this circuit properly, an address word of 8 bits is needed; 4 bits are used to address device 17, and the other 4 bits are used to address devices 1 through 16.

CHAPTER 5

Shift Registers

A shift register consists of a number of flip-flops connected together in such a way that the circuit can store a digital word for a time, and then can transfer it to another circuit on demand.

EIGHT-BIT SHIFT REGISTER

Fig. 5-1 shows an 8-bit shift register that uses Set-Reset master-slave flip-flops. It accepts serial data and is driven by the clock pulse. The register shown is circuit type 5491/7491.

When inputs A = B = 1, Gate 1 = 0 and Gate 2 = 1. These conditions put a 0 on the Reset (R) input and a 1 on the Set (S) input to flip-flop 1. When CP goes high, it puts a 0 on the CP inputs of the flip-flops. Since S = 1, this causes flip-flop 1 to go to the Q = 1 state. At the same time, the R and S inputs to the flip-flop are disabled. When the clock goes low, the CP input to the flip-flop goes high. This locks the flip-flop in the Q = 1 state and frees the S and R inputs to go to the next condition called for by inputs A and B.

Assume inputs A and B stay high. As a result of the first clock pulse, flip-flop 2 has its S input = 1 and its R input = 0. On the next clock pulse, therefore, flip-flop 2 will be driven to the Q = 1 position. At the same time, flip-flop 1 will remain in the Q = 1 state.

Before the next clock pulse arrives, let A or B (or both) go to 0. This sets the R input of flip-flop 1 to a 1 and the S input

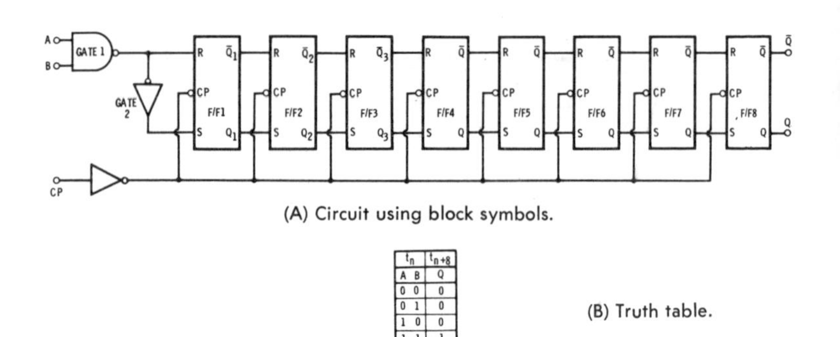

(A) Circuit using block symbols.

t_n		t_{n+8}
A	B	Q
0	0	0
0	1	0
1	0	0
1	1	1

t_n - BIT TIME BEFORE CP.
t_{n+8} - BIT TIME AFTER 8 CLOCK PULSES

(B) Truth table.

Fig. 5-1. Eight-bit shift register.

to a 0. Flip-flop 2 has Q = 1, which puts a 1 on the S input of flip-flop 3. The next clock pulse will, therefore, drive flip-flop 3 to the Q = 1 state; flip-flop 2 will stay in the Q = 1 state; and flip-flop 1 will be driven to the Q = 0 state.

If A and B are both set to 1 again, the next clock pulse will drive output Q of flip-flop 1 to 1, flip-flop 2 to 0, flip-flop 3 to 1, and flip-flop 4 to 1. After the eighth clock pulse, the first bit of data that entered the register will appear at the output of the eighth flip-flop. The process is summarized in the truth table, where t_{n+8} means the time slot after the eighth clock pulse. If we want to put in a specific 8-bit word, we need only change the input bit as required before each clock pulse.

To extract a word stored in the register, 8 clock pulses must be applied; the word will appear at the output in serial form. At the same time one word is being extracted, a different word can be loaded in. Alternatively, the register can be set to all 0s by setting B = 0 and clocking 8 times (or set to all 1s by setting A = B = 1 and clocking 8 times). One input, for example B, can be used as a control. Whenever B = 1, the circuit will follow A, entering a 0 if A = 0 and entering a 1 if A = 1.

Suppose you are working with a 16-bit word instead of an 8-bit word and need a serial-in/serial-out shift register. Fig. 5-2 shows how the type 5491/7491 can be operated in tandem

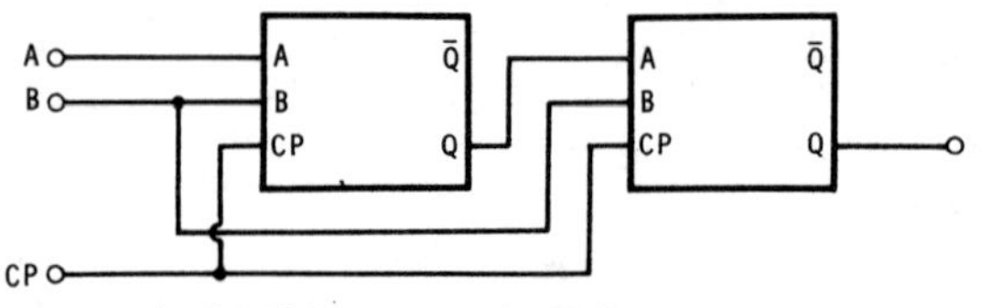

Fig. 5-2. Using two ICs in tandem operation.

to handle a 16-bit word. Longer word lengths can be handled by adding more units, connecting output Q to the next A input, and paralleling input B and the CP.

SERIAL-PARALLEL SHIFT REGISTER

Data can exist in both serial and parallel format, and changes from one form to the other are necessary. The shift register shown in Fig. 5-3, type 5496/7496, uses 5 master-slave type flip-flops and can convert data from serial operation to parallel operation and vice versa.

Master-slave flip-flops give top priority to their Clear and/or Preset inputs. In the circuits used in the 5496/7496 IC, the Clear input has priority over the serial input (D_S), but not over Preset. When Clear is set to 0, all the outputs (Q_A through Q_E) are driven to 0. When Preset is set to 1, the NAND gate associated with each flip-flop is free to follow its other input (P_A through P_E). Thus, if Preset Enable = $P_A = 1$, the output of Gate 1 = 0 and causes flip-flop A and output Q_A to go to 1. If input $P_A = 0$, however, Gate 1 = 1 and output Q_A is not affected. The other parallel inputs act in the same manner as input P_A.

For serial-in/serial-out operation, Preset Enable is set to 0 and Clear to 1. The circuit then operates like the previously considered register, type 5491/7491. The only difference between the two is that the data does not enter via a 2-input NAND gate but via a 1-input inverter. The data is transferred on the leading edge of a positive-going clock pulse. This means that the input data must be present at D_S (Fig. 5-3) before the circuit is pulsed, or else the data will not be entered in flip-flop A. Flip-flop B, however, is fed by flip-flop A, and thus data is always present at its input. Similarly, data is present at the input of flip-flops C, D, and E.

Since the outputs of the internal flip-flops are brought outside the package, the data entering serially at D_S is available in parallel form at outputs Q_A through Q_E. Thus, by using these outputs, the device will work as a serial-to-parallel converter. Note, however, that when a word is entered serially, the first bit to enter appears first at Q_A, then at Q_B, and finally at Q_E after the fifth clock pulse. In other words, the serial-to-parallel conversion is not complete until after the fifth clock pulse (parallel outputs prior to the fifth pulse will not be correct conversions). If the parallel outputs are being used to drive indicator circuits, the intermediate words may be acceptable. But if the parallel outputs are being fed to computing circuits, some

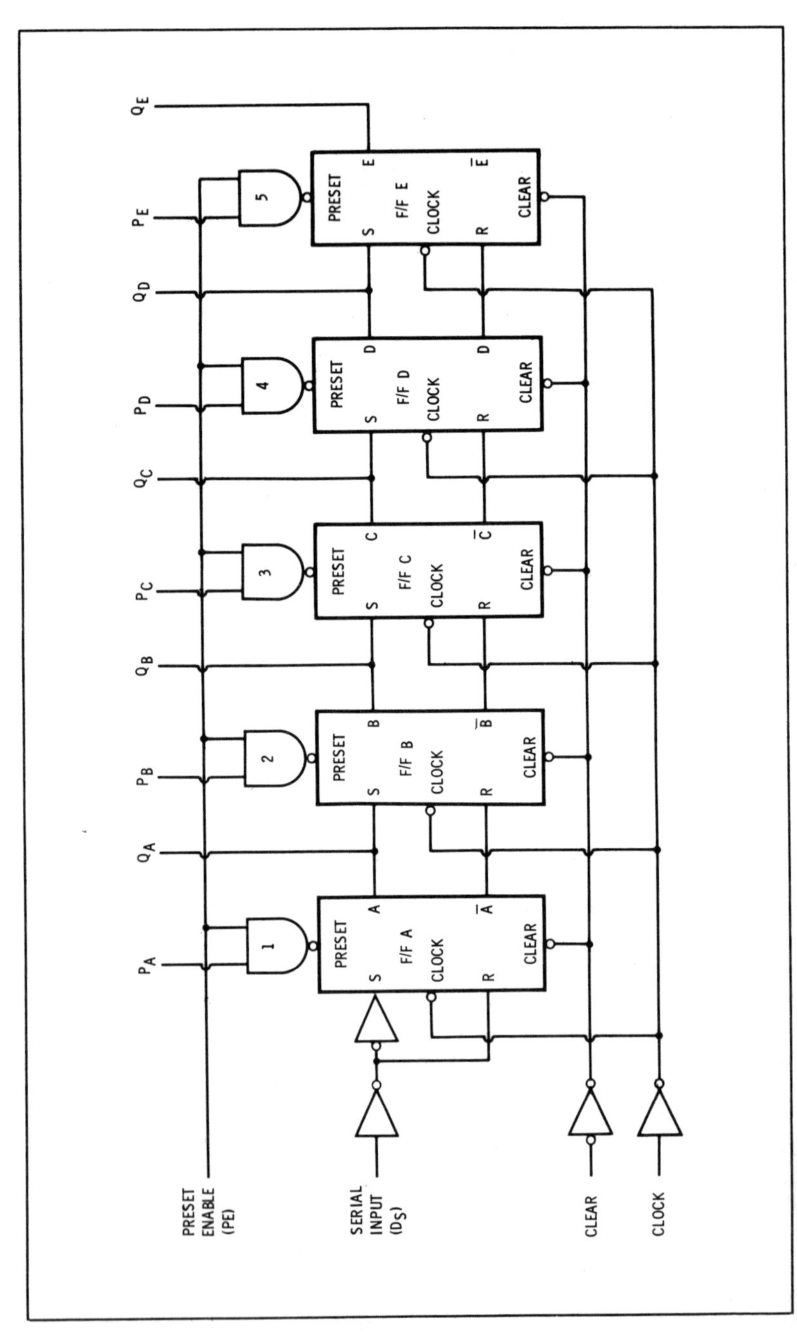

Fig. 5-3. Block diagram of a serial-parallel shift register.

form of output blanking or other control scheme may be necessary.

For parallel-to-serial conversion, data is applied to the P inputs. For example, when Preset Enable goes to 1, and $P_A = 1$, Gate 1 goes low. This is the activating signal for flip-flop A, and Q_A goes high. However, as mentioned above, if $P_A = 0$ when PE = 1, Gate 1 remains at 1 and the flip-flop is not affected; the output could be 1 or 0. To set in a parallel word consisting of both 1s and 0s, set Clear to 0 and PE to 1. Since PE has priority over Clear, all parallel inputs that are 1 will set their corresponding flip-flops to 1, while the Clear = 0 input will drive all the others to 0. To prevent driving all the flip-flops to 0, the Clear = 0 signal must be removed prior to or simultaneously with PE = 1. The word is then taken out serially by applying 1s or 0s to D_S and clocking the register. Note that the register can be set to all 0s, by keeping $D_S = 0$, while a word is being clocked out.

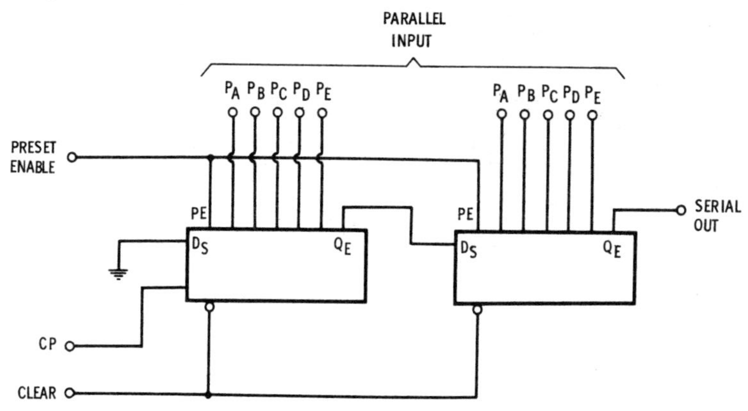

Fig. 5-4. Shift registers connected for tandem operation.

Registers can be combined to handle words longer than 5-bits, as shown in Fig. 5-4.

LEFT-SHIFT AND RIGHT-SHIFT REGISTERS

For shift registers discussed thus far, data has been entered at the left side—that is, at the left side of the schematic or drawing—and has then been shifted to the right (or, entered at the top and removed from the bottom). In any case, the data could not be moved forward and then backward, like maneuvering soldiers in ranks or boxcars on a railroad track. In some logical operations, a reverse or left-shift maneuver is needed.

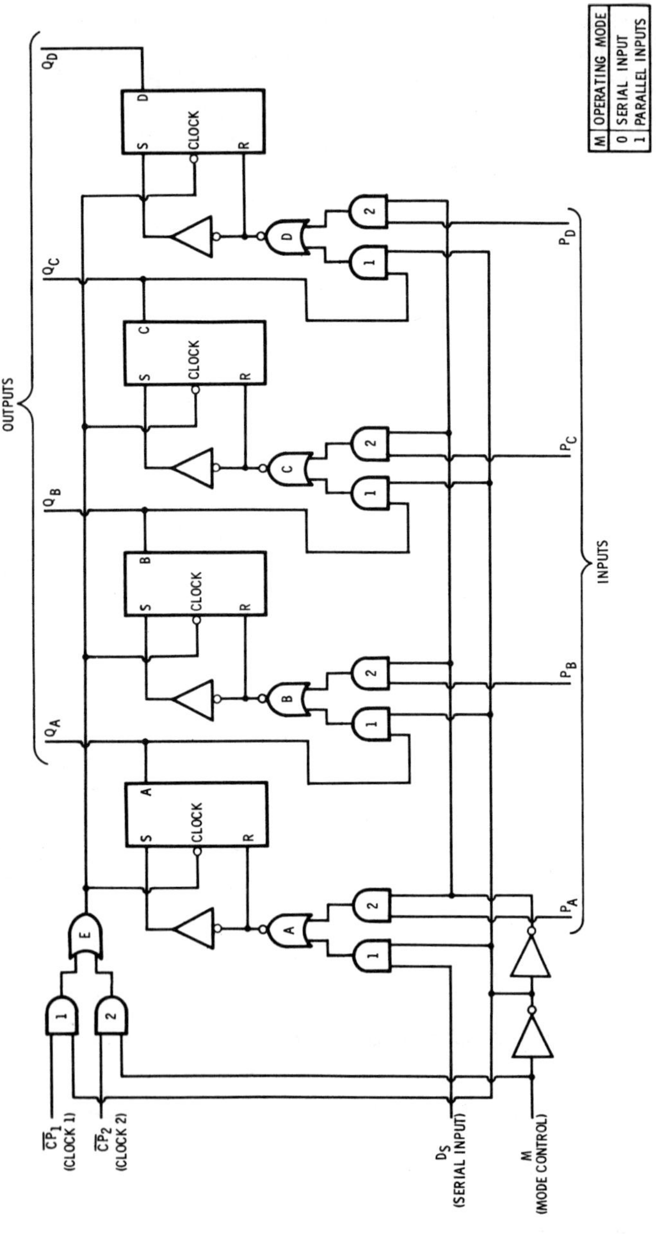

(A) Function block diagram.

M	OPERATING MODE
0	SERIAL INPUT
1	PARALLEL INPUTS

(B) Mode Control operation.

Fig. 5-5. Left- or right-shift register.

The shift register in Fig. 5-5A (type 5495A/7495A) can handle data in a serial or parallel form and can shift it left or right as required. The circuit is similar to previous registers but also has a Mode Control network that determines operation. Let the Mode Control input (M) be 0 (Fig. 5-5B). This causes all the AND gates marked 2 to have one input 0 and the gates are closed or inhibited—parallel inputs P_A through P_D cannot get into the register.

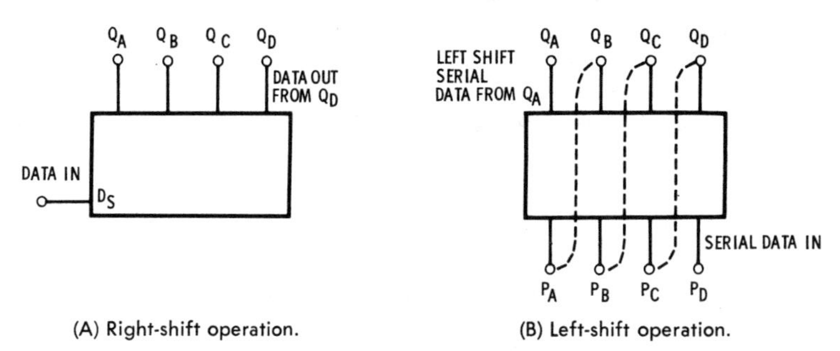

(A) Right-shift operation. (B) Left-shift operation.

Fig. 5-6. Operational method of Fig. 5-5.

The gates marked 1, however, all have a 1 input from the Mode Control circuit, so they are not inhibited. Data applied at the Serial input terminal will be fed into the register with each clock pulse. If the data at D_S is a 1, then Gate 1 = 1, Gate A = 0, and the inputs of the A flip-flop are S = 1, R = 0; if D_S = 0, S = 0 and R = 1. The data enters the register when the circuit is clocked by CP_1. The flip-flops are the same master-slave Set-Reset type used in the registers discussed previously. Data is entered on the negative edge of the clock pulse. Since the clock input circuit does not provide inversion, a negative-going clock signal is required. If a positive clock pulse is used,

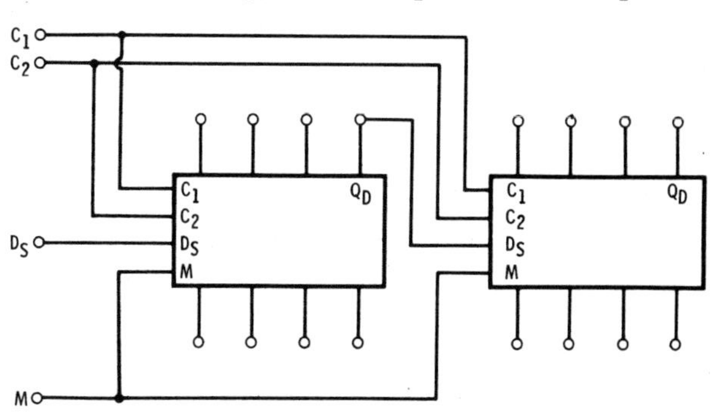

Fig. 5-7. Registers connected to provide expanded output.

the data will be entered on the trailing edge of the pulse. Since the data in each flip-flop is available at output pins, the circuit functions as a right-shift register and/or as a serial-to-parallel converter (Fig. 5-6A).

When the Mode Control is 1 (Fig. 5-5B), the "1" gates are inhibited and the "2" gates are enabled. Data applied at the serial input is blocked, but data applied at the parallel inputs (P_A through P_D) will enter the register whenever Clock 2 goes low. If data is taken out at outputs Q_A through Q_D, the register acts as a temporary store or memory. To obtain left-shift operation, serial data is fed into P_D ($M = 1$). Output Q_D is then applied to input P_C; output Q_C is applied to input P_B; output Q_B is applied to input P_A; and the output from Q_A is left-shifted data (Fig. 5-6B).

If left-shift and right-shift are to be obtained from the same clocking source, then clock inputs 1 and 2 can be tied together without affecting circuit operation.

Data has to be shifted left or right only as many places as required. This characteristic is useful in mathematical operations. Words longer than 5-bits can be handled as indicated in Fig. 5-7.

CHAPTER 6

Counters

Counters use flip-flops and gates to provide various functions such as binary counting, decimal counting, counting up, counting down, and generating a pulse when a preset count is reached. Counting is analogous to frequency division, since an output is generated only after a certain number of pulses have been fed into the counter. Thus, you may get one pulse out for every two pulses in, or one pulse out for every ten pulses in, etc. A binary counter, for example, is essentially a divide-by-2 circuit that generates a true output for every second pulse in.

FOUR-BIT BINARY COUNTERS

Fig. 6-1 is the circuit for a 4-bit binary counter (type 5493/7493) that can be used to count up to 16 or to provide simultaneous frequency division by 2, 4, 8, and 16. The flip-flops are master-slave type; the J and K inputs are open (which is the equivalent to having 1s as inputs); and the flip-flops will toggle on the negative edge of the clock pulse.

Consider first the reset function. When both R_O inputs 1 and $2 = 1$, the output of the reset gate is 0, and all flip-flops are driven to 0—that is, outputs Q_A through $Q_D = 0$. In normal counting, one or both reset inputs will be a 0, giving a 1 out of the reset gate and thus allowing the flip-flops to follow the clock pulses.

Except for the reset function, the IC consists of two completely independent circuits. Flip-flop A has its own input and

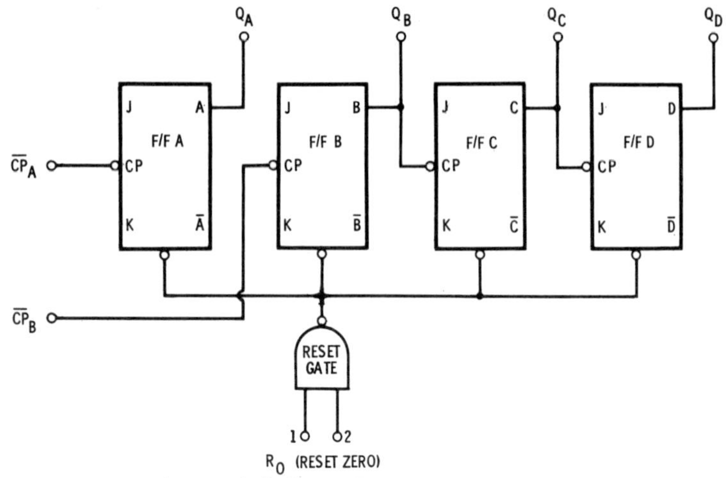

Fig. 6-1. Block diagram for a 4-bit binary counter.

output, while flip-flops B, C, and D work from one input and their outputs are interconnected.

Flip-flop A provides a divide-by-2 function. (It counts up to 2 since its output is one pulse out for every two pulses in.) Fig. 6-2 shows a master-slave, negative-edge-triggered flip-flop, such as circuit type 7473, set up to act as a divide-by-2 counter. When the Reset button is pressed, Q goes to 0 regardless of its previous state. When the Count button is pressed, the circuit will respond as shown in the truth table. If the Count button is not operated, the flip-flop obviously stays in the reset state (or count 0). On the first negative-going clock signal, Q goes to 1 and remains there when the clock returns to 1. The next negative-going count signal sets Q back to 0. Successive counts repeat the sequence.

If the number of pulses (1s) coming out of Q is compared with the number of pulses put in at the clock input, we see there are only half as many. Thus, the input frequency has been divided by 2. If a 60-Hz pulse train is applied to the clock input, a 30-Hz train comes out of Q.

Flip-flop A of the counter (Fig. 6-1) operates as described above. Flip-flops B, C, and D are similar to flip-flop A but are interconnected. If a pulse train is applied to CP of flip-flop B, the same divide-by-2 output will be present at Q_B as was present at Q_A. The output of flip-flop B is the clock input to flip-flop C. Thus, flip-flop C will toggle when Q_B goes to 0, as shown by the waveforms in Fig. 6-3. From flip-flop C, there are half as

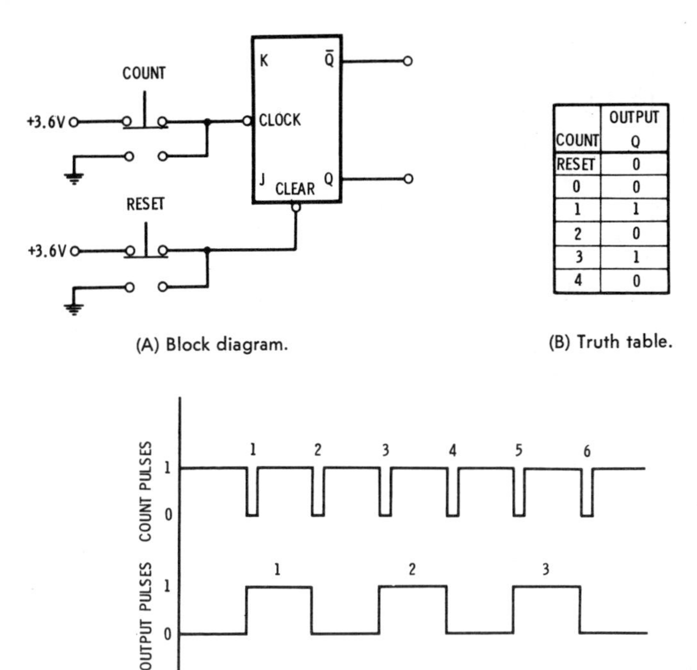

(A) Block diagram.

COUNT	OUTPUT Q
RESET	0
0	0
1	1
2	0
3	1
4	0

(B) Truth table.

(C) Input/output waveforms.

Fig. 6-2. Flip-flop used as a divide-by-2 counter.

many pulses as at Q_B. Output Q_C, in turn, acts as the clock input to flip-flop D, and the output from flip-flop D is half as many pulses as from flip-flop C. So, 60 Hz applied at the CP of flip-flop B gives a 30-Hz output at Q_B, 15 Hz at Q_C, and 7.5 Hz at output Q_D. The circuit starts at 000 and returns to 000 at the eighth pulse.

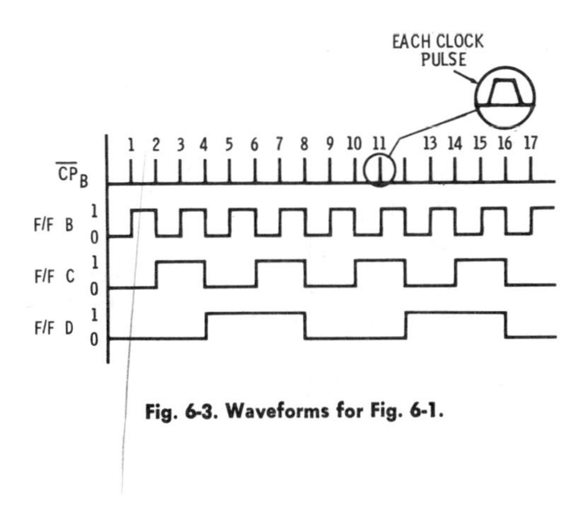

Fig. 6-3. Waveforms for Fig. 6-1.

COUNT	OUTPUT D	C	B
RESET (0)	0	0	0
1	0	0	1
2	0	1	0
3	0	1	1
4	1	0	0
5	1	0	1
6	1	1	0
7	1	1	1
8	0	0	0

Fig. 6-4. Eight-count truth table for Fig. 6-1.

As pulses are applied at the CP of flip-flop B, we see that outputs Q_B, Q_C, and Q_D are storing, remembering, or counting the number of input pulses. This is shown by the truth table in Fig. 6-4. The circuit can count from 0 to 7, where the binary number 000 is the first condition and the binary number 111 (which is equal to decimal 7) is the eighth condition. On the next input, the 3-bit counter overflows and the count starts over.

To count higher than 7, flip-flop A can be used in tandem with flip-flops B, C, and D. Output Q_A is connected to input $\overline{CP_B}$, and the signals to be counted are applied at input $\overline{CP_A}$. Conversely, the inputs can be applied to $\overline{CP_B}$ and, output Q_D can be used as the input to $\overline{CP_A}$; then output Q_A becomes the output of the counter. Four stages of binary counting will identify 16 numbers (0 through 15) as shown in Fig. 6-5. Overflow occurs on the sixteenth count.

Binary counters can be connected in tandem to count as high as desired. Each flip-flop added to the chain doubles the capacity of the counter. It is possible to count to 32 (0 through 31) with 5 flip-flops; to 64 with 6 flip-flops; etc.

DIVIDE-BY-TWELVE COUNTERS

The binary counter considered previously provides divide-by-2, by-4, by-8, etc., which are all powers of 2. In many cir-

COUNT	D	C	B	A
0	0	0	0	0
1	0	0	0	1
2	0	0	1	0
3	0	0	1	1
4	0	1	0	0
5	0	1	0	1
6	0	1	1	0
7	0	1	1	1

COUNT	D	C	B	A
8	1	0	0	0
9	1	0	0	1
10	1	0	1	0
11	1	0	1	1
12	1	1	0	0
13	1	1	0	1
14	1	1	1	0
15	1	1	1	1
16	0	0	0	0

Fig. 6-5. Sixteen-count truth table for Fig. 6-1.

cuits, however, division by other numbers is necessary. For these cases, binary counters with special internal interconnections and external gating can provide division by any number.

Divide-by-12 (divide-by-2 and divide-by-six) ability is provided by circuit type 5492/7492 IC, shown in Fig. 6-6. The only differences between this circuit and the previously considered counter are a few changes in the internal connections and the routing of the clock pulse. Reset is obtained as in the previous counter.

Flip-flop A provides divide-by-2 operation, while flip-flops B, C, and D provide divide-by-6. For divide-by-12, the two

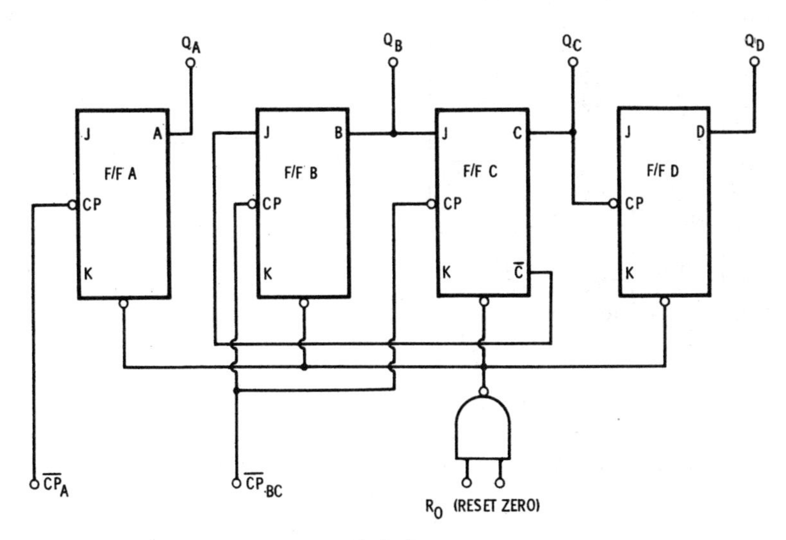

(A) Block diagram.

(B) Truth table.

COUNT	OUTPUT			
	D	C	B	A
0	0	0	0	0
1	0	0	0	1
2	0	0	1	0
3	0	0	1	1
4	0	1	0	0
5	0	1	0	1
6	1	0	0	0
7	1	0	0	1
8	1	0	1	0
9	1	0	1	1
10	1	1	0	0
11	1	1	0	1

Fig. 6-6. Divide-by-twelve counter.

sections work in tandem, in either sequence, A before or after B, C, and D.

Fig. 6-7 indicates how flip-flops B, C, and D provide the divide-by-6 function. The reset function sets all the outputs to 0 (line 1). After reset and prior to the first clock pulse, the clock input can be thought of as being high (although the clock may actually be high for only a short period before the negative transition). Thus, immediately after reset, the circuit is in the state shown by line 2.

LINE	COUNT	F/F D		F/F C				F/F B		
		CP	Q_D	CP	J	Q_C	$\bar{C}$	CP	J	Q_B
1	RESET	0	0	0	0	0	1	0	1	0
2	AFTER RESET	0	0	1	0	0	1	1	1	0
3	1	0	0	1	0	0	1	1	1	0
4	AFTER 1	0	0	0	1	0	1	0	1	1
5	2	0	0	1	1	0	1	1	1	1
6	AFTER 2	1	0	0	0	1	0	0	0	0
7	3	1	0	1	0	1	0	1	0	0
8	AFTER 3	0	1	0	0	0	1	0	1	0
9	4	0	1	1	0	0	1	1	1	0
10	AFTER 4	0	1	0	1	0	1	0	1	1
11	5	0	1	1	1	0	1	1	1	1
12	AFTER 5	1	1	0	0	1	0	0	0	0
13	6	1	1	1	0	1	0	1	0	0
14	AFTER 6	0	0	0	0	0	1	0	1	0
15	7	0	0	1	0	0	1	1	1	0

Fig. 6-7. Analysis table for Fig. 6-6.

At line 3, the clock input CP_{BC} in Fig. 6-6 goes high, which gives the same conditions as line 2. Line 4 shows the state of the circuit after the negative transition of the first pulse. Output Q_B has been driven to 1 (because its J and K inputs are both 1, causing the circuit to toggle). Input J to flip-flop C is also a 1; thus, flip-flop C is set up for a toggle. Flip-flop D has not been affected.

The next pulse sets up both B and C flip-flops and the state of the circuit after the negative transition is shown by line 6. Output Q_B goes to 0, Q_C goes to 1, and Q_D stays 0. At the same time, inputs J to flip-flops B and C go to 0, and the clock signal to flip-flop D goes high.

Pulse 3 goes high, setting up the circuit per line 7. When pulse 3 goes to 0 (line 8), Q_B goes to 0 because its J input was 0 and Q_C also goes to 0 because its J input was 0. When output Q_C goes to 0, it looks like a negative-going clock signal to flip-flop D, operating in the toggle mode, and flip-flop D, therefore, goes to 1.

Pulse 4 (line 10) sets outputs to: $Q_B = 1$, $Q_C = 0$, and $Q_D = 1$. Pulse 5 is shown by line 12 and pulse 6 is given on line 14.

(Note that line 14 is the same as line 1, and line 15 is the same as line 2.) Thus, the circuit will repeat the above sequence as long as pulses are fed into it.

The circuit does not count up to binary 6 but counts in binary (Q_D Q_C Q_B) as follows: 0 (000), 1 (001), 2 (010), 4 (100), 5 (101), and 6 (110)—binary 3 is missing. Nevertheless, six pulses are required to get one complete pulse at output Q_D; thus, the circuit divides by 6.

When flip-flop A is used as the input circuit and output Q_A is used as the clock pulse for the divide-by-6 circuit, divide-by-12 operation is obtained. The circuit does not count from 0 to 11 in binary (binary 6 and 7 are missing) but produces the truth table shown in Fig. 6-6B. The outputs are true for time periods immediately following negative-going transitions of the clock.

DECADE COUNTER

A decade counter needs 10 different output codes to represent numerals 0 through 9. Circuit type 7490, Fig. 6-8, consists of a binary counting stage (flip-flop A) and a quinary stage (flip-flops B, C, and D). The circuit is similar to the divide-by-six circuit, except that one AND gate has been added and the internal connections are different.

Consider the reset function first. All outputs are set to 0 by putting 1s on the "Reset to 0" gate. The circuit can also be set

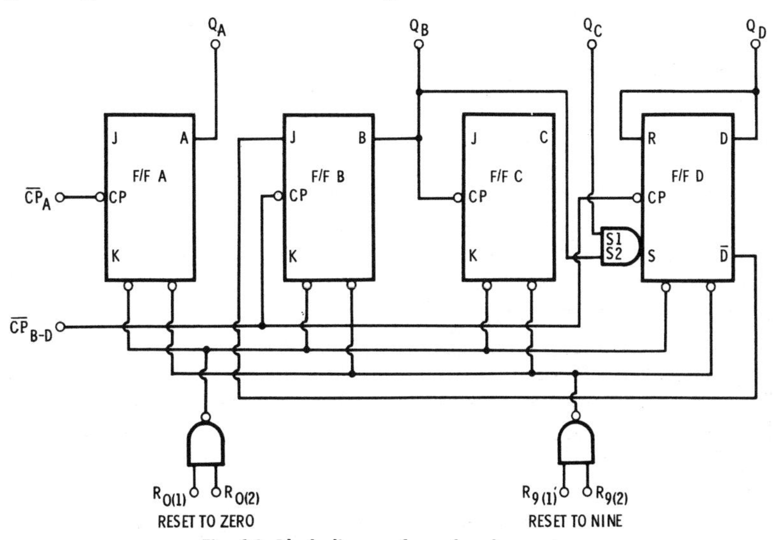

Fig. 6-8. Block diagram for a decade counter.

to BCD 9 by putting 1s on the "Reset to 9" gate. Note from the Reset truth table (Fig. 6-9B) that Reset-to-9 will take precedence over Reset-to-0. That is, if all four reset inputs are 1, the output will go to BCD 9.

BCD COUNT SEQUENCE

COUNT	OUTPUT			
	D	C	B	A
0	0	0	0	0
1	0	0	0	1
2	0	0	1	0
3	0	0	1	1
4	0	1	0	0
5	0	1	0	1
6	0	1	1	0
7	0	1	1	1
8	1	0	0	0
9	1	0	0	1

(A) BCD-counter mode.

RESET/COUNT

RESET INPUTS				OUTPUT
$R_{0(1)}$	$R_{0(2)}$	$R_{9(1)}$	$R_{9(2)}$	D C B A
1	1	0	X	0 0 0 0
1	1	X	0	0 0 0 0
X	X	1	1	1 0 0 1
X	0	X	0	COUNT
0	X	0	X	COUNT
0	X	X	0	COUNT
X	0	0	X	COUNT

X=EITHER 1 OR 0 MAY BE PRESENT.

(B) Divide-by-ten-counter mode.

Fig. 6-9. Truth tables for Fig. 6-8.

Operation of the divide-by-five (or count to five) circuit is detailed in the analysis table, Fig. 6-10. Line 1 shows the status of the circuit after being reset to 0. Line 2 shows the circuit after reset and prior to any negative-going transition of the clock pulse. Line 3 shows the clock going high and line 4 is the status of the circuit after the first pulse goes to 0. When $CP_{B\text{-}D}$ goes to 0, flip-flop B, with input $J = 1$, is in the toggle mode and goes high ($Q_B = 1$). Flip-flop C is in the toggle mode and toggles every time flip-flop B goes to 0. Flip-flop D is controlled by gate S and will go to 1 (on a negative-clock transition) whenever $S = 1$. This transition occurs on line 10 as the fourth

LINE	$\overline{CP}_{B\text{-}D}$	COUNT	F/F B			F/F C		F/F D						
			CP	J	Q_B	CP	Q_C	CP	S1	S2	S	R	Q_D	$\overline{D}$
1	X	RESET TO 0	X	1	0	0	0	X	0	0	0	0	0	1
2		AFTER RESET		1	0	0	0		0	0	0	0	0	1
3	1	1	1	1	0	0	0	1	0	0	0	0	0	1
4	0	AFTER 1	0	1	1	1	0	0	0	1	0	0	0	1
5	1	2	1	1	1	1	0	1	0	1	0	0	0	1
6	0	AFTER 2	0	1	0	0	1	0	1	0	0	0	0	1
7	1	3	1	1	0	0	1	0	1	0	0	0	0	1
8	0	AFTER 3	0	1	1	1	1	0	1	1	1	0	0	1
9	1	4	1	1	1	1	1	1	1	1	1	0	0	1
10	0	AFTER 4	0	0	0	0	0	0	0	0	0	1	1	0
11	1	5	1	0	0	0	0	1	0	0	0	1	1	0
12	0	AFTER 5	0	1	0	0	0	0	0	0	0	0	0	1
13	1	6	1	1	0	0	0	1	0	0	0	0	0	1
14	0	AFTER 6	0	1	1	1	0	0	0	1	0	0	0	1

Fig. 6-10. Analysis table for divide-by-five decade counter.

count goes low. This, in turn, puts a 0 on input J of flip-flop B and inhibits B from toggling on the next pulse.

Output waveforms Q_B, Q_C, and Q_D are shown in Fig. 6-11. The waveform for flip-flop A is not shown, but A is in the toggle mode and Q_A will be a square wave if its input clock is a constant-frequency pulse train.

The circuit can operate in two ways. If output Q_A is connected to input $\overline{CP}_{B\text{-}D}$ and the incoming count is applied to input A, the circuit will count from 0 to 9 and give a BCD output as shown in the BCD truth table (Fig. 6-9A).

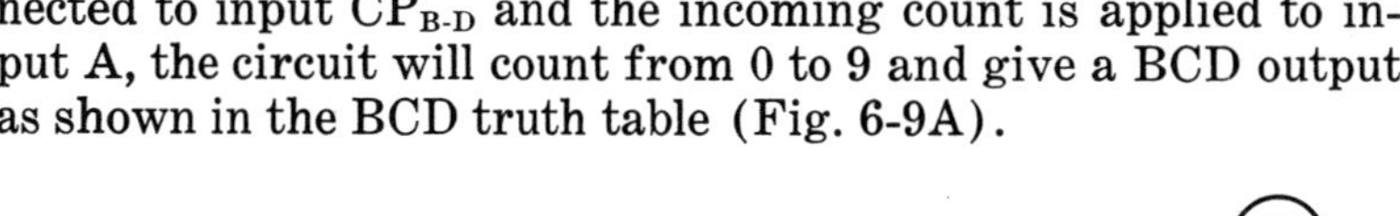

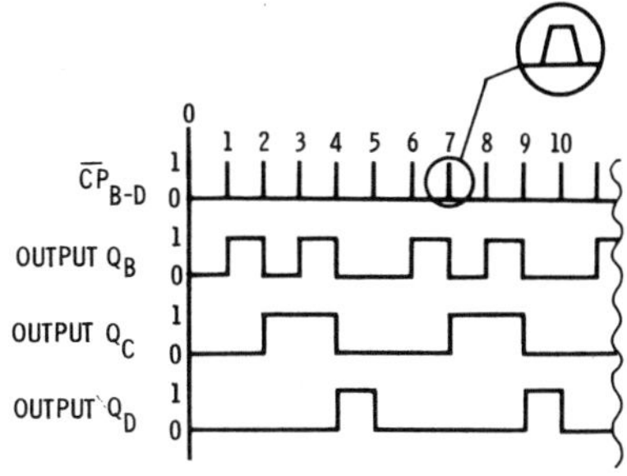

Fig. 6-11. Waveforms for Fig. 6-8.

For frequency division, a square-wave output (a wave with 50% duty cycle or high half the time and low half the time) is usually desired. In this case, the input frequency to be divided is applied at input $\overline{CP}_{B\text{-}D}$, and output Q_D is used to drive input $\overline{CP}_A$. Output Q_A is then a square wave at 0.1 the frequency of the input.

UP/DOWN BINARY COUNTER

Counting up from 0 is similar to addition, adding 1 for each input pulse. Counting down is equivalent to subtracting one count for each pulse. The synchronous 4-bit binary counter shown in Fig. 6-12 is circuit type 54193/74193. It will count up or down, depending on whether the count pulse is applied to a count-up circuit or a count-down circuit. It can be set to 0000 using the Master Reset (MR) input and can be preset to any number from 0000 to 1111 by use of the Parallel Load ($\overline{PL}$) input.

Consider first the reset function. When MR goes high, it puts 0s on the four NOR gates (which have active low inputs), and these in turn go high (to 1), which drives the four flip-flops to the $Q = 0$ state. The 0 input (from $MR = 1$) also acts to inhibit the AND gates of the parallel load circuit and prevents in-

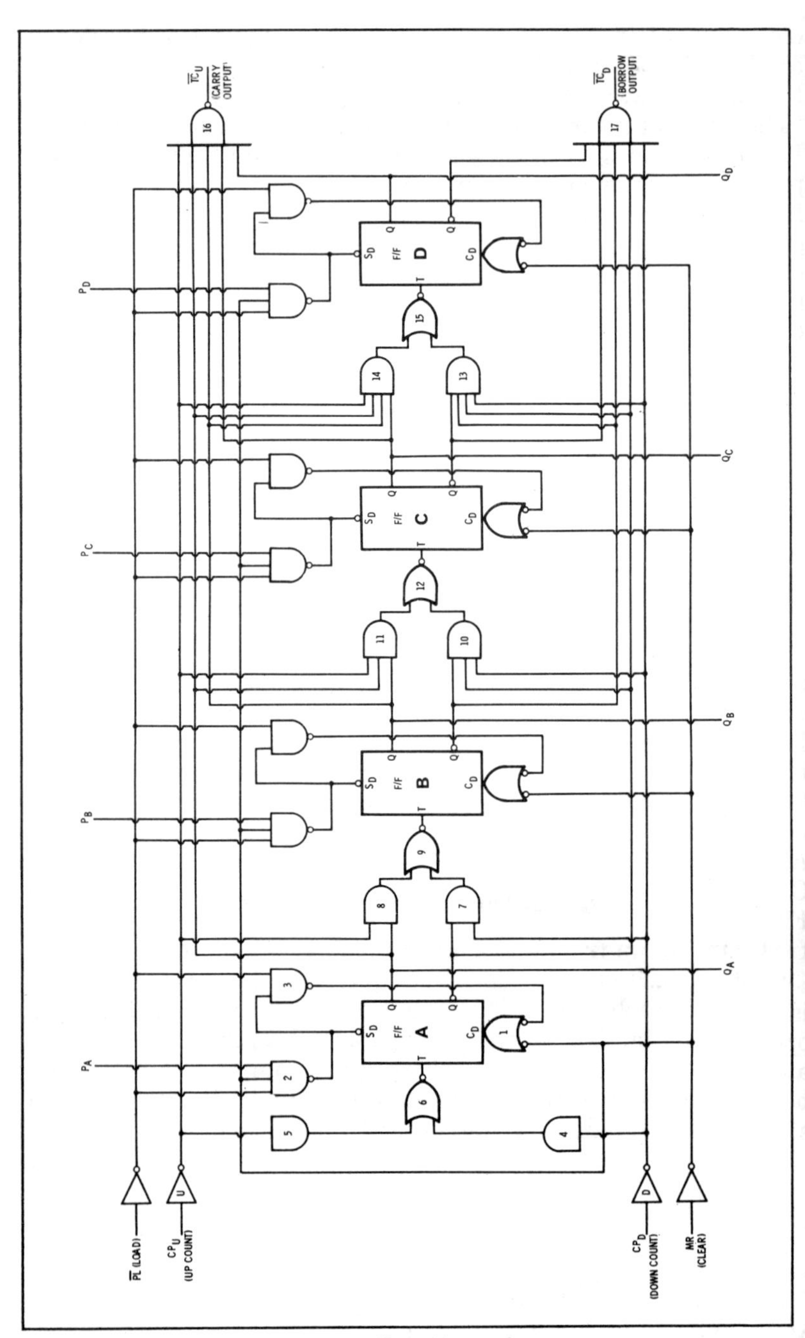

Fig. 6-12. Up/down binary counter.

correct reset. Thus, for flip-flop A, Gate 2 is a 1; Gate 3 can be a 0 or a 1 without affecting reset. MR overrides the other functions, as indicated in Fig. 6-13.

The Preset function operates similarly to the MR function. With MR = 0 and $\overline{PL} = 0$, Gate 2 has two 1s and P_A as the inputs. If $P_A = 1$, Gate 2 is satisfied and goes to 0; Q_A goes to 1. If $P_A = 0$, Gate 2 will be a 1; Gate 3 then has two 1 inputs and goes to 0. This drives Gate 1 to 0, and output Q_A goes to 0. The circuitry for flip-flops B, C, and D operates the same as flip-flop A. The counter is quiescent when MR = 0 and $\overline{PL} = CP_U = CP_D = 1$.

MR	$\overline{PL}$	CP_U	CP_D	MODE
1	X	X	X	RESET TO 0000
0	0	X	X	PRESET TO P_A, P_B, P_C, P_D
0	1	1	1	QUIESCENT
0	1	CP	1	COUNT UP
0	1	1	CP	COUNT DOWN

X= DON'T CARE CONDITION
CP= CLOCK PULSE

Fig. 6-13. Mode selection table for Fig. 6-12.

Circuit operation in the Count-Up mode is fairly complicated and is shown by the waveforms in Fig. 6-14. The starting condition for counting up is just after reset to 0000. The Down-Count input is held at 1, which makes Gate D = 0, setting Gates 7, 10, and 13 to 0. Gate 4 is also a 0, which frees Gate 6 to follow Gate 5.

The Up-Count sequence is a series of positive-going pulses. Assume input CP_U is 0 immediately after reset. This drives Gate U to 1, which sets Gate 5 to a 1 and, in turn, Gate 6 to a 0. Flip-flop A will now toggle when Gate 6 makes a transition from 0 to 1.

As count pulses enter the CP_U input, operation of the counter is shown by the waveforms in Fig. 6-14. (To emphasize the operating sequence, the waveforms are shown with exaggerated rising and falling edges. The gate being driven does not begin to respond until the driving gate has completed its excursion.) The sequence is as follows:

1. Input CP_U goes to 1.
2. Gate U goes to 0.
3. Gate 5 goes to 0.
4. Gate 6 goes to 1.
5. Flip-flop A toggles and Q_A goes to 1.

Nothing further will happen until the clock goes to 0.

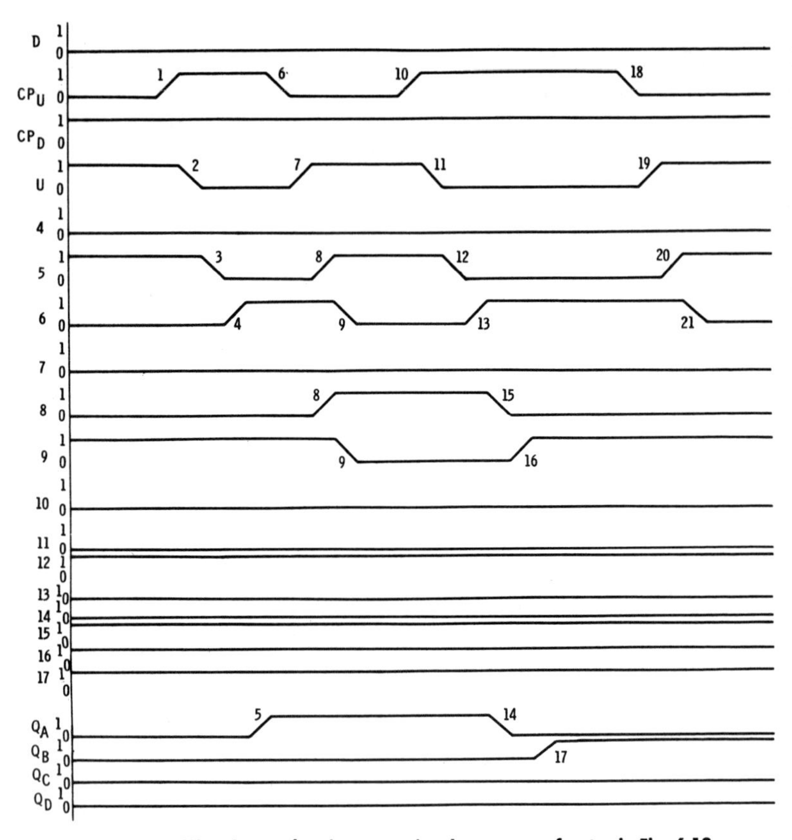

Fig. 6-14. Waveforms showing operational sequence of gates in Fig. 6-12.

6. The clock goes to 0.
7. Gate U goes to 1.
8. The next two events happen simultaneously:
   A. Gate 5 goes to 1.
   B. Gate 8 goes to 1.
9. Simultaneously:
   A. Gate 6 goes to 0.
   B. Gate 9 goes to 0.

Nothing further will happen until the clock goes high.

10. CP_U again goes to 1.
11. Gate U goes to 0.
12. Gate 5 goes to 0.
13. Gate 6 goes to 1.
14. Output Q_A goes to 0.

15. Gate 8 goes to 0.
16. Gate 9 goes to 1.
17. Flip-flop B toggles and output Q_B goes to 1.

Nothing further happens until the clock goes to 0.

18. CP_U goes to 0.
19. Gate U goes to 1.
20. Gate 5 goes to 1.
21. Gate 6 goes to 0.

Nothing further happens until the clock goes high.

The analysis can be continued in this manner and, the waveforms will show that the circuit operates per the truth table for counting up (Fig. 6-15).

COUNT PULSE	OUTPUT AFTER COUNT PULSE					
	D	C	B	A	CARRY OUTPUT	BORROW OUTPUT
0	0	0	0	0	1	0
1	0	0	0	1	1	1
2	0	0	1	0	1	1
3	0	0	1	1	1	1
4	0	1	0	0	1	1
5	0	1	0	1	1	1
6	0	1	1	0	1	1
7	0	1	1	1	1	1
8	1	0	0	0	1	1
9	1	0	0	1	1	1
10	1	0	1	0	1	1
11	1	0	1	1	1	1
12	1	1	0	0	1	1
13	1	1	0	1	1	1
14	1	1	1	0	1	1
15	1	1	1	1	0	1
0	1	0	0	0	1	0

COUNT UP SEQUENCE ↓ COUNT DOWN SEQUENCE ↑

Fig. 6-15. Truth table for Fig. 6-12.

From Fig. 6-13, we see that, for Count-Down operation, CP_U is always 1, Gate U = 0 and Gates 5, 8, 11, and 14 are always 0. Therefore, Gates 9, 12, and 15 will act as inverters and will follow, respectively, Gates 7, 10, and 13. When input CP_D goes to 0 after reset, Gate D goes to 1. Gate 4 goes to 1, driving Gate 6 to a 0, which prepares flip-flop A to toggle (when Gate 6 goes from 0 to 1).

Gate 7 has two inputs of 1 (Q = 1 and D = 1), so Gate 9 is driven to 0; thus flip-flop B is prepared to toggle when Gate 9 goes from a 0 to a 1. Flip-flops C and D are similarly prepared.

When input CP_D goes to 1, Gate D goes to 0, making Gate 4 go to 0, and causing Gate 6 to go to 1; flip-flop A toggles. At

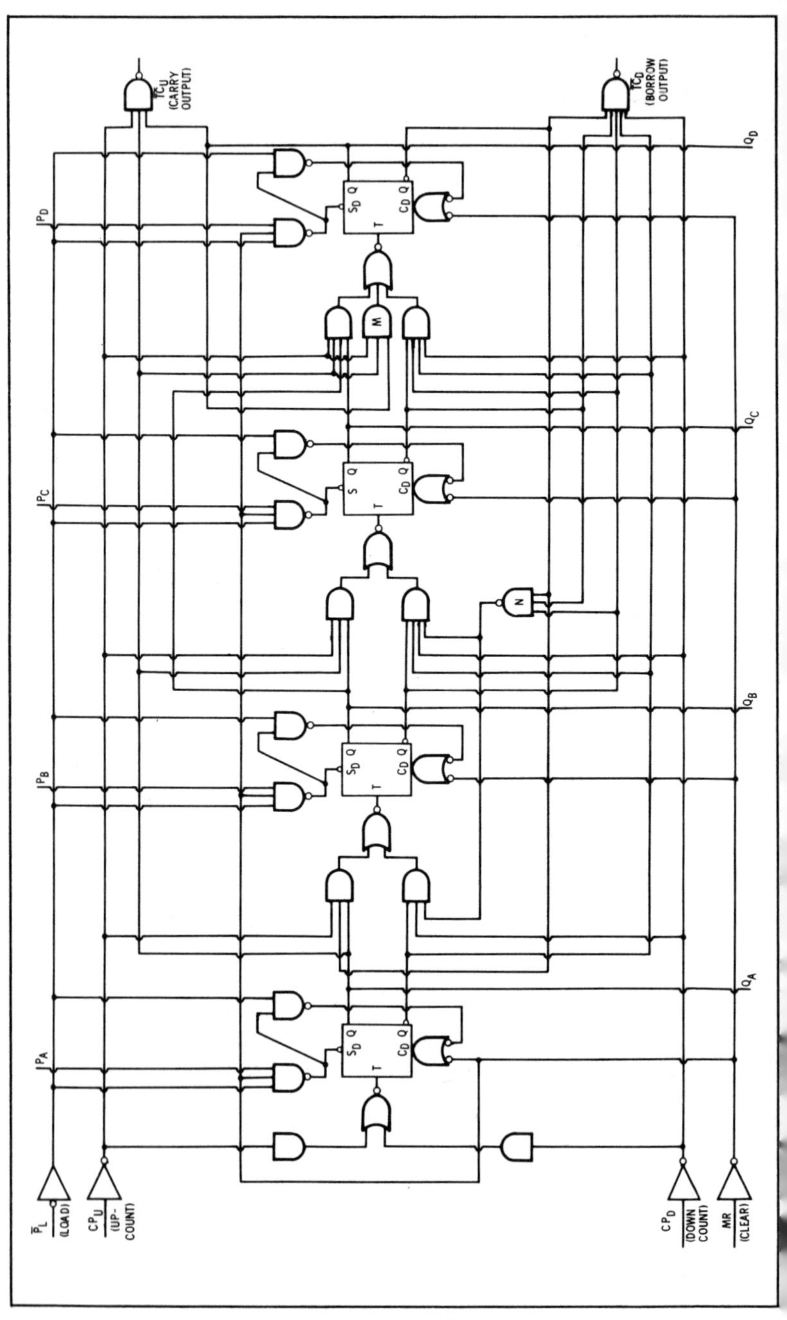

Fig. 6-16. Up/down BCD decade counter.

COUNT PULSE	D	C	B	A	TC_U	TC_D
	OUTPUT AFTER COUNT PULSE					
0	0	0	0	0	1	0
1	0	0	0	1	1	1
2	0	0	1	0	1	1
3	0	0	1	1	1	1
4	0	1	0	0	1	1
5	0	1	0	1	1	1
6	0	1	1	0	1	1
7	0	1	1	1	1	1
8	1	0	0	0	1	1
9	1	0	0	1	0	1
0	0	0	0	0	1	0

(COUNT UP SEQUENCE ↓; COUNT DOWN SEQUENCE ↑)

Fig. 6-17. Truth table for Fig. 6-16.

the same time, Gate 7 goes to 0, causing Gate 9 to go to a 1, and flip-flop B toggles. Similar action takes place at flip-flops C and D.

When input CP_D again goes to 0, Gate D goes to 1. Gate 4 goes to a 1, again driving Gate 6 to a 0. When CP_D goes to 1, flip-flop A toggles, but Gates 7, 10, and 13 inhibit flip-flops B, C, and D, respectively. As a result, the circuit follows the Count-Down sequence shown in the truth table in Fig. 6-15.

The Carry Output goes to 0 when the counter is full and the next count-up pulse occurs. Similarly, the Borrow Output goes

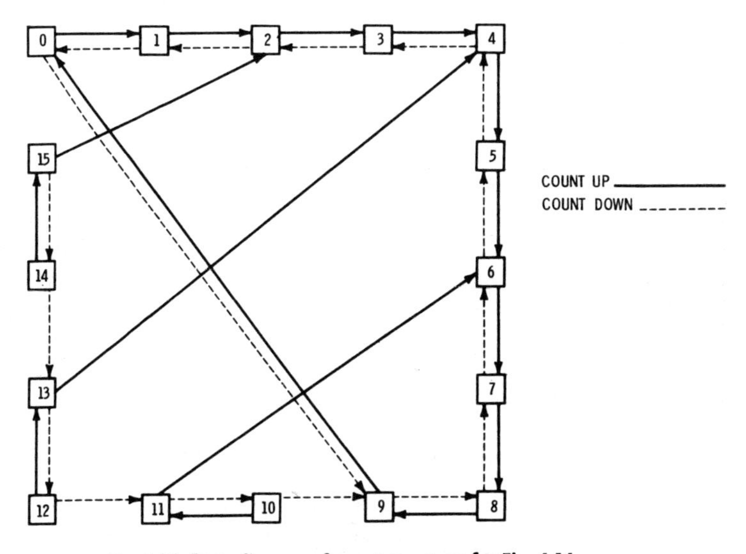

Fig. 6-18. State diagram of count sequence for Fig. 6-16.

to 0 when the counter is empty and the next down-count pulse occurs.

UP/DOWN DECADE COUNTER

A synchronous up/down BCD decade counter, similar to the up/down binary counter, is type 54192/74192 shown in Fig. 6-16. Circuit operation is the same as for the binary counter, except that the count sequence is forced back to the 0000 state on the tenth count. This is accomplished through the actions of additional Gates N and M.

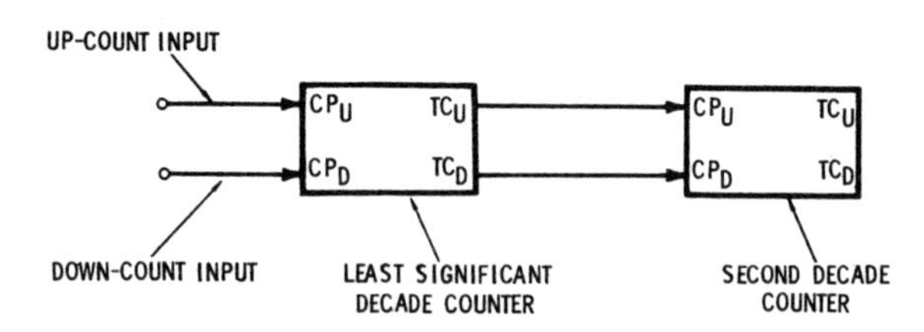

Fig. 6-19. Decade counters in tandem operation.

The counter can be preset to any count through the action of its parallel load circuit. Note that the counter can be preset to states that are not part of its regular count sequence. If, for example, the counter is preset to 1111, how will it respond on the next count pulse? The sequence of events is shown in Fig. 6-18 for all "out-of-normal-count" preloads. With the counter preset to 1111 (decimal 15), the next up-count will drive it to 0010 (decimal 2), from which point it will proceed through the normal decade count. If the counter is preloaded to 12, the next up-count will drive it to 13, while a down-count would drive it to 11. Two up-counts in succession will drive the circuit into the main sequence at state 4.

By operating two decade counters in tandem, as shown in Fig. 6-19, the count capacity can be increased to 100. The Carry Output signal of the first counter is used as the input to the Up-Count clock of the second counter. The Borrow Output signal is used as the Down-Count clock. More decades can be added in the same way. The binary counters shown in Fig. 6-12 can be operated in tandem in the same manner.

VARIABLE MODULO COUNTER

Type 9305 (Fig. 6-20) is a 4-bit counter with some extra gating and with the output of all four flip-flops available externally. The first flip-flop provides divide-by-2 operation and

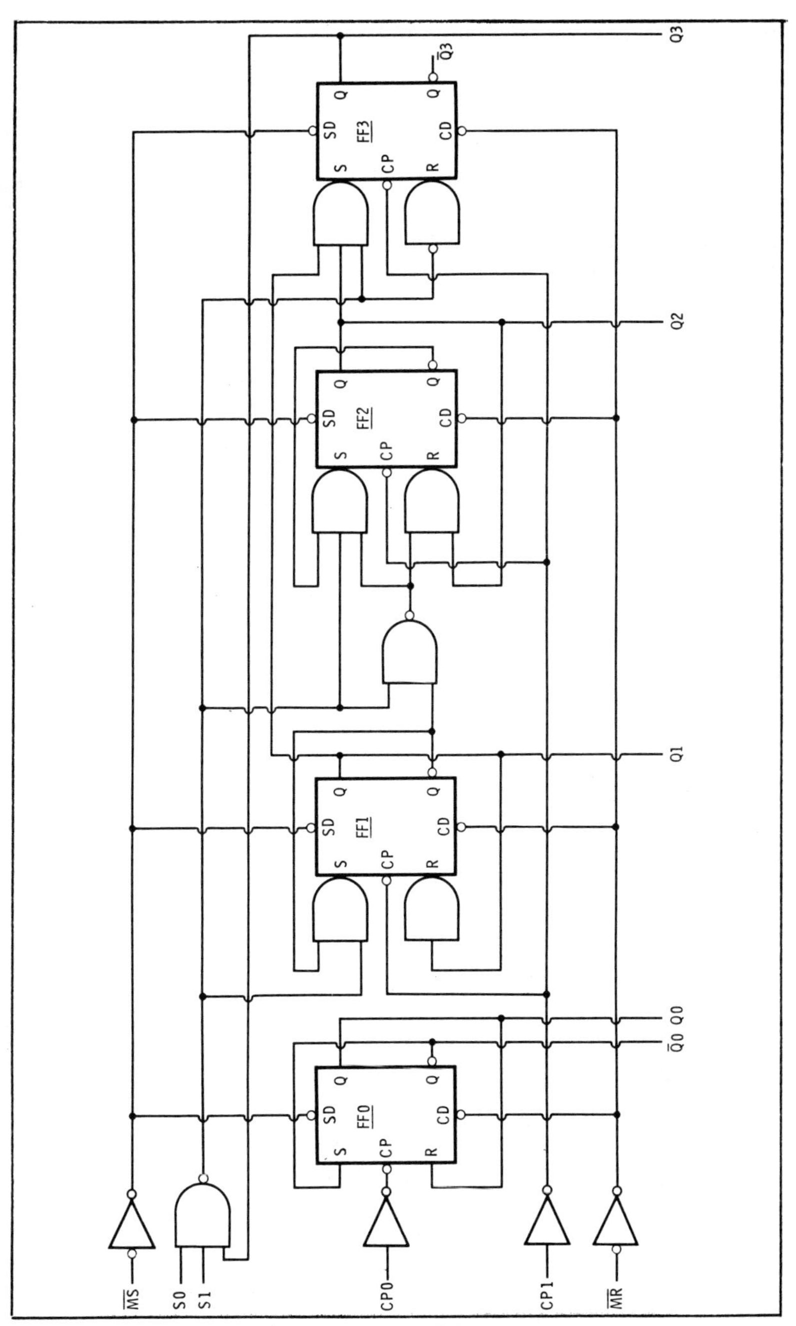

Fig. 6-20. Variable modulo counter.

the other three can be connected so as to count to 5, 6, 7, or 8. By feeding the output of one counter into the other, division by 10, 12, 14, and 16 is also possible.

All stages are cleared to 0 by bringing $\overline{MR}$ low; or set to all 1s by bringing $\overline{MS}$ low. With the first stage low, $\overline{Q}_0$ will be high and it feeds back to the S input of flip-flop 0. When the clock goes high, FF0 goes to the $Q_0 = 1$ state. This puts a 1 on the R input, and on the next positive clock, FF0 changes state again. Thus division-by-2 is obtained at the Q_0 output.

The other flip-flops are of the same type but the extra gates at the S and R inputs allow the terminal count to be varied. The four different counts available from the 3-stage group are obtained as indicated in the table. To count by 5, the two control inputs S_0 and S_1 are left open (which is equivalent to a 1), the input is CP_1 and the output is Q_3. For a 50% duty cycle divide-by-10, the signal from Q_3 is fed into CP_0 and the output taken from Q_0.

For divide-by-6, the signal from Q_1 is fed either to S_0 or S_1, and the other is left open. Input and outputs are the same as for divide-by-5, and divide-by-12 is obtained similarly to divide-by-10.

Divide-by -7 and -8 are obtained as shown in Table 6-1; divide-by -14 and -16 by using flip-flop 0.

Table 6-1. Counting by 5, 6, 7, or 8

Modulo	S_0	S_1
5	—	—
6	Q1 —	— Q1
7	Q2 —	— Q2
8	Q1 Q2	Q2 Q1

CHAPTER 7

Arithmetic Circuits

A whole group of special circuits has been developed for dealing with binary mathematics. Mathematical operations include addition, subtraction, multiplication, division, raising to a power, etc. Many of these operations can be performed with relatively simple adder circuits. Other operations require complex programs.

Even when operations are fairly simple, much effort has been made to develop special circuits and methods to reduce the time needed to complete an operation or to minimize the amount of electronics required. These circuits are beyond the scope of this book, but a few of the basic circuits will be discussed. These include adders, comparators, and a true/complement generator.

ADDERS

Binary addition follows the same rules as decade addition, except that things happen a lot quicker. In decade systems, each element or decade of a number represents any one of ten different levels or quantities (that is, 0, 1, 2, 3, 4, 5, 6, 7, 8, or 9); whereas in binary systems, each element represents only two levels (0 or 1). Thus, in Fig. 7-1A, the four-decade decimal number can have any value from 0000 through 9999, while the four-bit binary number shown in Fig. 7-1B, can have any value from 0000 through 1111. The 4-bit binary number can represent 16 levels (0 through 15), while the 4-decade number can count up to 9999 (including 0), which identifies 10,000 levels.

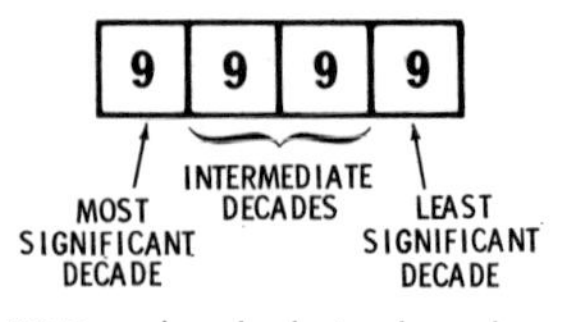

(A) Four-decade decimal number.

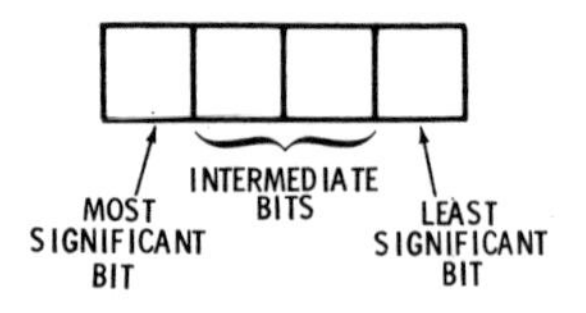

(B) Four-bit binary number.

Fig. 7-1. Representation of numerical displays.

The decade number system is far more efficient in terms of information content; the binary number system is more suited to electronic systems. Circuits can easily distinguish between two levels of signal but are subject to greater and greater error if they are asked to distinguish between 3 levels, 4 levels, etc.

Two binary numbers can be added as indicated in Fig. 7-2. Number A, consisting of 4 bits, is to be added to number B, also 4 bits long. When number A = 0000 and number B = 0000, the

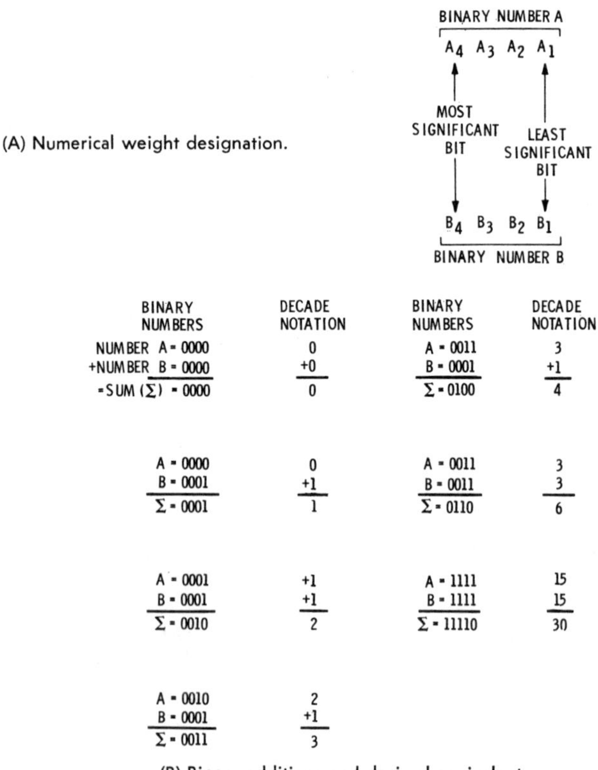

(A) Numerical weight designation.

(B) Binary additions and decimal equivalents.

Fig. 7-2. Addition of binary numbers.

sum (Σ) is also 0000, as shown in Fig. 7-2B. The sum of 0000 and 0001 is shown to be 0001. Then, when adding binary number 0001 to binary number 0001, we find that the space for the Least Significant Bit can no longer show the result by itself. Another space or the next most significant bit must be called into use. In other words, the slot or bin for the Least Significant Bit has filled up and overflowed into the next most important bin. (The same sort of overflow occurs in decade systems when 1 is added to 9, 2 to 8, etc.; the bin overflows and you generate a carry into the next bin.) Similar but more extended carries occur when you add larger numbers, as in Fig. 7-2B. Note that the addition of binary number 1111 and binary number 1111 (both 4-bit numbers) creates a 5-bit number, which means that this operation could not be performed correctly in a system using only 4-bit numbers.

Consider just the Least Significant Bit, numbers A_1 and B_1 in Fig. 7-2A. Note that this bin can, by itself, correctly represent the sum of $0 + 0$ and $1 + 0$; it cannot, by itself, represent the sum of $1 + 1$, which requires two bits to give a binary 10. Therefore, any circuit that is required to add two one-bit numbers must be capable of generating a 2-bit output. The Least Significant Bit in such an output is called the *sum,* and the Most Significant Bit is called the *carry.*

When adding the least significant bits of two numbers, we only have to deal with two bits, since the carry will by definition always be 0. Such circuits are called half-adders. Circuits that deal with bits having more weight than the least significant bits must handle the carry from the previous stage. These circuits are called full-adders. The operation of addition will be clarified by considering some specific circuits.

Two-Bit Full Adder

The 2-bit full adder type 5482/7482 circuit shown in Fig. 7-3A will add two 2-bit numbers and generate the proper carry. The numbers to be added are inputs A_2, A_1 and inputs B_2, B_1. The output (Fig. 7-3B) is the sum of the two numbers plus a carry bit to show whether the second bin has overflowed or not.

Line 1 of the truth table (Fig. 7-4) indicates the addition of 00 to 00. Consider first the case where A_1 and B_1 are the least significant bits of a number. For this condition, we do not have a carry bit from a lower-level addition, and input C_{IN} is always zero.

With $A_1 = B_1 = C_{IN} = 0$, Gates 1, 2, 3, and 4 are all closed. The output of Gate 5 is a 1 and the output of Gate 6 (Σ_1) is 0.

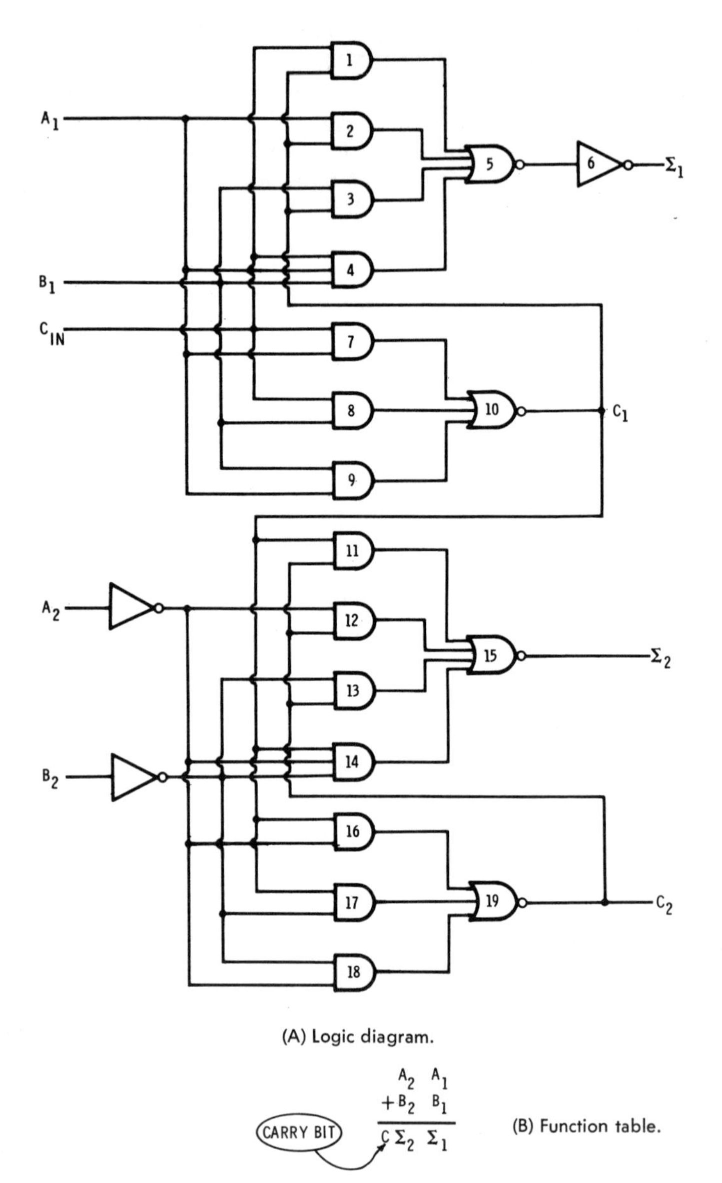

(A) Logic diagram.

(B) Function table.

Fig. 7-3. Two-bit full adder.

Also, Gates 7, 8, and 9 are closed so the output of Gate 10 = 1. With $A_2 = B_2 = 0$, we note that Gate 14 has all 1s as inputs and is therefore open; thus, NOR Gate 15 is satisfied and its output (Σ_2) is 0. We note also that Gates 16, 17, and 18 are all open and thus output $C_2 = 0$. The circuit, therefore, has generated the correct output for the specified input.

Line 2 of the truth table indicates the addition of 01 and 00. With Gates 7, 8, and 9 still closed as in the previous addition, the output of Gate 10 is a 1; therefore, Gate 2 has all 1s as inputs, Gate 5 is 0, and Gate 6 is 1. The rest of the gates have the same status as in the previous addition.

LINE	INPUT				OUTPUT					
					WHEN $C_{IN} = 0$			WHEN $C_{IN} = 1$		
	A_1	B_1	A_2	B_2	Σ_1	Σ_2	C_2	Σ_1	Σ_2	C_2
1	0	0	0	0	0	0	0	1	0	0
2	1	0	0	0	1	0	0	0	1	0
3	0	1	0	0	1	0	0	0	1	0
4	1	1	0	0	0	1	0	1	1	0
5	0	0	1	0	0	1	0	1	1	0
6	1	0	1	0	1	1	0	0	0	1
7	0	1	1	0	1	1	0	0	0	1
8	1	1	1	0	0	0	1	1	0	1
9	0	0	0	1	0	1	0	1	1	0
10	1	0	0	1	1	1	0	0	0	1
11	0	1	0	1	1	1	0	0	0	1
12	1	1	0	1	0	0	1	1	0	1
13	0	0	1	1	0	0	1	1	0	1
14	1	0	1	1	1	0	1	0	1	1
15	0	1	1	1	1	0	1	0	1	1
16	1	1	1	1	0	1	1	1	1	1

Fig. 7-4. Truth table for Fig. 7-3.

A line-by-line analysis of the circuit can be carried out to verify the truth table for all input states of A_2, A_1 and B_2, B_1.

When the two bits to be added are not the least and next least significant, the carry bit from a lower-level addition must be handled. When the carry bit from a lower level is 0, the circuit will operate as described above. When the carry bit is 1, then the circuit must operate as indicated for the second set of outputs in the truth table—that is, when $C_{IN} = 1$. Considering line 1 in the truth table, with $C_{IN} = 1$, we see that Gates 7, 8, and 9 are closed, Gate 10 is a 1, Gate $1 = 1$, Gate $5 = 0$, and $\Sigma_1 = 1$. Again, the circuit can be analyzed line by line to verify the truth table.

Note the use of inverters to turns 0s into 1s (and vice versa) to make the truth table come out right. This type circuit design is perfectly all right as long as the circuit works correctly for all conditions, and as long as the propagation delays introduced by such extra stages do not interfere with the timing requirements of the system.

Four-Bit Adder

Two 2-bit adders can easily be combined to form a 4-bit adder as shown in Fig. 7-5. However, the circuit for a 4-bit binary full adder is also available in a single device as shown

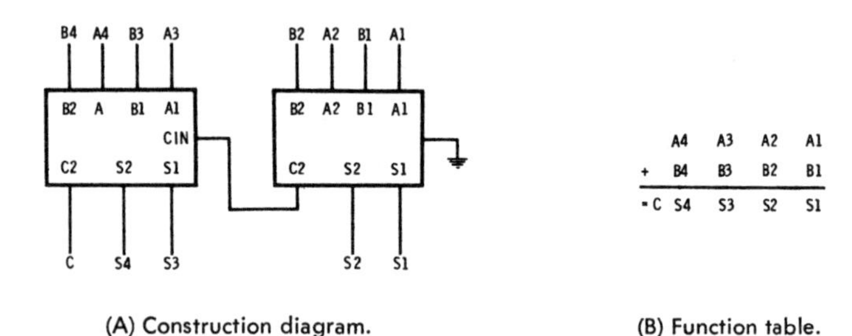

(A) Construction diagram. (B) Function table.

Fig. 7-5. Four-bit addition using two 2-bit adders.

in Fig. 7-6 (a type 5483/7483 circuit). The circuit is the same as in Fig. 7-5, except that the carry bit from bin 2 to bin 3 is made internally and not brought outside the package. Also, carry C4 represents the carry across four bits. Four-bit adders can be combined to make 8-bit adders, 16-bit adders, etc.

Gated Adders

The two adders so far discussed add two numbers as soon as the information is received. A gated, 1-bit, full adder (type 5480/7480), is shown in Fig. 7-7.

First, ignore Gates 11, 12, 13, 14, 15, and 16. Compare the remaining portion of the circuit with the A_1 B_1 C_{IN} portion of Fig. 7-3A. The circuits are identical, except that the inverted carry and the inverted sum outputs are brought outside. The inverted carry is labeled $\overline{C_{n+1}}$ but is the same as C_1 of Fig. 7-3A. Thus, the truth table for Fig. 7-3 applies to the adding circuit of Fig. 7-7 (except that inputs A_2 and B_2 and outputs Σ_2 and C_2 do not apply, and an output for C_1 must be added).

The gating portion of Fig. 7-7A consists of diode-transistor logic (DTL), which is fully compatible with TTL logic. DTL allows use of the wired-OR connection, which is forbidden in TTL except for special circuits. In any case, Gates 12 and 15 actually use a permanently-wired connection, although they perform the OR-logic function as indicated in Fig. 7-7B. As a consequence of this arrangement, when input A* is used, inputs

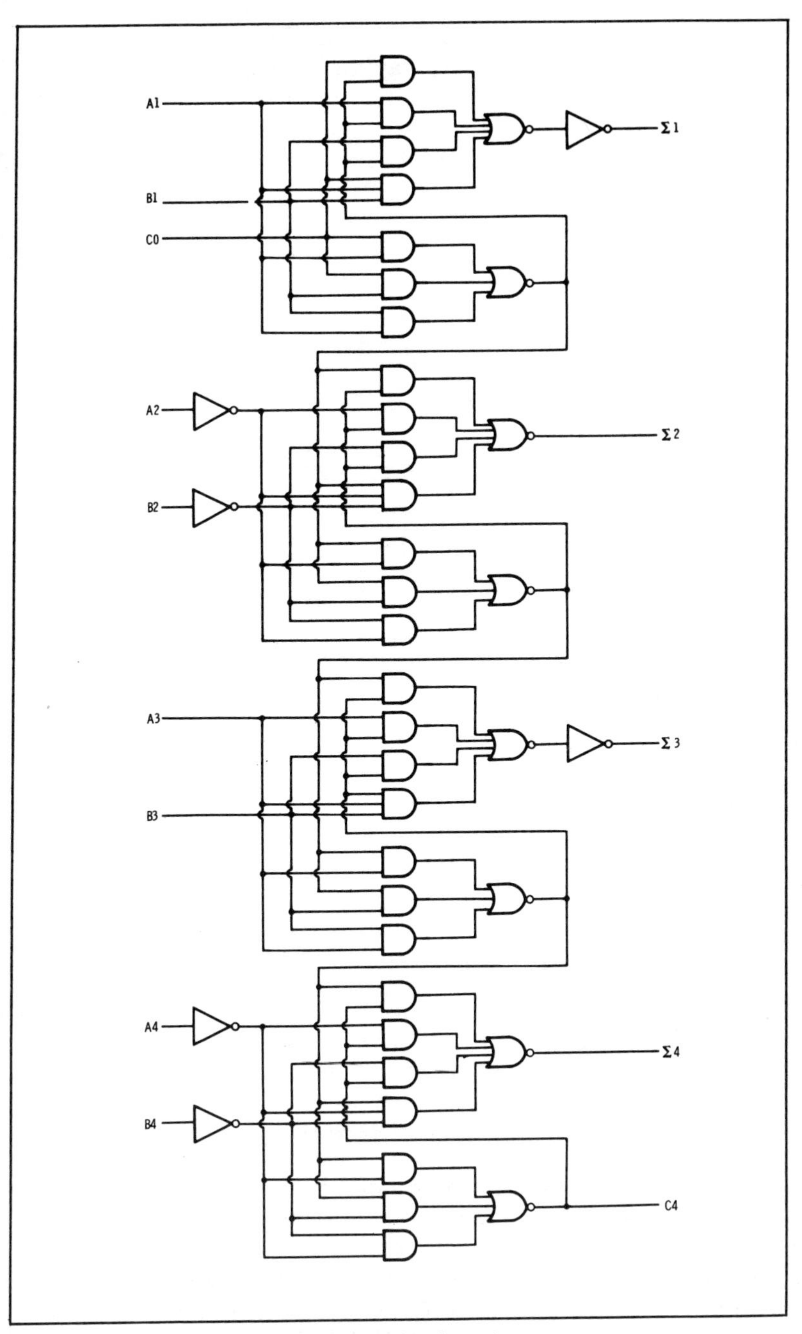

Fig. 7-6. Four-bit adder logic diagram.

A_1 and A_2 must be connected to ground. Thus, Gate 11 will be high but will follow input A*, staying high if A* is high. Conversely, when A_1 and A_2 are used as inputs, input A* must be left open. The same rules apply to inputs B_1, B_2, and B*.

The gated adder can be used to perform subtraction as well as addition.

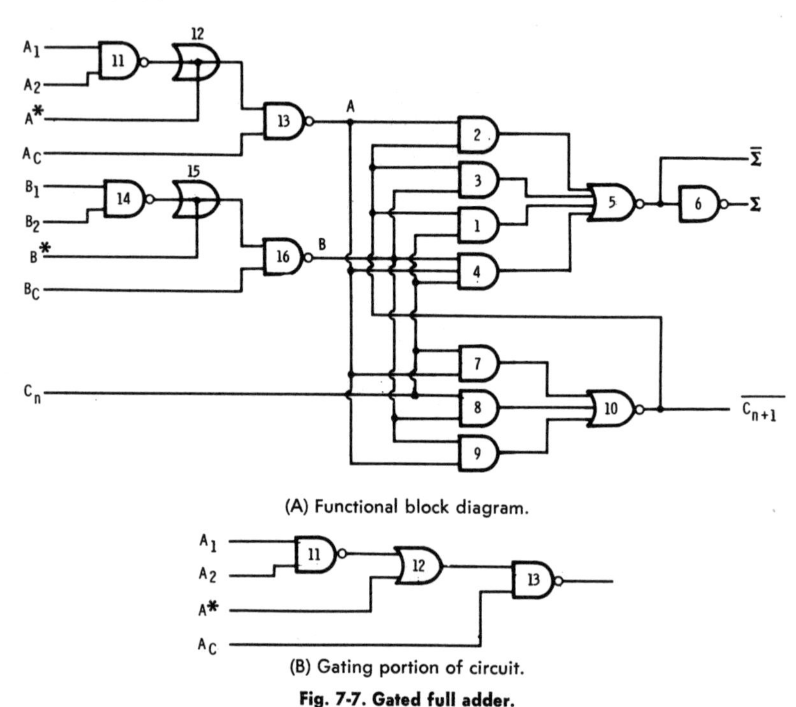

(A) Functional block diagram.

(B) Gating portion of circuit.

Fig. 7-7. Gated full adder.

TRUE/COMPLEMENT CIRCUIT

In binary mathematics, subtraction is usually performed by taking the complement of the number to be subtracted and adding it to the other number. An end-around carry or other mathematical process is then applied so that whatever subtraction algorithm is being used is satisfied, and the answer comes out right.

What is the complement of a number? In decimal notation, a 1-digit number can have any value from 0 through 9. When the number slot is empty, the number contained in the slot is 0, and the number of units that can be added to the slot without it overflowing is 9. When the slot contains 5 units, the number of units that be added without overflowing is 4. The number of units that can be added to the slot without causing overflow is the complement of the number already in the slot. Thus, 9 is the complement of 0, 4 is the complement of 5; 5 is the complement of 4; etc. The key number in the above system is 9, and the complements are called the *nine's complements*.

In binary mathematics, a slot can hold only a 0 unit or a 1 unit. Thus, the complement of 0 is 1 and the complement of 1 is 0. The complement is obtained by changing the 0 to 1 and the 1 to 0. As the number of bits is increased to 2 and more (that is, A_2 A_1 A_0), the same rule holds for a straight binary sequence where binary 000 means no units and 111 means all

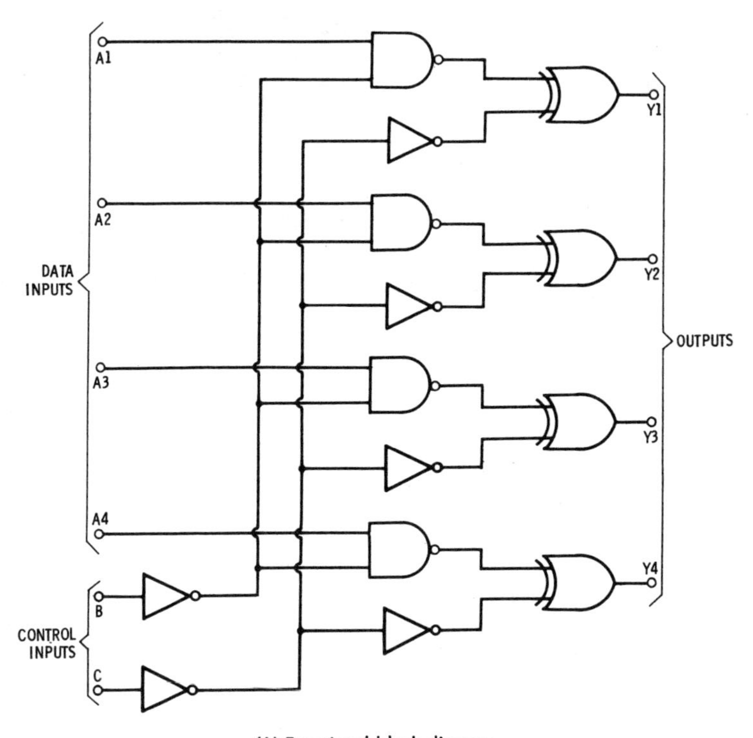

(A) Functional block diagram.

(B) Truth table.

CONTROL INPUTS		OUTPUT			
B	C	Y1	Y2	Y3	Y4
0	0	$\overline{A1}$	$\overline{A2}$	$\overline{A3}$	$\overline{A4}$
0	1	1	1	1	1
1	0	A1	A2	A3	A4
1	1	0	0	0	0

Fig. 7-8. Four-bit, true/complement, zero/one element circuit.

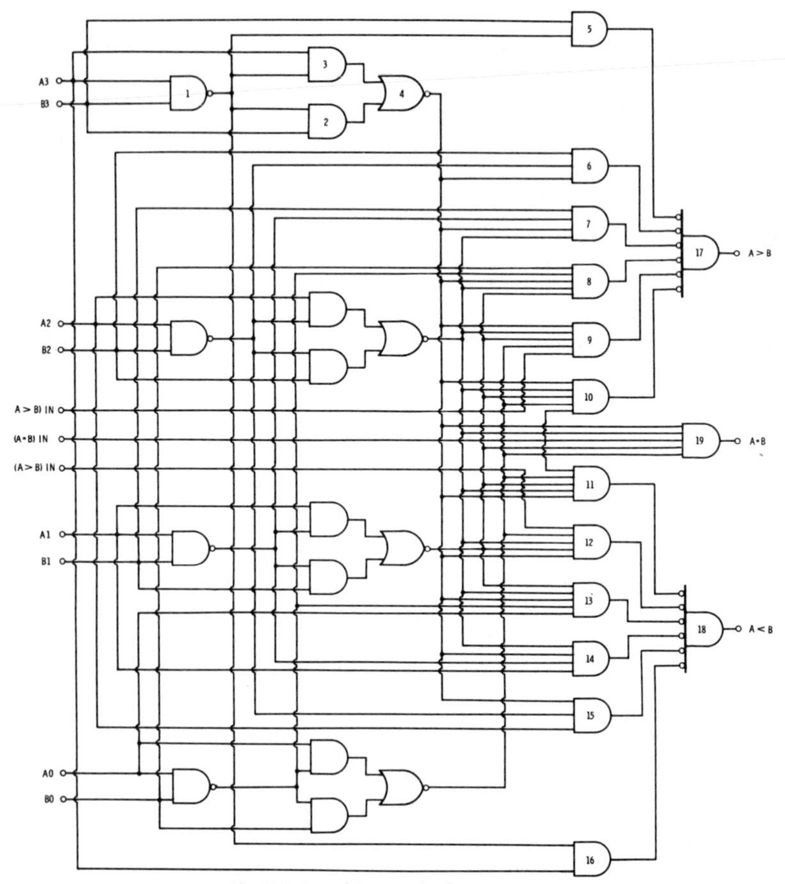

Fig. 7-9. Four-bit magnitude comparator.

slots (of a 3-bit number) are full. For special binary codes, such as excess-3 and excess-2, the complement of a number is not necessarily obtained by changing all 1s to 0s and all 0s to 1s. In these cases, more complicated definitions of complement are required.

In any case, the need arises to generate the complement of binary words and numbers. Fig. 7-8 shows a 4-bit true/complement, zero/one element circuit (monolithic circuit types 54H87, 74H87) that will generate the complement of a number or will pass the number through unchanged. Further, the circuit will also generate all 1s or all 0s. The circuit can be used to load registers in addition and subtraction schemes, or preload counters, etc., in other applications.

Circuit operation is straightforward and is summarized in the truth table in Fig. 7-8B. With B = C = 0, the outputs give the inversions (the complements) of the input bits. With B = 0 and C = 1, the outputs are all 1; with B = 1 and C = 0, the outputs are the same as the inputs; with B = C = 1, the outputs are all 0.

COMPARATOR

The need often arises to compare one digital number with another. Is number A larger than B, equal to it, or smaller? If B is smaller than A, for example, a digital control system might be required to keep adding pills to a bottle. If A equals B, the system might be told to stop. If B should exceed A, an alarm might sound. Many mathematical equations can be solved in a similar manner.

COMPARING INPUTS				CASCADING INPUTS			OUTPUTS		
A3, B3	A2, B2	A1, B1	A0, B0	A > B	A < B	A = B	A > B	A < B	A = B
A3 > B3	X	X	X	X	X	X	H	L	L
A3 < B3	X	X	X	X	X	X	L	H	L
A3 = B3	A2 > B2	X	X	X	X	X	H	L	L
A3 = B3	A2 < B2	X	X	X	X	X	L	H	L
A3 = B3	A2 = B2	A1 > B1	X	X	X	X	H	L	L
A3 = B3	A2 = B2	A1 < B1	X	X	X	X	L	H	L
A3 = B3	A2 = B2	A1 = B1	A0 > B0	X	X	X	H	L	L
A3 = B3	A2 = B2	A1 = B1	A0 < B0	X	X	X	L	H	L
A3 = B3	A2 = B2	A1 = B1	A0 = B0	H	L	L	H	L	L
A3 = B3	A2 = B2	A1 = B1	A0 = B0	L	H	L	L	H	L
A3 = B3	A2 = B2	A1 = B1	A0 = B0	L	L	H	L	L	H

Fig. 7-10. Truth table for Fig. 7-9.

A 4-bit magnitude comparator (type 5485/7485) is shown in Fig. 7-9. Two 4-bit words, A0 A1 A2 A3 and B0 B1 B2 B3 are applied. Consider bits A3 and B3. Since these are the most significant bits, Word A will be greater than Word B if A3 is greater than B3; that is, if A3 = 1 and B3 = 0. Similarly, Word A will be less than Word B if A3 = 0 and B3 = 1. If A3 = B3, the decision as to whether Word A is greater or less than Word B depends on bits A2 and B2. The same considerations apply to the next two levels of bits. For the two words to be equal, the bits must match on every level.

In normal operation, the inputs marked A < B, A = B, and A > B are held high. With A3 = 1 and B3 = 0, Gate 1 goes to a 1 driving Gate 3 to a 1, which drives Gate 4 to 0. Gate 4, in turn, drives Gates 6 through 15 to 0. With Gate 5 = 0 (because B3 = 0), Gate 17 has all 0s as inputs, which satisfies it, and the output A > B goes high. At the same time, Gate 16 goes high and Gate 18 is driven low. Thus, the A < B output goes low. Gate 19 is driven low by Gate 4 = 0, and thus the A = B output is low.

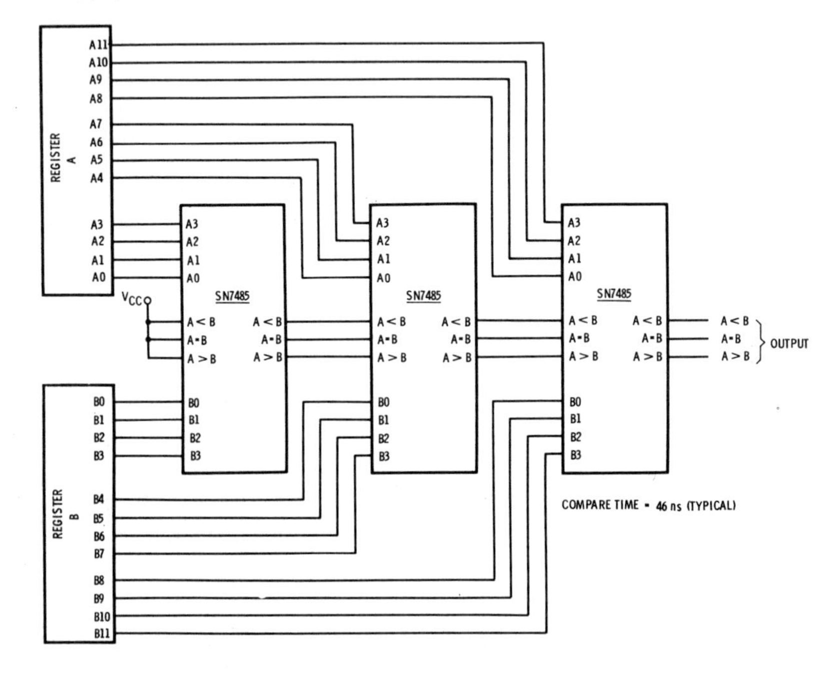

Fig. 7-11. Cascaded comparators.

When A3 = 0 and B3 = 1, Gate 1 goes to 1, Gate 2 goes to 1, Gate 3 goes to 0, and Gate 4 goes to 0. Again, Gates 6 through 15 are driven to a 0. Gate 5, however, is driven high while Gate 16 is driven low. Thus, the A < B output goes high while A > B goes low; Gate 19 is also low.

When A3 = B3 = 1, Gate 1 goes to 0, which drives Gates 2 and 3 to 0 and causes Gate 4 to go high. Gates 6 through 15 plus Gate 19 are now free to follow their other inputs. Gates 5 and 16 are driven low, which allows Gates 17 and 18 to follow their other inputs. When A3 = B3 = 0, Gate 1 goes high, but Gates 2 and 3 are held to 0 by their second input and Gate 4 is high. The same output states are obtained.

When A3 = B3, the state of the outputs is determined by A2 and B2 in a similar manner. If A2 and B2 are also equal, outputs are determined by A1 and B1, and then by A0 and B0. When all bits are equal, Gate 19 is satisfied and goes high.

For words longer than 4-bits, comparisons can be made as shown in Fig. 7-11. In this case, the signals for the A < B, A = B, and A > B inputs are obtained from the preceding stages. These cascaded inputs allow a "tree" of comparators to operate as a single, large comparator.

EXCLUSIVE OR AND EXCLUSIVE NOR

The exclusive OR (X-OR) and exclusive NOR (X-NOR) are very useful in many logic circuits and especially in arithmetic operations. The basic circuit and truth table of quad X-OR gate 7486 is shown in Fig. 7-12. If either but not both inputs is true (high), the output is high. If both inputs are high, or both low, the output is low.

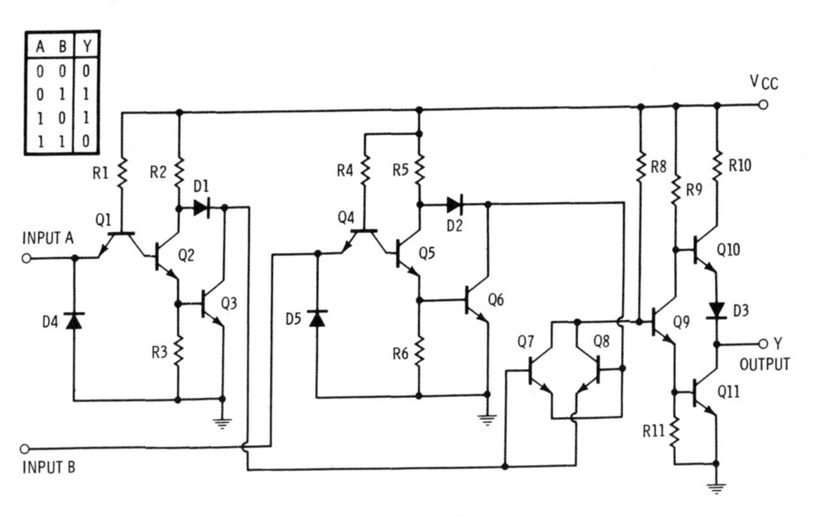

Fig. 7-12. Exclusive OR gate.

Looking at the output circuit, if Q9 is off, Q10 will be on and Q11 will be off, thus the output is high. If Q9 is on, Q11 will be on, Q10 will be off and the output will be low. Q9 will be off if either Q7 or Q8 is on; Q9 will be on if both Q7 and Q8 are off.

To turn Q8 or Q7 on, two conditions must be met: its emitter must be brought low and its base brought high. When input A is high, the emitter of Q8 and base of Q7 are low. If input B is also high, the emitter of Q7 and base of Q8 are also low. Thus Q7 and Q8 are off, Q9 is on, and the output is low.

If input B is low, however, while A remains high, the emitter of Q7 is low and the base of Q8 is high; thus Q8 has emitter low

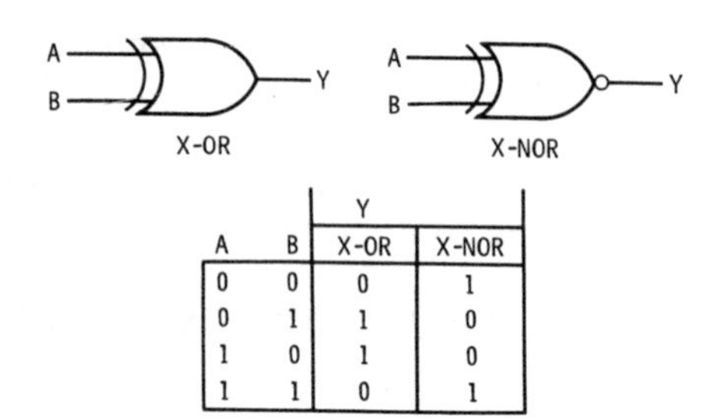

A	B	Y X-OR	Y X-NOR
0	0	0	1
0	1	1	0
1	0	1	0
1	1	0	1

Fig. 7-13. Exclusive OR and exclusive NOR logic.

and base high and turns on. Q9 is turned off and the output goes high.

The circuit is symmetrical, so if input A goes low and B goes high, Q7 turns on the output is high.

If both inputs are low, the base and emitters of both Q7 and Q8 are high and these transistors are off. Q9 is on and the output is low.

The circuit for the X-NOR is similar to the X-OR but the output is the negative of the X-OR gate. Logic symbols are shown in Fig. 7-13.

CHAPTER 8

Parity and Priority

In transmitting digital information from one device or instrument to another, noise spikes and other interfering electrical signals can cause errors. A positive-going noise spike can cause a 1 to appear where a 0 should be; a negative-going spike may wipe out a 1, causing a 0 to appear instead.

A little noise on an analog signal (such as a voice message or a musical recording) causes a slight degradation in the quality and/or intelligibility of the message, but it does not make it wrong. An error in a digital signal, however, can create extremely wrong interpretations. If a computer tells a machine to add $10 to one account and deduct $10 from another account, but the machine at the end of the line gets a command to deduct $1,000,000 from one account and pay it to another, a monumental error has occurred.

An error of $1,000,000 in the transfer of funds is not likely to go unnoticed for long and, thus, the system's problem of transfering funds tends to be self-correcting. But what if an error of only a few dollars occurs? This may go unnoticed. In other cases, errors can be far more dangerous and difficult to detect. What about a computer that is controlling an atomic reactor? Or a Boeing 747? In critical cases, an error-detecting scheme of some sort is vital.

Many error-detecting and correcting schemes have been devised. One of the easiest ways is to transmit the same message twice and compare the two received messages bit by bit to make sure they correspond. If they don't, the message can be transmitted again and again.

Another method is to use a Hamming code. In this technique, extra bits are inserted into the message in such a way that transmission errors can not only be detected but also corrected. The capability for correcting a wrong message arises from the redundancy supplied by the extra bits.

PARITY GENERATOR

One of the simplest and most economical error-detecting schemes is the use of parity bits. Assume you are sending a 3-bit message which can consist of any word from 000 to 111. Now, add a special fourth bit of such a value that the number of 1s transmitted is always an even amount. The word transmitted will then be as shown in Fig. 8-1. The extra bit is called a parity bit since it assures that all the words are on a par with

PARITY BIT	MESSAGE BITS
0	0 0 0
1	0 0 1
1	0 1 0
0	0 1 1
1	1 0 0
0	1 0 1
0	1 1 0
1	1 1 1

Fig. 8-1. Message bit with parity bit added.

respect to whether they have an even number or an odd number of 1s. When the message is received, a parity check is performed. If there are an even number of 1s, the word is assumed to be correct. The parity bit, whether 0 or 1, is then discarded.

Obviously, the parity formula can be changed so that the number of transmitted 1s add up to an odd number instead of an even number. Odd parity, as it is called, is used more often then even parity since odd parity requires at least one 1 in every word, even if the data word is 000.

A circuit to test an 8-bit word for parity and to generate the required parity bit is shown in Fig. 8-2. The device, circuit type 54180/74180 IC, will generate even or odd parity.

Line 1 of the analysis table (Fig. 8-3) shows both Parity Select inputs low, which causes both outputs to be high, regardless of the number of input bits. Line 2 shows both Select inputs high, which drives both outputs low.

Line 3 shows all input bits low or 0, and thus the number of

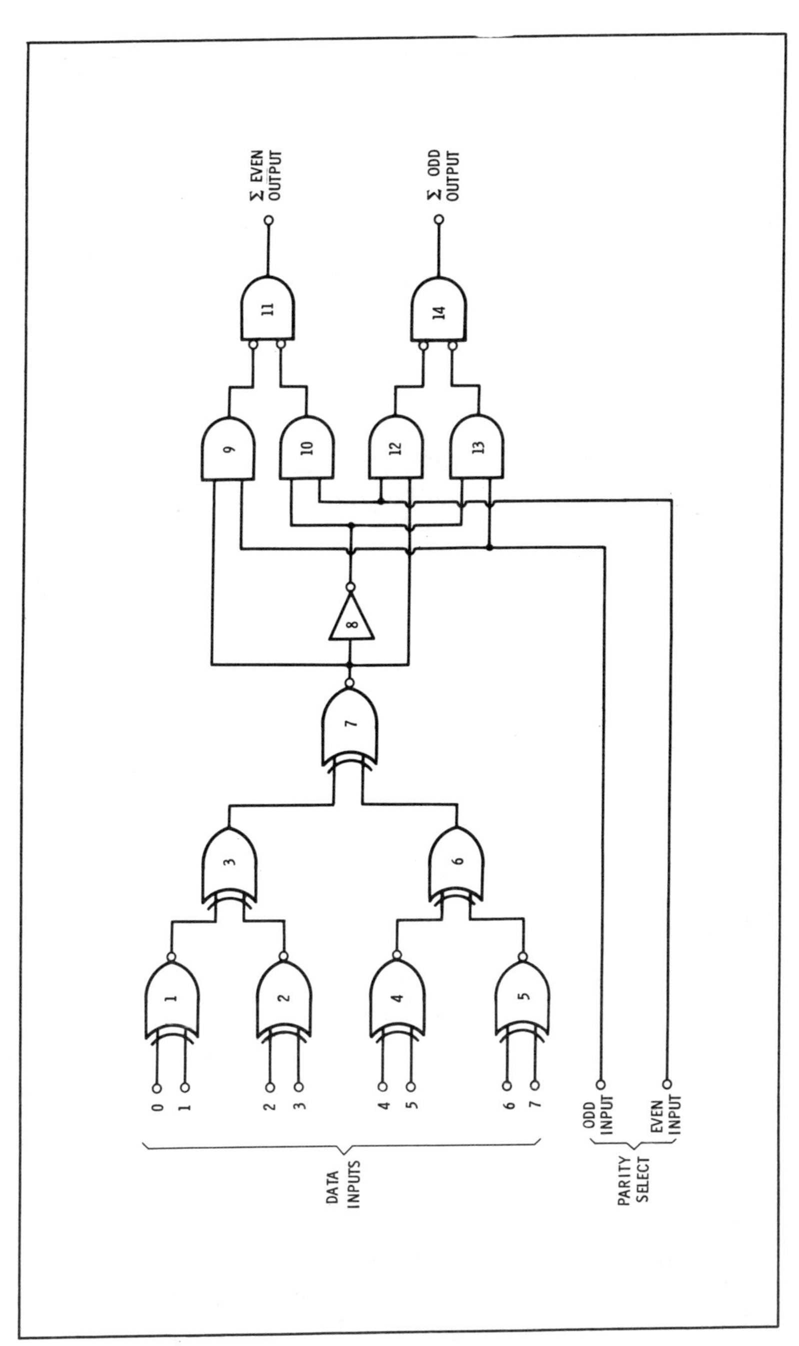

Fig. 8-2. An 8-bit odd/even parity generator/checker circuit.

LINE	INPUTS (ODD OR EVEN NUMBER)	PARITY SELECT		INPUTS								GATES													
		EVEN	ODD	0	1	2	3	4	5	6	7	1	2	3	4	5	6	7	8	9	10	Σ EVEN 11	12	EVEN 13	Σ ODD 14
1	X	0	0																	0	0	1	0	0	1
2	X	1	1																	1	0	0	1	0	0
3	EVEN	1	0	0	0	0	0	0	0	0	0	1	1	0	1	1	0	1	0	0	0	1	1	0	0
4	EVEN	0	1	0	0	0	0	0	0	0	0	1	1	0	1	1	0	1	0	1	0	0	0	0	1
5	EVEN	1	0	0	0	1	0	1	0	0	0	1	0	1	0	1	1	1	0	0	0	1	1	0	0
6	ODD	1	0	0	0	0	0	0	0	0	1	1	1	0	1	0	1	0	1	0	0	1	1	0	0
7	ODD	0	1	0	0	0	0	0	0	0	1	1	1	0	1	0	1	0	1	1	0	0	0	0	1

X = IRRELEVANT

Fig. 8-3. Analysis table for Fig. 8-2.

1s in the message is 0 or even. With Even Parity Select high, the internal gates take up the states shown; the output marked Σ Even (Gate 11) will be high; and output Σ Odd (Gate 14) will be low. Since a 0 is required for the parity bit, the output of Gate 14 can be added to the transmitted word as indicated in Fig. 8-4. The Temporary Storage shown in Fig. 8-4 can be a shift register, a memory circuit, or other circuit. For example, if the word is to be transmitted serially, a multiplexer can be used to hold the word plus its parity bit.

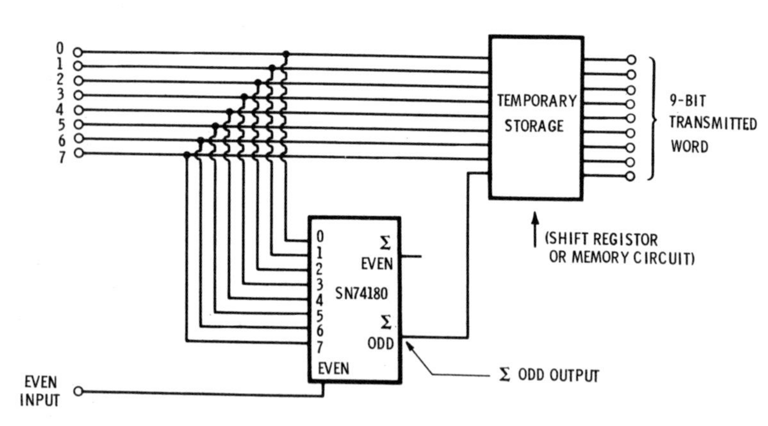

Fig. 8-4. Circuit for adding parity bit.

Line 4 shows the circuit when the Odd Parity Select line is left high, while line 5 simply shows that the scheme holds when the number of 1s is increased to two. Lines 6 and 7 show input words with an odd number of bits.

When the word with parity bit is received, it is tested by a parity tree similar to Gates 1 through 7, except that an extra bit must be examined. If the predetermined parity—odd or even—is found to be correct, the transmission is assumed to be correct. Note, however, that this scheme will not catch a word in which two bits are wrong (two 1s or 0s interchanged, or two 1s added or subtracted). More elaborate parity checks and special codes can be used to detect multiple errors.

PRIORITY ENCODER

An aircraft is coming in for a landing under control of its autopilot. The height-above-ground measuring system tells the control computer that the plane is too high for its position on the glide slope; therefore, something should be done about it (such as nosing down a little, lowering the flaps a little more, or reducing engine speed). At the same time, the speed-measuring system is telling the control system that the airspeed has fallen too close to the stall-out limit, and that something must be done about it also (such as increasing engine speed, or raising the flaps, etc.). Obviously, it is impossible to increase and decrease engine speed at the same time, so the control system must choose which of the two situations is the most important and act accordingly.

A basic control scheme for a system monitoring eight variables is shown in Fig. 8-5. The variables may be oil temperature, fuel-flow rate, boiler pressure, etc. If oil temperature rises too high, the bearings of a large expensive machine will experience excess wear. If the fuel-flow rate rises too high, it is a signal that fuel is being wasted by a leak or poor combustion. If the boiler pressure rises too high, the boiler can explode and destroy the entire system. In a situation like this, we would assign the highest priority to high boiler pressure. As soon as it exceeded its preset limit, we would want the control system to act to reduce the boiler pressure, no matter what this might

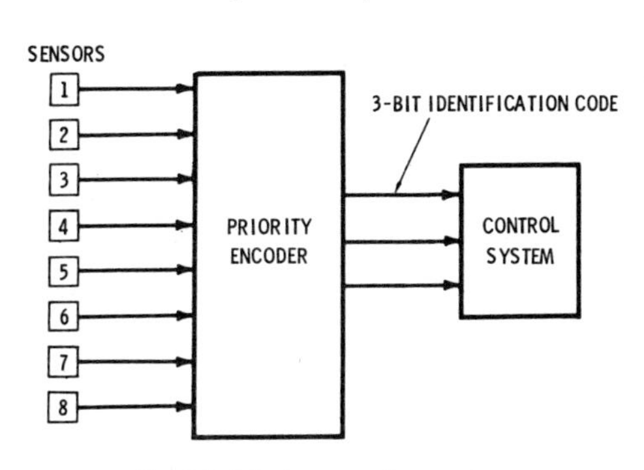

Fig. 8-5. Priority control system.

do to the other variables. In designing a control system, therefore, limits are determined for all the variables. Then, priorities are assigned so that the control system knows which operation to perform when it is asked to do two or more contradictory things at the same time.

The priority encoder shown in Fig. 8-6 has 8 active low inputs and 3 outputs. Input $\overline{7}$ has the highest priority. Whenever it is low, the output generates the 3-bit word 000, regardless of the states of the other inputs. If input $\overline{7}$ is high, the encoder will produce an output corresponding to the next lowest pri-

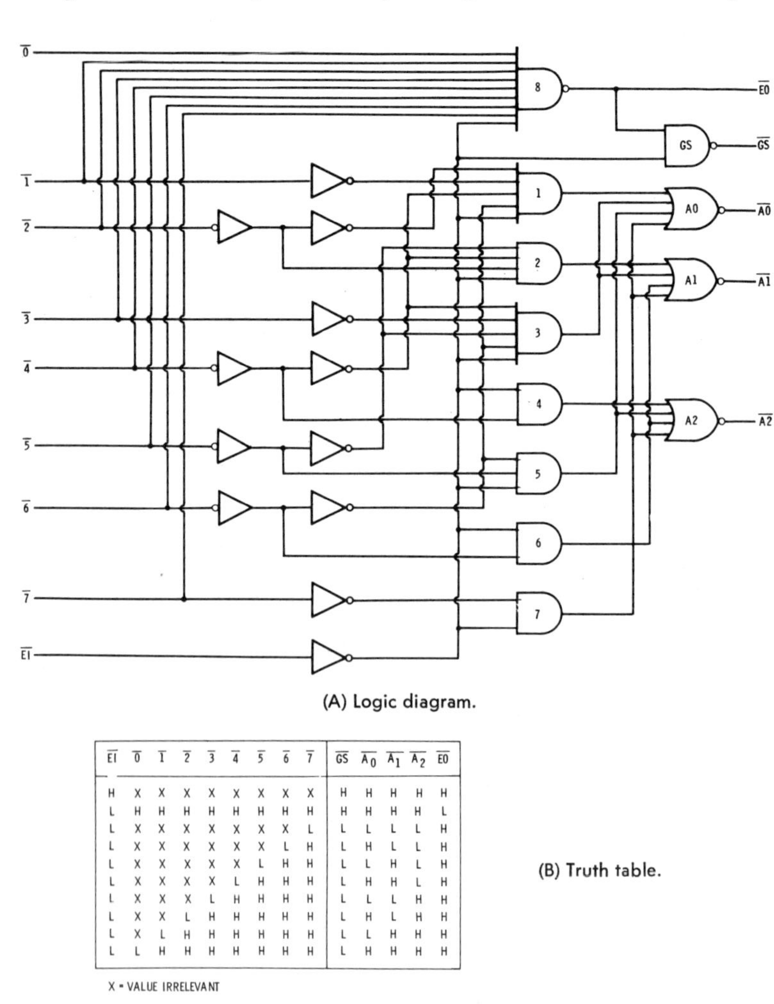

(A) Logic diagram.

$\overline{EI}$	$\overline{0}$	$\overline{1}$	$\overline{2}$	$\overline{3}$	$\overline{4}$	$\overline{5}$	$\overline{6}$	$\overline{7}$	$\overline{GS}$	$\overline{A_0}$	$\overline{A_1}$	$\overline{A_2}$	$\overline{EO}$
H	X	X	X	X	X	X	X	X	H	H	H	H	H
L	H	H	H	H	H	H	H	H	H	H	H	H	L
L	X	X	X	X	X	X	X	L	L	L	L	L	H
L	X	X	X	X	X	X	L	H	L	H	L	L	H
L	X	X	X	X	X	L	H	H	L	L	H	L	H
L	X	X	X	X	L	H	H	H	L	H	H	L	H
L	X	X	X	L	H	H	H	H	L	L	L	H	H
L	X	X	L	H	H	H	H	H	L	H	L	H	H
L	X	L	H	H	H	H	H	H	L	L	H	H	H
L	L	H	H	H	H	H	H	H	L	H	H	H	H

X = VALUE IRRELEVANT

(B) Truth table.

Fig. 8-6. Eight-input priority encoder.

ority input. If only 1 input is active, the encoder responds with the corresponding output as shown in the truth table. If two or more inputs are active, the output produces the code for the input having the highest priority.

Input $\overline{EI}$ is an enabling or clock input. Output gate GS is a group output which goes to 0 when one or more of the 8 inputs is active. Output $\overline{GS}$ is a 1 if all inputs are inactive. Output $\overline{EO}$ combines the information from input $\overline{EI}$ and output $\overline{GS}$. When enable input $\overline{EI}$ goes low—which constitutes an interrogation of the encoder—$\overline{EO}$ goes low if all inputs are inactive and high if one or more is active.

Circuit operation is as follows: When input $\overline{EI}$ is high, it puts 0s on Gates 1 through 8 and Gate GS. This, in turn, puts 0s on Gates A0, A1, and A2, driving them to 1. Gate 8, with a 0 input, is driven to 1, and Gate GS, with a 0 input, is 1. Thus, all outputs are high.

When input $\overline{EI}$ goes low, it removes its inhibiting affect and allows the gates to follow their other inputs. If input $\overline{0}$ is active (that is, 0), Gate 8 is driven to 1; therefore, Gate GS has two 1s as inputs and is driven to 0, while $\overline{EO}$ is 1. Gates 1 through 7 all have one or more inputs = 0 and, thus, these gates remain at 0. Output gates A0, A1, and A2 are not affected.

With input $\overline{EI}$ low, let input $\overline{1} = 0$ (with the other inputs inactive). Gate 8 and $\overline{EO}$ go to 1 and $\overline{GS}$ goes to 0. Gate 1 now has all inputs = 1 and goes to 1; Gate A0 goes to 0. Gates 2 through 7 all have at least one input = 0, and they are not affected. Gates A1 and A2 stay high. If, in addition to $\overline{1} = 0$, in-

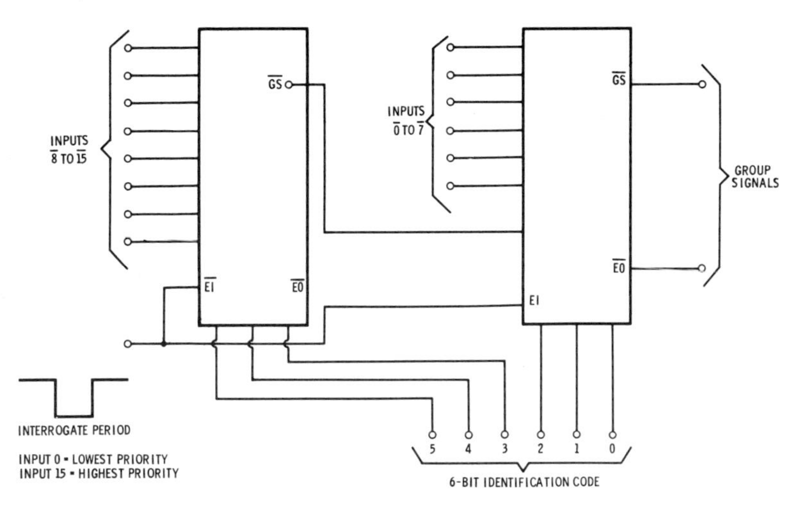

Fig. 8-7. Diagram for expanded encoder operation.

put $\overline{0}$ also = 0, no change in the output occurs; the priority of input $\overline{1}$ over input $\overline{0}$ has been identified.

As the other inputs become active, the circuit responds similarly, producing the 3-bit output code shown in the truth table. Priority levels can be increased by using more encoders as shown in Fig. 8-7. More inputs can be handled by using more encoders in a similar manner.

CHAPTER 9

Memories

Three basic types of memory functions have been developed so far in TTL. The first type is the random-access read-write memory. It is similar to a magnetic core memory, since you put data into the memory on command and then read it out as required, one word at a time. The second type is called a read-only memory. In this type circuit, the information is put into the circuit at the time it is manufactured and cannot be changed thereafter. This type of memory is very useful for storing data that does not change with time, such as trigonometry tables, code conversion schemes, and microprograms for computers. A third type memory is called an associative or content-addressable memory. A major advantage of this type memory is its speed of response when searching for information.

A memory must perform three functions. First, it must provide a way for information to be put into it. Its contents may be changeable in a read-write memory and fixed in a read-only memory. Second, it must retain the information stored in it. Finally, it must deliver the information when asked for it.

Very small memories are sometimes organized to store single bits of information. Thus, a 16-bit memory has 16 different locations for storing a bit. Each location is isolated and independent of every other location. If you want to know whether bit location 12 is holding a 1 or a 0, you have to ask the memory the equivalent of, "What information is in position 12?" In order to single out bit position 12, an addressing scheme is needed that will allow bit 12 to be interrogated without disturbing the other locations. An address scheme is also required when information is loaded into bit 12.

Large memories are usually organized in terms of words rather than single bits. Circuit type 5488/7488 (a high-speed monolithic IC) is organized as 32 words of 8 bits each. It is a 256-bit read-only memory but its contents are available only as 32 different words. Thus, instead of having to address 256 different bit locations, only 32 word locations have to be addressed. The addressing scheme is much simpler.

The major advantage of semiconductor memories over magnetic core memories has been operating speed. Semiconductor memories operate as much as 100 times faster than core memories. Core memories, on the other hand, cost less than semiconductor memories. Thus, many systems today use large, relatively slow core (or magnetic tape, disc, etc.) memories for storing large masses of information. Small fast semiconductor memories are used for temporary storage of information that is being processed. A major disadvantage of semiconductor memories is that they will lose the information stored in them when power is lost—the memory is said to be volatile since the information vanishes when the power is cut off. This does not apply to read-only memories. They hold their information whether the power is on or off.

RANDOM-ACCESS MEMORY (RAM)

Fig. 9-1 shows the arrangement of the 16-bit active-element memory, circuit type 5484/7484. The storage section consists of 16 flip-flops arranged in a 4-by-4 matrix. Each flip-flop can be addressed by energizing one of the 4 X-input lines plus one of the 4 Y-input lines. By using a matrix arrangement, the address function requires only eight inputs, instead of the 16 that would be required if each flip-flop had its own input address line. As the number of bits in a memory increases, the matrix scheme becomes more and more efficient: a 64-bit memory needs 8 + 8 or 16 inputs rather than 64; a 256-bit memory needs 16 + 16 or 32 inputs rather than 256; etc.

Data does not enter the memory via just one input, however, but is entered via a "Write 1" and a "Write 0" input. Similarly, the outputs are obtained from a "Sense 1" and a "Sense 0" amplifier.

A storage flip-flop is shown at Fig. 9-2. In normal storage operation, assume the flip-flop is holding a 0, and, therefore, transistor Q_0 is on (saturated). Then, its collector and the base of transistor Q_1 will be low, causing Q_1 to be off, and its collec-

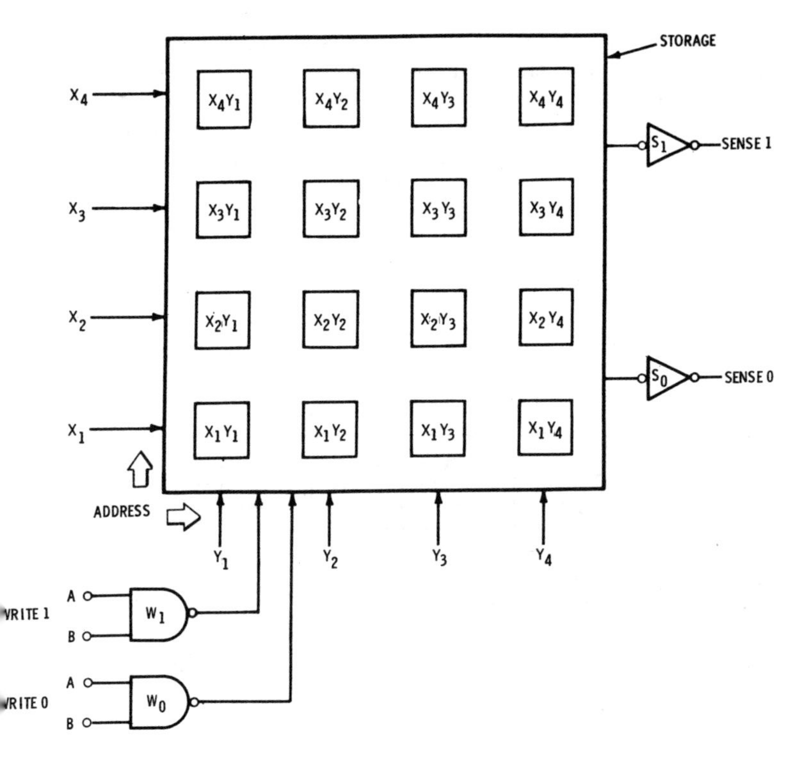

Fig. 9-1. RAM storage arrangement diagram.

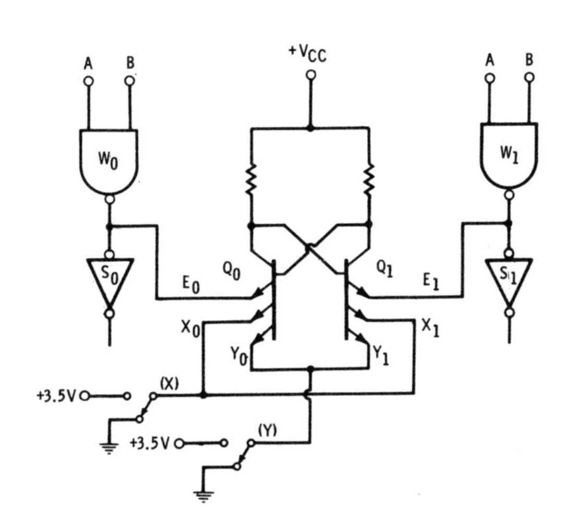

Fig. 9-2. Schematic of a storage flip-flop.

tor and the base of transistor Q_0 to be high. Inputs for writing will all be low and, thus, Gates W_0 and W_1 will be high, causing emitters E_0 and E_1 to be high. The current flowing through transistor Q_0 will flow out the X_0 and Y_0 lines, which are both grounded. The outputs of the sense amplifiers will be high.

To read the state of a bit, the X and Y address lines are brought to a 1. If only the X emitters are brought high, the current that was flowing out of X_0 and Y_0 flows out of emitter Y_0 only. Similarly, if only Y_0 is brought high, the current flows

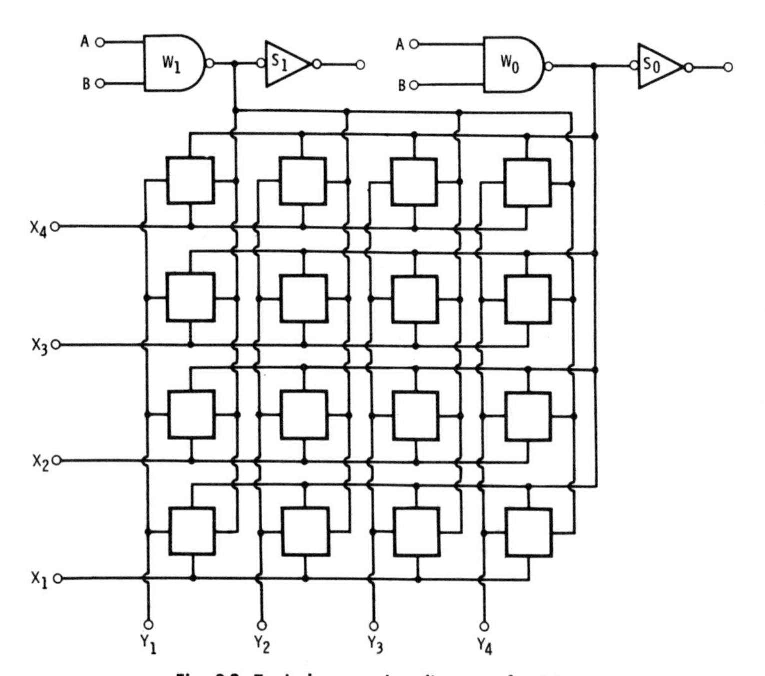

Fig. 9-3. Typical connection diagram of a RAM.

out of emitter X_0. In either case, the status of the circuit stays the same. But when both X and Y emitters are brought high, the current is diverted into the E_0 emitter and flows into the input of gate S_0. The result is that the output of the "Sense 0" amplifier falls to 0. The "Sense 1" amplifier is not affected and its output stays high. For the conditions where the flip-flop is storing a 1, Q_1 will be the saturated transistor; when X and Y are brought high, the current from E_1 causes the "Sense 1" amplifier to go to 0, while gate S_0 stays high.

Suppose that bit location X_3Y_2 is to be interrogated. When address lines X_3 and Y_2 are brought high, all the flip-flops in row X_3 have their X emitters raised, while all the flip-flops in column Y_2 have their Y emitters raised. Only the flip-flop at X_3Y_2 has both the X and Y emitters raised. Thus, only it acts on the sense amplifiers and only one sense amplifier goes low.

To write data into the flip-flop at X_3Y_2, the X_3 and Y_2 address lines are brought high, as in reading. To write a 0, both inputs of the "Write 0" gate are brought high, which drives W_0 to 0. If Q_0 is already on, nothing changes. However, if Q_0 is off, the potential of E_0 falls sufficiently below that of E_1 so that transistor Q_0 turns on and transistor Q_1 turns off. This action occurs because the sink impedance of W_0, when low, is less than the input impedance of S_1. Once the flip-flop has taken on the desired state, it remains there after address and write inputs are brought low. Writing a 1 into a flip-flop is the same as above, except that the Write 1 amplifier is used, and transistor Q_1 is driven on.

When writing in a 1 or 0, only the flip-flop that is addressed is affected. In all the other flip-flops, the low X and/or Y inputs prevent the Write amplifier from changing the state of the flip-flop.

A memory very similar to the type 5484/7484 memory just described is circuit type 5481/7481. It has only one input to each write amplifier; thus, it does not require an additional gating or clocking signal.

FUNCTION	INPUTS						STORED BIT	OUTPUTS	
	ADDRESS		WRITE 0		WRITE 1				
	X_n	Y_n	A	B	A	B		S_1	S_0
QUIESCENT	0	0	0	X	0	X	0 OR 1	1	1
READ	1	1	0	X	0	X	0	1	0
	1	1	0	X	0	X	1	0	1
WRITE 1	1	1	0	X	1	1	GOES TO 1	0	1
WRITE 0	1	1	1	1	0	X	GOES TO 0	1	0

Fig. 9-4. Functional table for Fig. 9-1.

REGISTER FILE

In very high speed systems, it is often desired that the content of a memory be available even while new information is being entered. Fig. 9-5 shows a high-speed buffer memory (4-by-4 register file) that allows simultaneous reading and writing.

This buffer memory (circuit type 54170/74170) is organized into 4 words, each 4 bits long. Word 1 is stored in the 4 flip-flops (actually, latches) in the left column; word 2, in the next column; and so forth. The memory has two address systems, one for writing and one for reading. The address systems consist of a 2-bit code plus an enable signal. The Write address system consists of code W_AW_B and enable G_W. For example, to write new data into word 1, W_A, W_B and G_W are brought low. (See the Write Function truth table.) This drives Gates 49, 50, and 47 high, and the latches of word 1 respond to the data on inputs 1D through 4D. If input 1D is a 1, then the latch for bit 1 of word 1 goes to $Q = 1$; if input 1D is a 0, the latch goes to $Q = 0$.

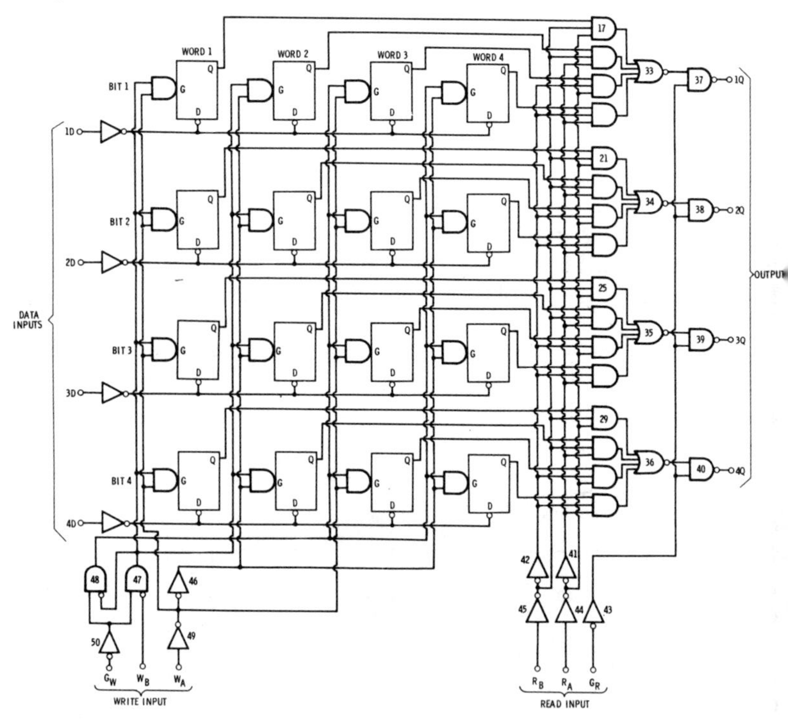

Fig. 9-5. Functional block diagram for a Register File.

Let the Write Function advance to word 2 and readout the contents of word 1 at the same time. To select readout of word 1, Read inputs R_A, R_B, and G_R are brough to 0; this applies two 1s to Gates 17, 21, 25, and 29. If bit 1 of word 1 is a 1, Gate 17 turns on. Gate 33 then has two inputs 0 and one input a 1. Its output is 0. The output gate (37) has one input of a 1 (from $G_R = 0$), but, since the input from Gate 33 is a 0, the output 1Q is high. Similarly, if $Q_1 = 0$, the signal will propagate through the read-address system and appear at the output as a 0. The other three bits of word 1 appear at the outputs in the same manner.

Thus, the memory is seen to operate somewhat differently than the 16-bit memory considered previously. The data appears on only one output, instead of two; it appears in true form, rather than in complementary form; it appears in groups of 4-bits at a time, instead of as single bits. With this

WRITE INPUTS			WORD
W_B	W_A	G_W	
L	L	L	1
L	H	L	2
H	L	L	3
H	H	L	4
X	X	H	NONE

(A) Write function.

READ INPUTS			OUTPUTS			
R_B	R_A	G_R	1Q	2Q	3Q	4Q
L	L	L	W0B1	W0B2	W0B3	W0B4
L	H	L	W1B1	W1B2	W1B3	W1B4
H	L	L	W2B1	W2B2	W2B3	W2B4
H	H	L	W3B1.	W3B2	W3B3	W3B4
X	X	H	H	H	H	H

W0B1 - THE FIRST BIT OF WORD 0, ETC.

(B) Read function.

Fig. 9-6. Truth tables for Fig. 9-5.

memory, reading of any word can occur simultaneously with the writing of any word (including the word being written); whereas in the previous memory, only the bit being written in could be read out simultaneously.

READ-ONLY MEMORY (ROM)

Read-only memories tend to be larger in terms of storage capacity than random-access memories. This characteristic follows naturally from the fact that no write-in circuits are required. All that is needed is an address system and an output circuit.

Most ROMS are designed to fill the specific needs of one circuit and, usually, one customer. Thus, they are special circuits, rather than standard off-the-shelf devices. Once the customer decides what information the ROM has to store, he transmits this data to the IC manufacturer. The manufacturer creates a special photo-mask that contains the data and uses it as the final masking step in manufacturing the ICs. The process is relatively expensive if only a few ICs are needed but becomes less expensive when the cost is spread over a few hundred or more ROMs.

Certain types of stored information are useful in more than one application, so a few standard ROMs have been developed to meet these needs. Code conversions, reference tables, and display and readout systems may be able to use standard ROMs.

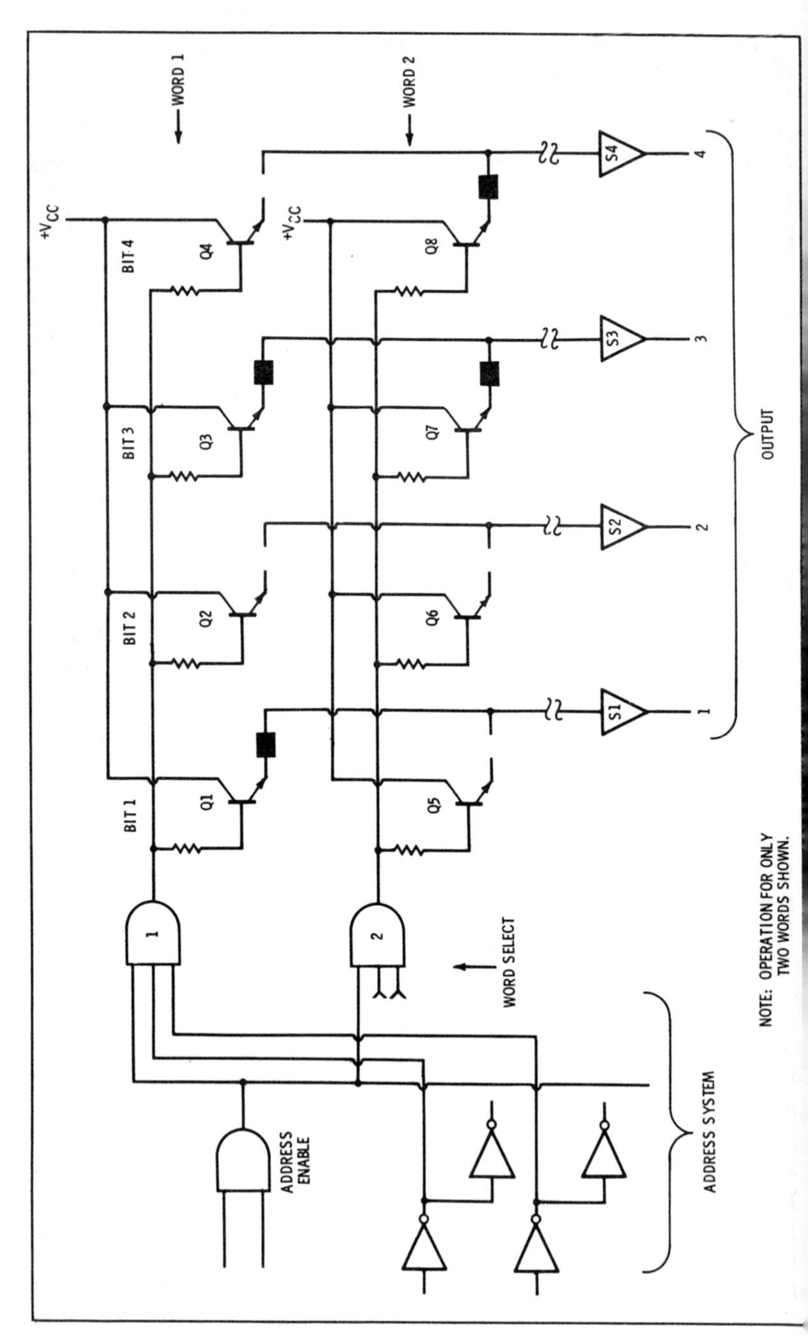

Fig. 9-7. Operating principle of a Read-Only memory.

The operating principle of a ROM is very straightforward and is shown in Fig. 9-7. Only two words are shown, each 4 bits long. Assume the address system has selected and enabled word 1 and, therefore, Gate 1 is high. As a result, the bases of all the storage transistors of word 1 are high. The square block in the emitter circuit of bit 1 is a metal connection that allows the circuit of the transistor to be completed and, thus, current will flow through transistor Q_1. This current into Gate S_1 causes S_1 to go high. For bit 2, the connection between the emitter of transistor Q_2 and the input of Gate S_2 has been removed, and Gate S_2 stays at 0. Similarly for bit 3 ($S_3 = 1$) and bit 4 ($S_4 = 0$).

The transistors of word 2 are also connected to the output amplifiers, but, since the bases of these transistors are low, no current flows even when the emitter is left connected. When word 2 is selected and enabled by the address system, the output changes to the pattern set into the ROM for word 2. For manufacturing reasons, the ROM is made initially with all links in place. The ROM is customized to a specific application by removing links for those locations where 0s are desired.

Various types of organizations are available in ROMs. Fig. 9-8A shows a 32-word by 8-bit ROM, monolithic type 5488/7488. Operation is very straightforward. Simply apply the address code (see word select table) of the desired word, put the enable low, and read out the data.

A variation of the ROM is known as a programmable ROM or PROM. Instead of programming the memory during the final masking stage, the circuit is provided with connections that can be destroyed by feeding the PROM a higher than normal voltage. PROMs can thus be permanently programmed individually to whatever pattern is required.

CONTENT ADDRESSABLE MEMORY

Some systems require what can be called a searching operation or function. Suppose a system is being used to monitor aircraft entering and leaving the airspace of a landing field. The display system for the tower operator includes a cathode ray tube (crt) on which he can call up information about all planes in the area. He may, for example, want a display of all planes flying at a certain altitude. Or, he may want a display of all planes that are within a 10-mile radius of the landing strip.

Each plane will have its own indentification number and will be represented by a digital word in the monitoring system. The

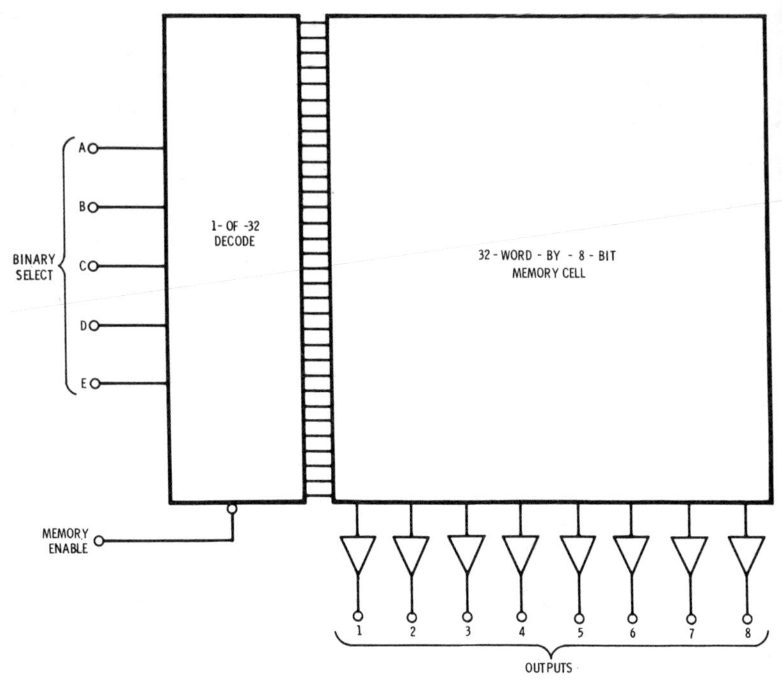

(A) Logic block diagram.

WORD ADDRESSED	INPUTS					
	BINARY SELECT					ENABLE
	E	D	C	B	A	G
0	L	L	L	L	L	L
1	L	L	L	L	H	L
2	L	L	L	H	L	L
3	L	L	L	H	H	L
4	L	L	H	L	L	L
5	L	L	H	L	H	L
6	L	L	H	H	L	L
7	L	L	H	H	H	L
8	L	H	L	L	L	L
9	L	H	L	L	H	L
10	L	H	L	H	L	L
11	L	H	L	H	H	L
12	L	H	H	L	L	L
13	L	H	H	L	H	L
14	L	H	H	H	L	L
15	L	H	H	H	H	L

WORD ADDRESSED	INPUTS					
	BINARY SELECT					ENABLE
	E	D	C	B	A	G
16	H	L	L	L	L	L
17	H	L	L	L	H	L
18	H	L	L	H	L	L
19	H	L	L	H	H	L
20	H	L	H	L	L	L
21	H	L	H	L	H	L
22	H	L	H	H	L	L
23	H	L	H	H	H	L
24	H	H	L	L	L	L
25	H	H	L	L	H	L
26	H	H	L	H	L	L
27	H	H	L	H	H	L
28	H	H	H	L	L	L
29	H	H	H	L	H	L
30	H	H	H	H	L	L
31	H	H	H	H	H	L
ALL	X	X	X	X	X	H

(B) Word Select table.

Fig. 9-8. A 256-bit Read-Only memory.

word may be sectioned, as indicated in Fig. 9-9A, where a certain group of bits provide plane identification; another group of bits give the altitude of the plane; another group, its distance from the field; and so on. As the plane moves through the area, the information is continually updated by various radars and transponders.

Assume the control tower operator wants to check all planes at altitudes from 5000 to 6000 feet and that the digital word representing these altitudes is 1101. One way to do this would be to check the digital words associated with all the planes in the area to see if their altitude field is 1101. Any plane having the altitude of interest is displayed on the crt. All other plane images are blanked out.

A content addressable memory allows a simultaneous search of its entire contents to see if it contains data of the desired type. TTL compatible memory device, type 93402 (Fig. 9-10) is a high-speed 16-bit associate random-access memory. It is a 4-word by 4-bit memory circuit that generates a match signal when it contains a word having the same bit pattern as the word being applied to it. The words in the memory can also be changed and read out as required.

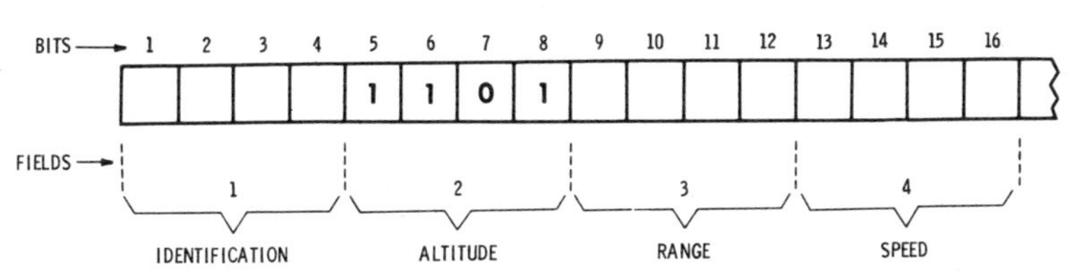

Fig. 9-9. Possible organization of a digital word for an aircraft monitoring system.

Memory storage elements are flip-flops; Gates 17 and 18 store bit 1 of word 1. In the quiescent state, all inputs are high; memory output bits $\overline{O}_0$ are high; and match signals M are high (except for match signal $\overline{M}_0$). With address bit $\overline{A}_0$ high, Gate 14 is low and Gate 19 is low, regardless of the state of Gates 17 and 18. Therefore, output $\overline{O}_0$ for bit 1 is high. The other bits of word 1 are obtained in a similar manner. With the address bits of the other words also high, their "19" gates will also be low. Thus, all outputs are high.

To read out word 1, input $\overline{A}_0$ is brought low. Gate 19 will now have one input high and will follow Gate 17. If Gate 17 is low, Gate 19 will be low and output $\overline{O}_0$ will be high. If Gate 17 is high, Gate 19 will be high and output $\overline{O}_0$ will go low. Thus, the output takes up the state of Gate 18 when word 1 is addressed. Suppose that words 1 and 2 are addressed simultaneously by bringing both $\overline{A}_0$ and $\overline{A}_1$ low. If both "19" gates stay high, the output will be low. However, if either of the "19" gates goes low, the output will go high. Gate 19 is actually a wired-OR circuit and if any gate goes low, the common tie-point

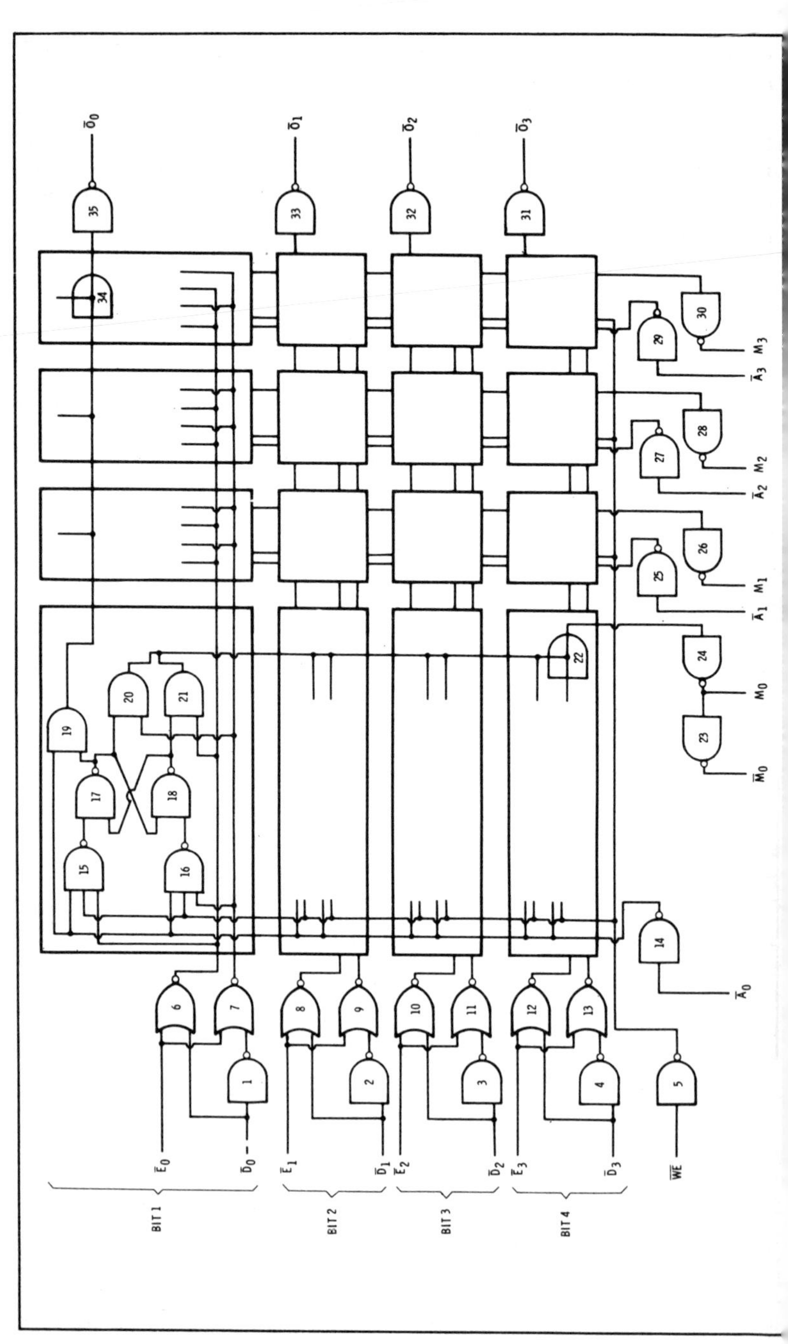

Fig. 9-10. A 16-bit associative/content addressable memory.

goes low. For the straight Read function, therefore, the memory is addressed one word at a time as with other memories.

A word is written into the memory by applying it to inputs $\overline{D}_0$ through $\overline{D}_3$, and by bringing the bit enables ($\overline{E}_0$ through $\overline{E}_3$), write enable ($\overline{WE}$), and the address bit low. With $\overline{WE} = 0$ and $\overline{A}_0 = 0$, Gate 15 is free to follow Gate 6, and Gate 16 is free to follow Gate 7. With $\overline{E}_0 = 0$, Gates 6 and 7 will follow $\overline{D}_0$ or Gate 1. If $\overline{D}_0 = 0$, Gate 6 goes to a 1; this satisfies Gate 15, which goes to 0. A 0 into Gate 17 drives it to a 1. Gate 18, with two inputs of a 1, goes to a 0. With $\overline{D}_0 = 0$, Gate 1 is 1 and Gate 7 is a 0; thus, Gate 16 remains high. If $\overline{D}_0 = 1$, Gate 1 goes to a 0, Gate 7 goes to a 1, and Gate 6 to a 0. As a result, Gate 16 is satisfied, which puts a 0 into Gate 18, driving it to a 1, while Gate 17 is driven to a 0.

Searching the memory for a match is accomplished by applying the four bits to be matched at inputs $\overline{D}_0$ through $\overline{D}_3$ and then bringing the $\overline{E}$ inputs low. First, let all $\overline{E}$ inputs be high. Then Gates 20 and 21 of each bit in the memory will have one input low, and none of the "20" and "21" gates will be satisfied. As a result of this, Gate 24 will be driven high. The group of gates driving Gate 24 are connected in a wired-AND configuration. If any gate is high, it brings the common tie-point high, and Gate 24 is driven low.

	WRITE ENABLE	BIT ENABLE INPUTS				DATA INPUTS				BIT STORED IN WORD 1				MATCH OUTPUTS						
LINE	$\overline{WE}$	$\overline{E}_0$	$\overline{E}_1$	$\overline{E}_2$	$\overline{E}_3$	$\overline{D}_0$	$\overline{D}_1$	$\overline{D}_2$	$\overline{D}_3$	B1	B2	B3	B4	M_0	M_1	M_2	M_3	$\overline{M}_0$	$\overline{A}_{0-3}$	$\overline{O}_{0-3}$
1	1	1	1	1	1	X	X	X	X	X	X	X	X	1	1	1	1	0	X	
2	1	0	1	1	1	0	X	X	X	0	X	X	X	1	?	?	?	0	X	
3	1	0	1	1	1	1	X	X	X	0	X	X	X	0	?	?	?	1	X	
4	1	0	1	1	1	0	X	X	X	1	X	X	X	0	?	?	?	1	X	
5	1	0	1	1	1	1	X	X	X	1	X	X	X	1	?	?	?	0	X	
6	1	0	0	1	1	0	0	X	X	0	1	X	X	0	?	?	?	1	X	
7	1	0	0	1	1	0	1	X	X	0	1	X	X	1	?	?	?	0	X	
8	1	0	0	1	1	1	0	X	X	0	1	X	X	0	?	?	?	1	X	
9	1	0	0	1	1	1	1	X	X	0	1	X	X	0	?	?	?	1	X	

Fig. 9-11. Truth table for Fig. 9-10.

Circuit operation is indicated by the truth table (Fig. 9-11). In line 1, all the enable inputs are high and a match is indicated for all words in the memory. For this condition, the state of the $\overline{D}$ inputs is irrelevant and, thus, the inputs are said to be "masked." In line 2, $\overline{E}_0$ is brought to a 0, which unmasks bit $\overline{D}_0$. The bits stored in the memory for word 1 will affect output $\overline{O}_0$. If the data bit $\overline{D}_0$ is a 0 and the bit in storage is 0, output M_0 is driven high since bit 0 matches while bits 1, 2, and 3 are masked. If bit 1 of word 2 is also a 0, M_1 goes to a 1, but if it is 1, M_1 is a 0. Similar action occurs for words 3 and 4. Lines 3, 4, and 5 show circuit status for $\overline{D}_0$ and bit 1 of word 1.

In line 6, data inputs $\overline{D}_0$ and $\overline{D}_1$ are both unmasked by setting $\overline{E}_0 = \overline{E}_1 = 0$. No match is obtained in lines 6, 8 and 9, but it is in line 7. The other M outputs will be either high or low depending on the data stored in bits 1 and 2 for words 2, 3, and 4.

The same considerations apply as the other data inputs are unmasked. If the data in all four words is the same as the input or "descriptor" data, then four "match" signals are obtained. A priority circuit can be used to process the matching words one at a time.

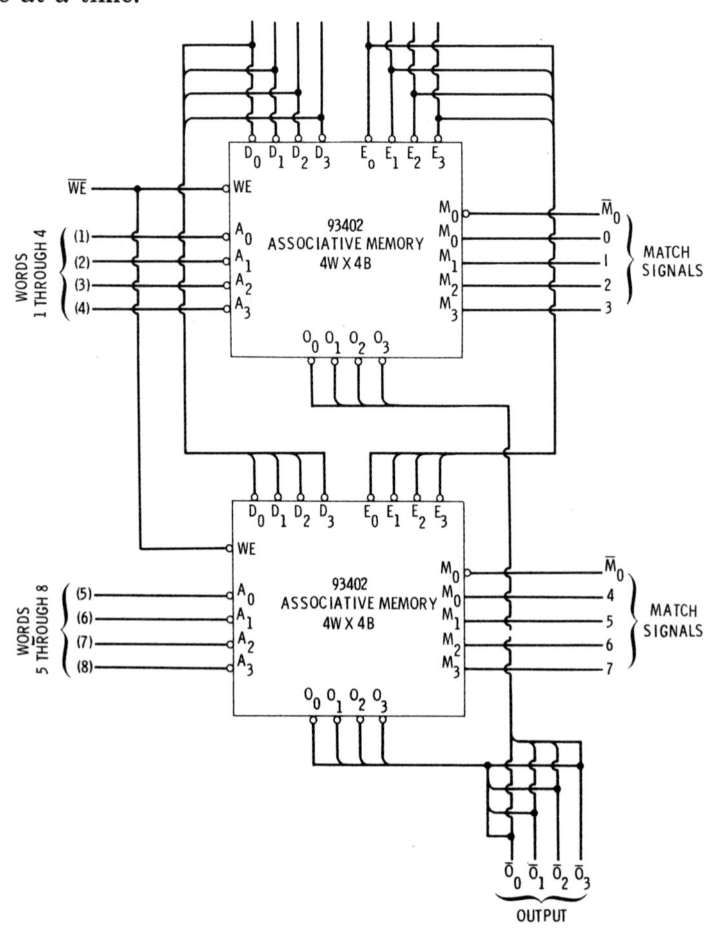

Fig. 9-12. Diagram for expanding word length.

A content addressable memory (or CAM) of larger size can be formed by connecting a number of the basic devices together. As shown by Fig. 9-12, a CAM of 8 words-by-4 bits can be formed from two memory units. The outputs are open-collector circuits and, thus, can be tied together. If a match is obtained for the bits being compared, the outputs will be the wired-OR function. The memory can be expanded to more words, in the same manner, by tying together the D inputs, the E inputs, and the O outputs.

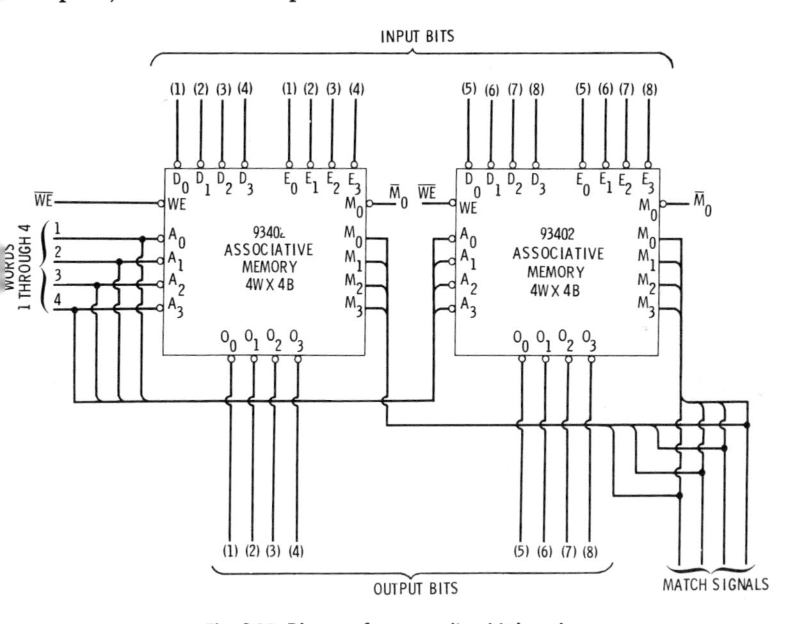

Fig. 9-13. Diagram for expanding bit length.

Expansion to handle 8-bit words can be accomplished as indicated in Fig. 9-13. Match outputs are also open-collector circuits and can be tied together, giving four match signals for a 4-word, 8-bit memory. Expansion to more words and more bits can be obtained by combining the schemes shown in Figs. 9-12 and 9-13.

CHAPTER 10

Special Circuits

A number of special circuits have been developed to aid the use of TTL in various applications. Many of these circuits fall into the category of interface circuits, since they allow TTL to work into or from other types of electronic circuits, including other digital logic families and analog or linear circuits.

INTERFACE DRIVER

Linear IC, type 75450, is a dual peripheral driver consisting of two NAND gates and two isolated transistors (Fig. 10-1A). The transistors are rated at 300 mA continuous collector current, and the NAND gates require the usual +5-volt supply.

The IC can be used to drive two lamps or two relays, each connected as shown in Fig. 10-1B. When the gate is low, the transistor is off and the load is connected to ground through a very high impedance. When the gate is high—which requires at least one input to be a 0—the transistor is on and the load is connected to ground through a very low impedance. Current then flows through the load from +V to ground. The diode suppresses transients when the transistor is turned off.

Two type 75450 devices can be used to drive an ac load as shown in Fig. 10-1C. To operate as an ac source, the A transistors are turned on together while the B transistors are held off. Then, the A devices are turned off and the B transistors are turned on, and so forth.

If any possibility exists that an A and a B transistor can be on simultaneously, current-limiting resistor R1 must be made

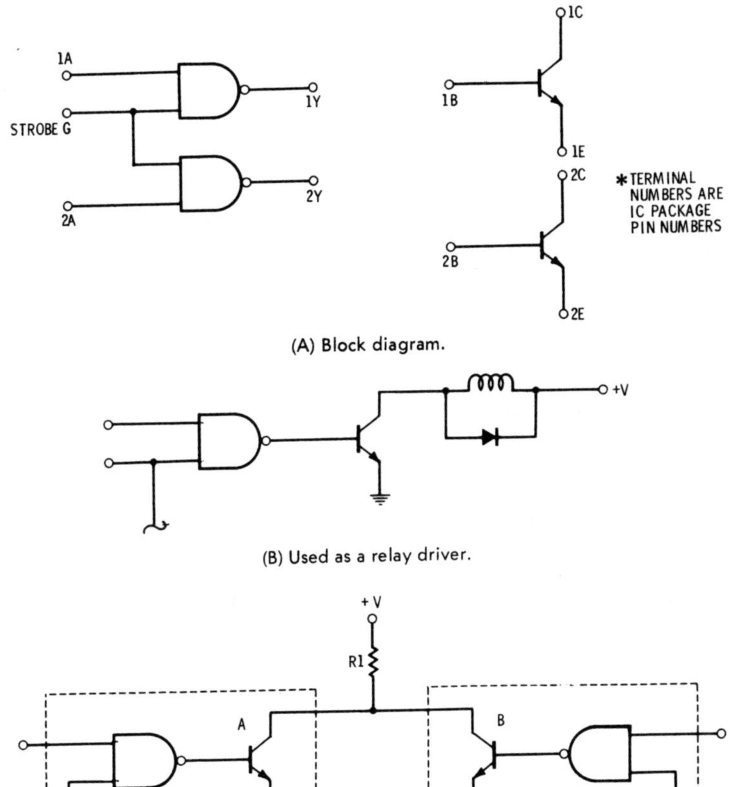

(A) Block diagram.

(B) Used as a relay driver.

(C) Used as an ac source.

Fig. 10-1. Dual peripheral driver.

large enough to keep the transistors from burning out. If the load is inductive, the circuit must be analyzed to prevent turn-off transients from destroying the transistors.

ONE-SHOT MULTIVIBRATOR

Sometimes one pulse must be delayed, relative to another, to prevent improper operation of a circuit. In other cases, a signal source does not generate pulses as such, but the information obtained from the source is required in the form of pulses. Sometimes pulses need to be lengthened or shortened to be compatible with other signals. The one-shot multivibrator shown in Fig. 10-2A can be used for these functions.

Operation is straightforward. With either A_1 or A_2 low and B high, a single positive-going pulse is generated at Q. Typically, the width of the pulse is 30 nanoseconds but can be increased to as long as 40 seconds by adding a resistive-capacitive timing circuit as shown in Fig. 10-2B.

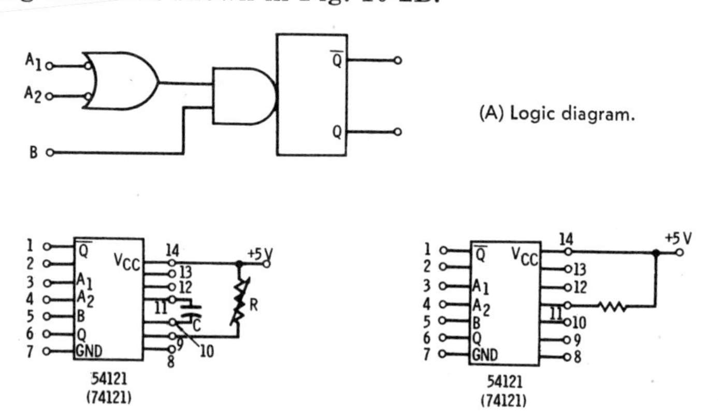

(A) Logic diagram.

(B) Addition of R-C timing circuit.

(C) Pulse width stabilizing circuit added.

Fig. 10-2. A one-shot multivibrator.

The value of capacitor C can vary from 10 pF to 10 μF, and the value of resistor R can range from 0 to 40,000 ohms. Pin 9 is connected to an internal resistor of about 2000 ohms, and this resistance is in series with the external resistor. The connection shown in Fig. 10-2C stabilizes the width of pulses generated by the one-shot multivibrator.

Fig. 10-3 shows the pulse lengths that can be obtained for various values of C and R. With $C = 1\ \mu F$ and the total timing resistance (the sum of external R and internal 2K resistor) = 10K, the curve shows a typical pulse width of 7 milliseconds.

LATCHES

One major use of latches is as a temporary storage of data between a data source and an indicator. If the input to an indicator (such as a 7-segment readout tube) changes more than a few times a second, the result is an unreadable flicker. By storing the information temporarily, thus keeping the indicator from changing more often than once or twice a second, useful and readable outputs are obtained (although some intermediate readings may be lost).

Fig. 10-4A shows a one-bit latch that is incorporated in a 4-bit bistable latch (circuit types 5475/7475 and 5477/7477) and in an 8-bit bistable latch (circuit type 54100/74100). The

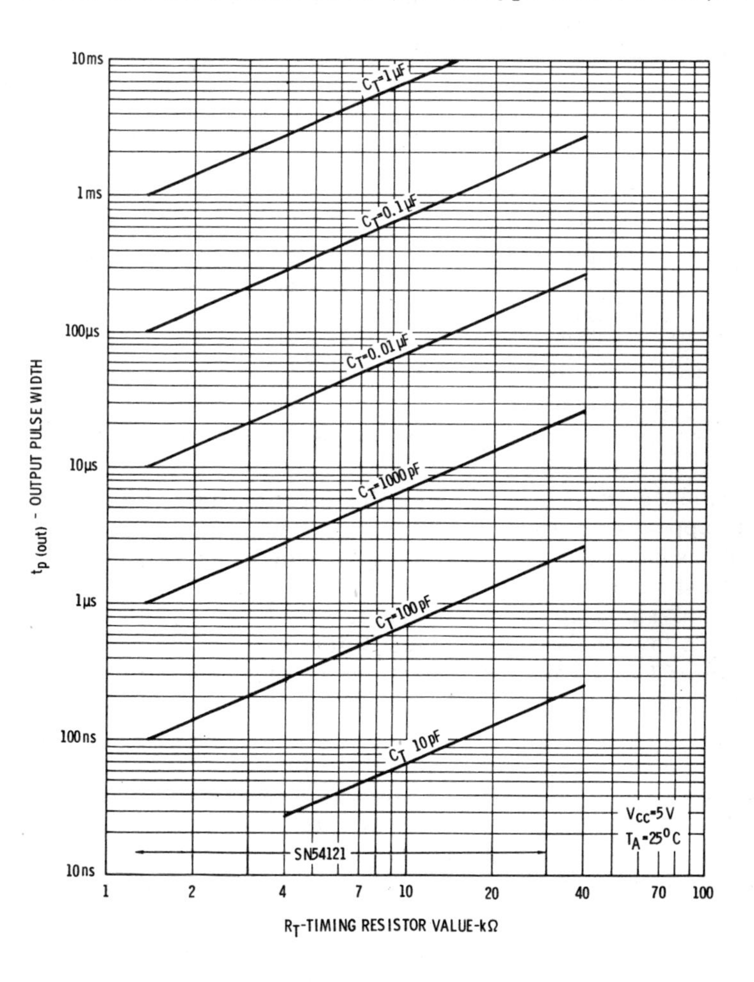

Fig. 10-3. Typical characteristics.

major differences between the ICs are the internal clock connections and the available outputs. Circuit type 5475/7475 has both Q and $\overline{Q}$ outputs for each of four latches, while type 5477/7477 and type 54100/74100 have only Q outputs.

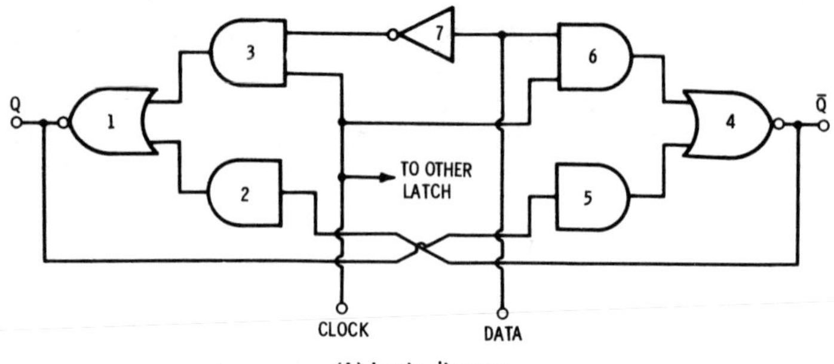

(A) Logic diagram.

t_n	t_{n+1}
D	Q
0	0
1	1

t_n = BIT TIME BEFORE CLOCK NEGATIVE - GOING TRANSITION.
t_{n+1} = BIT TIME AFTER CLOCK NEGATIVE - GOING TRANSITION.

(B) Truth table.

LINE	CLOCK	DATA	1	2	3	4	5	6	7	Q	$\bar{Q}$
1	0	0			0			0	1	Q	$\bar{Q}$
2	1	0	0	1	1	1	0	0	1	0	1
3	1	1	1	0	0	0	1	1	0	1	0
4	0	1			0			0	0	Q	$\bar{Q}$

(C) Analysis table.

Fig. 10-4. One-bit latch.

Whenever the clock is high, the information on the data input appears on the Q output and Q will follow the data. When the clock goes low, Q no longer follows the data but stays in its last state.

In analysis table (Fig. 10-4C), line 1 shows both the clock and data low. This causes Gates 3 and 6 to be a 0 and, thus, NOR Gates 1 and 4 will be determined by prior conditions. Line 2 shows the clock high and data low. Gate 3 is now high and this drives Gate 1 to 0. The other gates follow as shown in the analysis table; Q goes to 0; $\bar{Q}$ goes to 1. In line 3, both clock and data are high. Now Gate 6 is high; this drives Gate 4 to a 0, and the other gates are driven to the conditions shown. In line 4, the clock is 0 and data is 1. Again, Gates 3 and 6 are low, and the circuit remains in the state it was in when the clock went low.

SCHMITT TRIGGERS

Although digital ICs can work with signals that are less than pure square waves, they normally are not able to handle signals that have excessively slow rise or fall times or that have too much noise. Slow rise and fall times can cause gates to go into oscillation, while too much noise causes false operation. Further, when an input signal is in the intermediate or forbidden region between a high and a low, the output still tends to follow the input and the ambiguity can be propagated down the chain. The Schmitt trigger is a circuit that converts slow or noisy signals into signals having satisfactory leading and trailing edges, and with noise removed.

The TTL Schmitt trigger (which is usually an inverter) is designed to go to the low state when the input rises to about 1.65 volts or more and to remain low until the input falls below about +0.85 volt, at which point the output goes high. The output then stays high until the input again rises to 1.65 volts or above. A circuit with these characteristics is said to have hysteresis. The normal TTL circuit does not have hysteresis, and when the input is between the minimum for a 1 and above the maximum for a 0, the output is also somewhere between high and low.

The logic symbol for an inverter type Schmitt trigger is shown in Fig. 10-5A, while Fig. 10-5B shows how the circuit

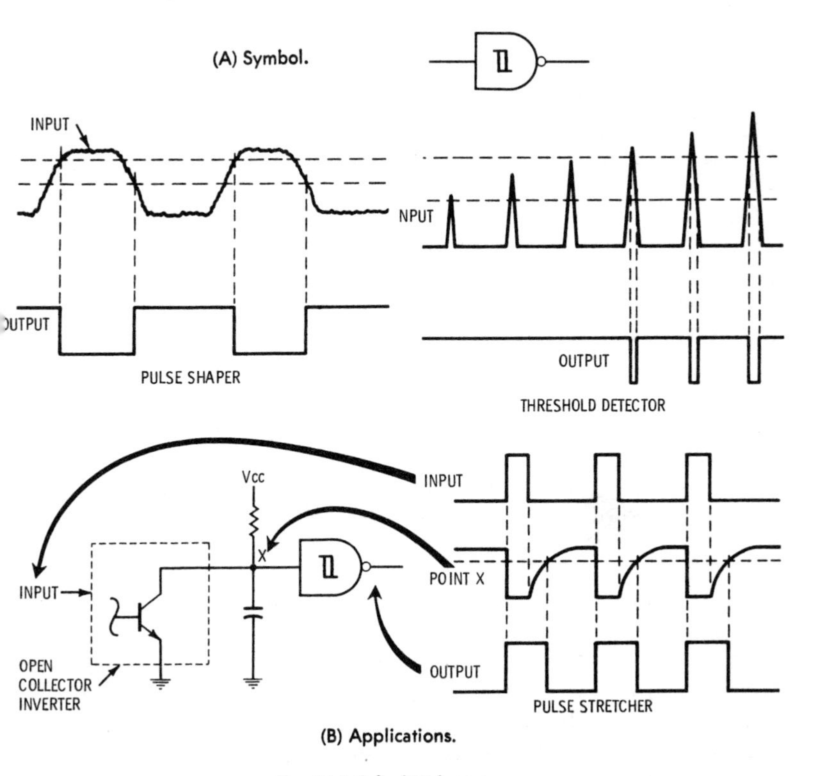

Fig. 10-5. Schmitt trigger.

can be used to convert a slow moving input to a sharp-edged digital signal, how to remove noise, convert sine waves to square waves, detect signals above the threshold of the device, and how it can act as a pulse stretcher.

Fig. 10-6 shows the circuit of type 7414, which is a hex Schmitt trigger. Note that the input circuit is not the emitter of a transistor but is a diode, which is typical of diode-transistor-logic (DTL). The output circuit, however, is the usual TTL totem pole.

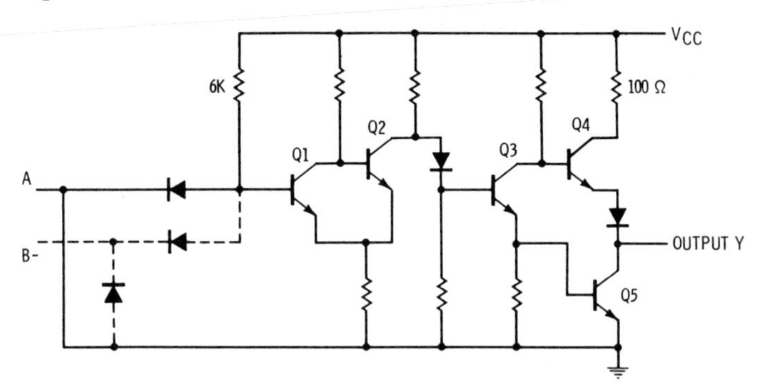

Fig. 10-6. Schmitt trigger inverter.

When input A is low, current flows through the 6K resistor and diode to ground. This brings the base of Q1 low, the base of Q2 high, the bases of Q3 and Q5 are low, and the base of Q4 is high. Thus output Y is high. As the input begins to increase, Q1 begins to turn on. Because the emitter resistor is common to Q1 and Q2, the emitter voltage of Q2 rises with Q1 when its base voltage begins to fall. When the input has risen far enough (typically to +1.85 V) Q1 is fully on and the base and emitter of Q2 are nearly at the same potential, so Q2 turns off. Once Q2 turns off, Q3 turns on. With Q3 on, Q5 is driven on while Q4 is turned off.

Now let the input voltage start to decrease. When input A drops low enough, Q1 begins to turn off. Q2, however, will be held off until the voltage drop across Q1 rises enough to turn Q2 on. This voltage is normally about 0.85 V.

Some Schmitt triggers have more than one input, usually in the form of diodes, as shown dotted in Fig. 10-6, and performing a NAND logic. Type 74132 is a quad 2-input NAND Schmitt trigger, while type 7413 is a dual 4-input NAND Schmitt trigger.

Hysteresis is also used in certain other circuits, especially those that act as data receivers. Line receivers of this type can also act as conventional Schmitt triggers.

ZERO-CROSSING DETECTOR

When turning ac loads such as transformers and meters on and off, it is often desirable, or necessary, to do so when the ac voltage or current is near zero. By turning such loads off and on when the power is near zero, power line transients are greatly reduced or eliminated. In addition, the controlling device, whether mechanical or semiconductor, only has to handle a small amount of power rather than transient voltages and currents which can be many times larger than normal full load values.

Signetics type 8T363 (Fig. 10-7) is a dual zero-crossing detector whose output is low when the input voltage is +30 mV above 0, and is high when the input is 30 mV lower than 0.

The input circuit consists of Q1 and Q2 as a differential pair, with Q3 acting as a common load. Q4 provides temperature compensation for the input circuit, which is returned to −6 V. D1 is a 6-volt zener diode, which allows the IC to be operated with a −12-volt supply instead of −6 volts.

In normal operation, the STROBE input is high. Then, as long as the input voltage is negative (but not negative enough to cause Q1 to break down) Q1 is turned off. The voltage at point

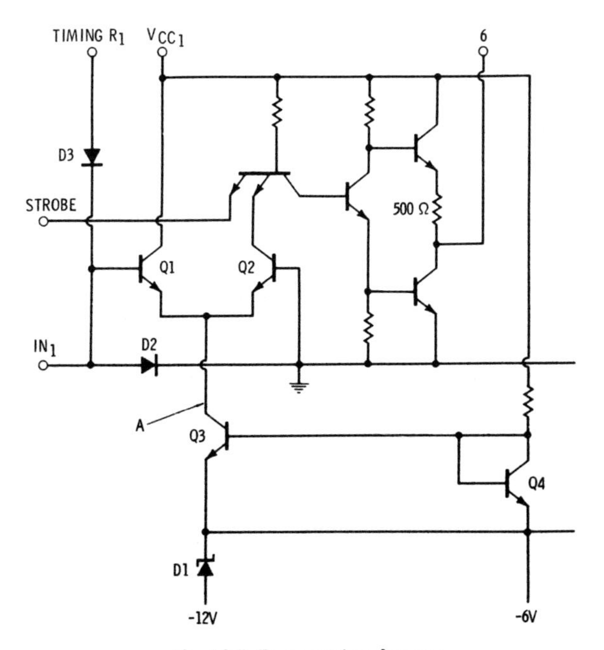

Fig. 10-7. Zero-crossing detector.

A for these conditions is sufficiently below ground potential (0 volts) so that Q2 is on. The rest of the circuit forms a typical 2-input NAND gate. With one emitter of the input transistor conducting strongly (via Q2), the output is high.

When the input signal rises to 0 volt and above, Q1 turns on. When Q1 is on, point A rises above ground and Q2 is turned off. With Q2 off, the NAND circuit sees two high inputs and goes low. D2 limits the input voltage to about +0.6 volt. D3 can be connected to ground to keep the input from going too negative. It also provides a second input that allows the device to be used as a high-stability one-shot multivibrator.

LINE DRIVERS AND RECEIVERS

All signal transmission lines, whether twisted pairs, coaxial cables, or wires in a ribbon or flat cable, have similar characteristics. Each wire of the line has inductance and a series resistance; the wires together form a capacitor, and the leakage from one wire to the other is equivalent to a resistance (usually referred to as conductance, which is the reciprocal of resistance). Also, each wire forms a stray capacitance with other nearby conductors. As the length of the line is increased, the inductance, series resistance, capacitance and conductance all increase proportionately.

When a signal is fed into one end of a transmission line, the impedance that the driving circuit sees is a complicated function of the line parameters. In general, however, the impedance the driving circuit sees is low, usually from about 50 ohms as a minimum to about 150 ohms maximum, although some lines have a little higher impedance. (The impedance of some twin-wire flat tv lead-in cable is as high as 500 ohms.) The impedance that a line would have if it were infinitely long is called its characteristic impedance.

Assume that a high-current driver is feeding a receiver over a transmission line several hundred feet long. The input impedance of the receiver is usually very high, and thus the transmission line looks like an open circuit to the driver. When the driver suddenly applies a step voltage to the line, what happens?

First of all, the driver must supply current to charge the capacitance of the line and to supply leakage current. The voltage step applied by the driver will travel down the line toward the open end. When the voltage wave reaches the open end, a surprising thing happens. Instead of simply rising to the level of the input and stopping, the voltage wave keeps rising and goes higher than the input. Now the open end of the line has a higher voltage than the driven end, and this voltage wave begins to travel back down the line toward the input. The voltage wave returning to the input is known as a reflected wave. When it reaches the driver, it will usually be absorbed by the low impedance of this circuit but multiple reflections can occur. Eventually, the voltage on the wires of the transmission lines will stabilize to the same level as the output voltage of the driver. In the meantime, reflected waves can be interpreted by the receiver as a series of separate signals.

Fortunately, reflected waves can be eliminated by terminating the line in its characteristic impedance. When a step wave of voltage reaches the end of a properly terminated line, the voltage is in effect fooled into thinking it is being fed into an infinitely long cable. Since a voltage wave never gets to the end of an infinite cable, it will never return and reflections do not occur.

Because the impedance of most transmission lines is low, the driving circuit must have sufficient current capacity to supply this load, plus the input circuits of all receivers placed on the line. For a logic level of +3.0 V, a line impedance of 50 ohms itself requires 60 mA. Since this is above the normal level of TTL output circuits, special line drivers are usually needed.

Most transmission lines are terminated by a parallel resistor having the same value as the line's characteristic impedance. Some lines, however, are terminated by a series resistor.

The time required for a step wave of voltage to travel down a transmission line is large with respect to the time delay of a TTL circuit. For a twisted pair line 600 feet long, for example, the time required for the receiving end of the terminated line to rise to 50% of the input signal level is approximately 110 ns. For the signal to rise to 90% of the input would require 29×110 ns = 3190 ns = 3.19 μs.

Thus, if the system uses a typical TTL gate as a receiver, the data transmission rate would have been reduced about 100 times below normal TTL operating rate.

To solve this problem, special line receivers have been developed. These devices have a high impedance differential input circuit that can work with signals as low as 25 mV. With these receivers, it is no longer necessary for the signal at the end of the transmission line to rise to 90% or even 50% of the input, but only 10% or so. The time required for the signal to rise to 10% for the line considered above is 0.17×110 ns = 18.7 ns. This is much closer to the normal delay of TTL circuits. When the transmission line is operated in this way, the signal appearing at the receiver is in effect attenuated by 90% from that fed into the line. The allowable attenuation and the length and characteristics of the line combine to determine the maximum operating frequency. Megahertz rates can be obtained for lines several hundred feet long. For very long lines, operating frequencies must be drastically reduced to those common in telephone systems. Data rates for long telephone lines range from about 2400 bps up to a maximum of about 9600 bps.

The system designer must consider several other factors. Included in these are common mode and differential mode impedances, dc offsets, noise levels, error rates, and the specific characteristics and capabilities of driver, receiver, and transmission lines. In bus organized or party line systems, multiple drivers and receivers are fed by, and drive, the same line or lines.

Types 8T13 and 8T14, by Signetics, are matched line drivers and receivers, respectively, although the 8T13 is a dual circuit, while the 8T14 is a triple circuit.

The logic of one line driver, shown in Fig. 10-8A, consists of two AND gates driving an OR gate. The schematic (Fig. 10-8B) shows a typical TTL input AND-OR structure, but the output circuit is different. The output consists of Q10, which has an uncommitted emitter, plus Q8, which provides short-circuit protection. A short circuit could occur not only mechanically, but also if two drivers attempt to drive a party line or bus in opposite directions at the same time. The uncommitted emitter output allows more than one device to drive a common data bus high so as to feed a number of receivers.

Because of Q8, the extra diode D1, and the low impedance in the collector of Q10, the output voltage/current curve has the shape shown in Fig. 10-9. When Q10 is on and the load

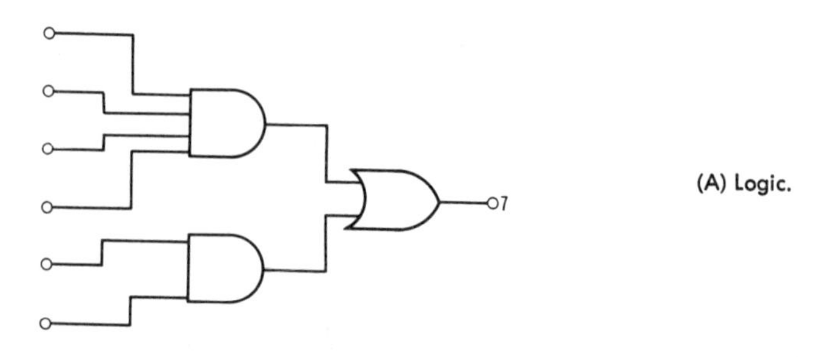

(A) Logic.

Fig. 10-8.

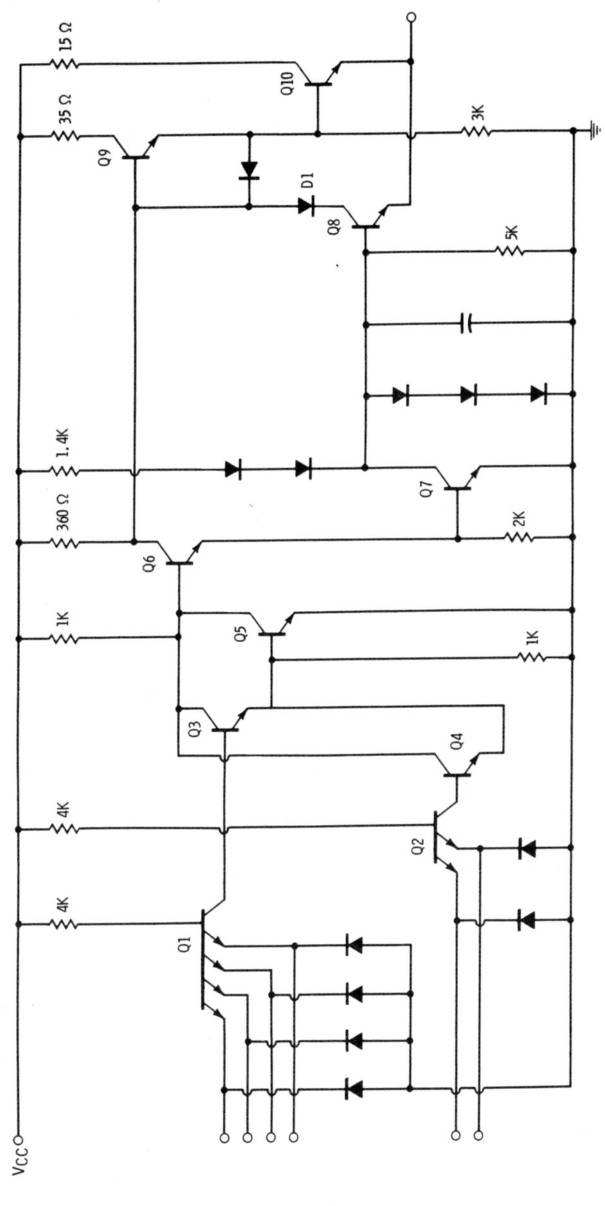

(B) Schematic.

Line driver.

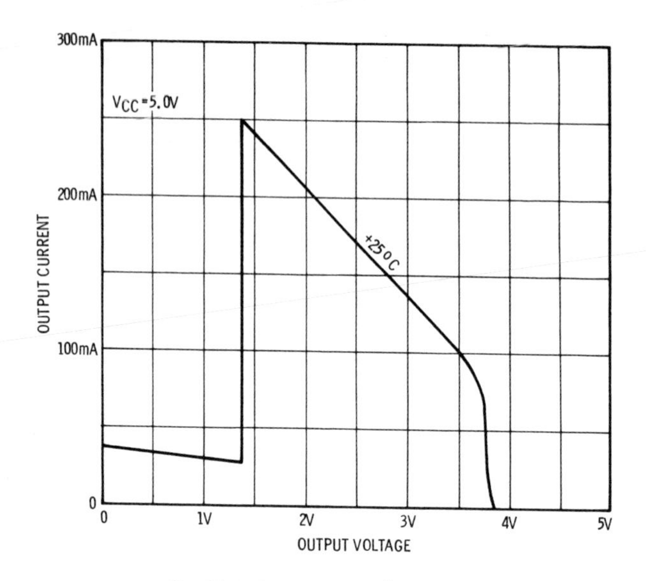

Fig. 10-9. Output voltage/current curve.

impedance is high, the output voltage is nearly 4 V. As the load impedance is decreased, output current increases and rises toward a maximum of about 250 mA. The output voltage for this condition has fallen to about 1.4 V. The voltage at the base of Q8 is 3 diode voltage drops above ground, or about $3 \times 0.6\ V = 1.8\ V$. With its emitter at about 1.4 V and base at about 1.8 V, Q8 turns on. With Q8 on, current flows through D1 and Q8 to the load, thereby diverting current from Q9, turning it off and on as a result, turning Q10 off. The circuit remains in this state until the input conditions change and cause Q6 to turn on.

Because of the low output impedance of the circuit, it can drive a 50-ohm load in parallel with a fairly large capacitance. For example, with a load capacitance of about 4000 pF, signal rise time is approximately 80 ns; with 1000 pF, rise time is approximately 24 ns.

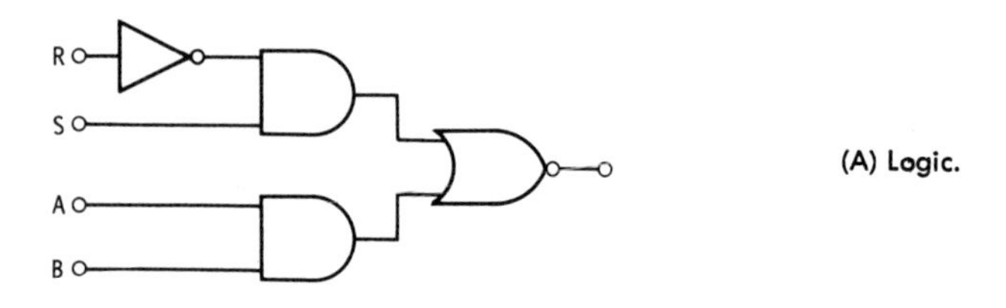

(A) Logic.

Fig. 10-10. A

The 8T14 is a triple receiver, with the logic shown in Fig. 10-10A. The R input drives the differential amplifier shown in Fig. 10-10B. Transistors Q3, Q5 and Q6 act as a constant current load to Q1 and Q2. When the voltage at R is low, Q1 is off and Q2 supplies collector current to Q3. When the voltage at R rises above the threshold level, Q1 turns on to supply collector current to Q3 and thus causes Q2 to turn off. Once

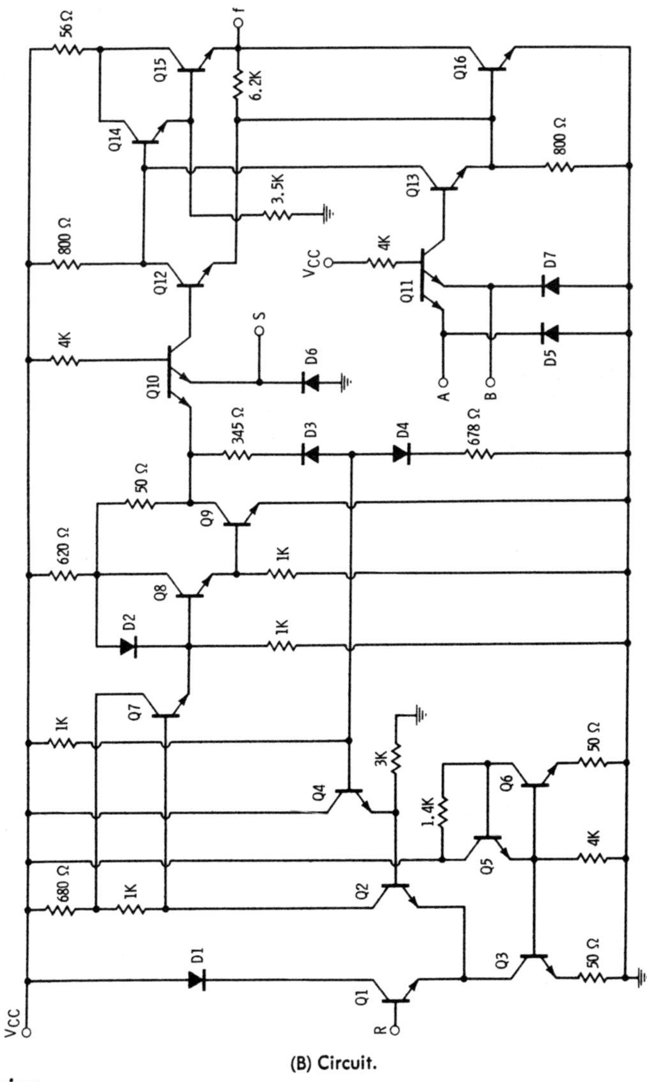

(B) Circuit.

line receiver.

Q1 turns on, D1 acts to hold it on even when the input voltage drops below the turn-on value. Thus the circuit has about 0.5 V hysteresis.

The voltage at the collector of Q2 is fed through Q7, Q8, and Q9 to control one of Q10's two emitters. When Q2 is on, Q7 is off, Q8 is on, Q9 is on, and Q10 is on. When Q2 is off, Q7 is on, Q8 is off, Q9 is off, the driven emitter of Q10 is high and Q10 is off. The rest of the circuit implements the AND and OR functions of the logic diagram. When Q2 is on, Q9 is also on, and when Q2 is off, Q9 is also off.

Q4 is connected as an emitter-follower. When Q9 is on, the signal at the base of Q4 has two paths to ground; one path is through D4 and a 678-ohm resistor, and the other path is through D3, a 345-ohm resistor, and Q9. When Q9 is off, the signal at the base of Q4 has only one path to ground, through D4 and the 678-ohm resistor. Thus, the voltage at the base of Q4 is higher when Q9 is on than it is when Q9 is off. Therefore, once Q2 has been turned on by input R going low, it is latched on and the constant current load is supplied entirely by Q2. Input R must now rise to its minimum high level before Q1 can be turned on again.

Because of the hysteresis of the circuit, it can also be used, with external components, as a Schmitt trigger, to convert sine waves to square waves, as a one-shot, and even as an oscillator. In the 54/74 family, types 74128 and 74S140 are 50/75 ohm line drivers. Type 74128 is basically a 2-input NOR gate with the output circuit modified to deliver up to 42 mA in the high state, and sink up to 48 mA in the low state. Type 74S140 is a 4-input NAND with current rating of 40 mA for high, and 60 mA for low. These circuits do not provide hysteresis on the inputs.

The TTL families have similar circuits.

CHAPTER 11

Increasing TTL Speed and Device Density

Standard TTL is presently being used in many digital systems. It has been a popular form of logic for some time. However, as circuit designers became familiar with the characteristics of the family, they began to push against the normal operating limits. At the same time, TTL began advancing from single-gate packages to multiple-gate packages and then to complete functions, such as flip-flops, counters, decoders, etc.

First of all, designers wanted higher speed so they could do certain jobs faster, especially repetitive or time-consuming jobs. Other designers were building computers for use in outer space or in remote locations on earth. They wanted low-power operation so they could run the systems for a long time on batteries. And, of course, all designers would be delighted to obtain both lower power and higher speed at the same time.

In the search for an optimum density of component packaging, the first stage has become known as *small-scale integration* (SSI). Further steps in circuit integration have produced *medium-scale integration* (MSI) and *large-scale integration* (LSI). No hard and fast boundaries separate SSI, MSI, and LSI. Generally accepted definitions are that packages or chips with up to 10 or 12 gates represent SSI; packages containing 10 to 100 gates are MSI; packages with more than 100 gates are LSI. Beyond LSI is something that has been called *very large-scale integration* (VLSI). A VLSI device would have 1000 or more gates.

PROPAGATION TIME

What is meant by operating speed in digital systems? A typical gate in standard TTL has an average propagation delay of about 10 nanoseconds. This means that once the specified input conditions have been met, the output will change to the new state within about 10 ns. For a 2-input NAND gate, the delay in going to a 0 output (from a 1 output) is specified as 7 ns (typical) to 15 ns (maximum); the delay in going to a 1 output (from a 0 output) is specified as 11 ns (typical) to 22 ns (maximum). Measuring such delays is difficult and requires accurate test fixtures, correct operating procedures, and precise definitions of waveshape rise and fall times—when is the output 0 and when is it 1? In practical usage, propagation delay can be translated into the maximum frequency at which a system can operate. A master-slave flip-flop in standard TTL, for example, can be toggled continuously without error as long as the clock frequency is kept below about 30 MHz. (The typical clock frequency is 35 MHz for the type 5470/7470 flip-flop.) At higher frequencies the flip-flop may not respond correctly.

HIGH-SPEED TTL

The first modification to standard type 54/74 TTL was designed to increase the operating speed. Fig. 11-1 shows the schematic of a basic NAND gate in standard TTL, and Fig. 11-2 shows the schematic for high-speed TTL. High-speed TTL uses lower values of resistance; therefore, the amount of charge storage in these elements and their associated stray capacitances is reduced. Note, also, that high-speed TTL removes the output diode and adds an extra transistor in a Darlington configuration to aid in changing the output from 0 to 1. As a result of this change, the delay in driving the output to 0 (from a 1) becomes 6.2 ns (typical) to 10 ns (maximum). The delay in driving the output to 1 (from a 0) becomes 5.9 ns (typical) to 10 ns (maximum). Flip-flops made for high-speed TTL technology can be operated at toggle frequencies of 50 MHz.

Darlington outputs are also used in some regular TTL gates such as 5440/7440, a dual 4-input NAND buffer.

One very important parameter—operating voltage—was kept constant at 5-volts dc. Thus, standard and high-speed TTL can be used in the same system without adding special power

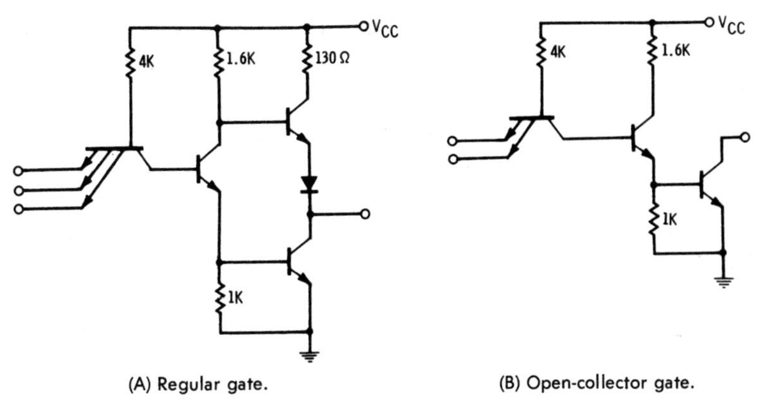

(A) Regular gate.

(B) Open-collector gate.

Fig. 11-1. Standard TTL NAND gate.

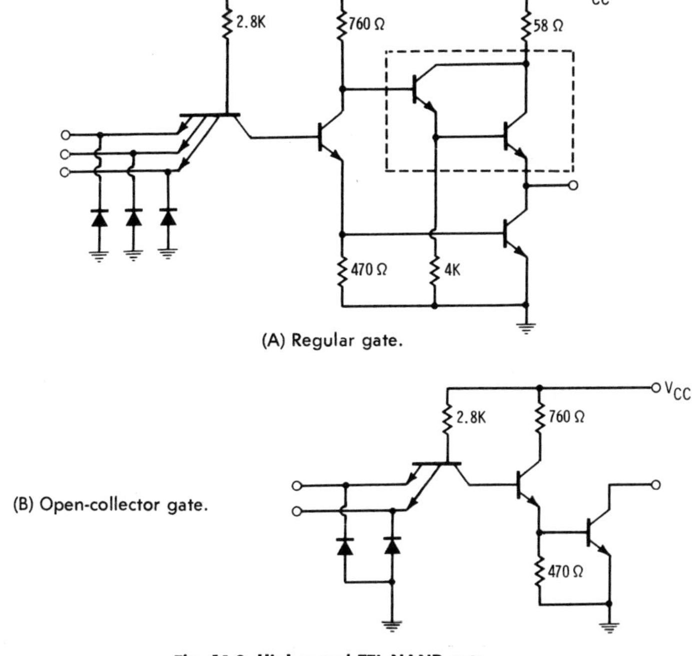

(A) Regular gate.

(B) Open-collector gate.

Fig. 11-2. High-speed TTL NAND gate.

supplies. In all succeeding families of type 54/74 TTL, the operating voltage is kept at 5 volts.

Another notable change incorporated into high-speed TTL (in the type 54/74 family, it is called type 54H/74H) is the addition of clamping diodes on the inputs. Fig. 11-3 shows how these diodes prevent the input lines from overshooting, which, if not suppressed, can lead to false operation. Overshooting and related transient effects become more severe as operating speed increases. The input diodes were found to be so advantageous in type 54H/74H circuits that they have been retrofitted to standard TTL, even though they may not be shown on some drawings. Their inclusion in standard TTL costs practically nothing (other than a change in the masking), and the reduction of coupling problems aids system design.

High-speed TTL has been made available primarily in a number of gating circuits and some assorted flip-flops. Unless the extra speed is actually needed in a circuit, standard TTL is normally used.

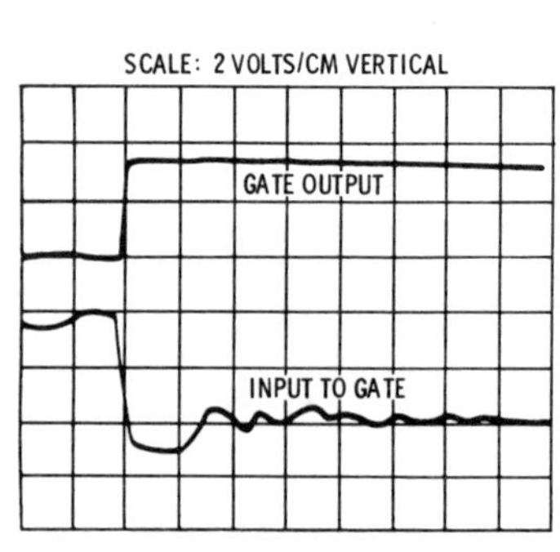

(A) TTL gate with clamp diodes.

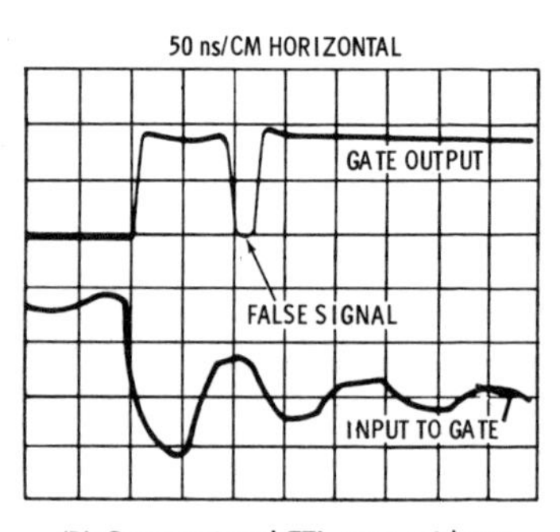

(B) Conventional TTL gate without clamp diodes.

Fig. 11-3. Effect of input clamping diodes.

One of the major prices paid for high-speed TTL is higher power consumption by each gate. In normal operation, standard TTL has an average standby power dissipation of 10 mW per gate. On the other hand, high-speed TTL has a standby power dissipation of 22 mW per gate—more than twice as much. Not only does the higher power requirement place more of a burden on the power supply, it also means that each IC package will give off more heat (assuming an equal number of gates in each package). Thus, the cooling system requires extra attention, and special fans or heat sinks may be needed.

Because type 54H/74H TTL has lower impedances than standard 54/74 TTL, it uses more input and more output current. Gates in type 54H/74H circuits can usually drive or fan out to 9 other H gates. Also, one H gate can drive 20 standard gates. Gates in standard type 54/74 circuits can also drive H gates, but the fan-out from standard to H gates is 1, rather than the usual 10.

LOW-POWER TTL

Since lower circuit impedances in H-type TTL caused power consumption to go up, wouldn't higher circuit impedances cause the power consumption to go down? The answer is yes, and low-power TTL or LPTTL (type 54L/74L) is the result of this idea. The circuit for a basic gate is shown in Fig. 11-4. Again, the operating voltage is kept at 5 volts.

LPTTL has characteristics similar to standard and high-speed TTL, but it pays for its low power consumption in operating speed. Power consumption is down to 1 mW per gate, but propagation delay is up to 33 ns per gate. As a result, the flip-flop toggle frequency is 3 MHz (typical).

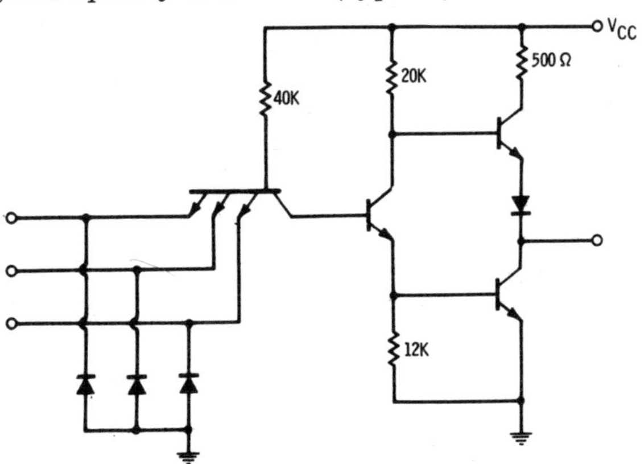

Fig. 11-4. Low-power TTL NAND gate.

ACTIVE BYPASS TTL

The next modification to come along was the use of an active network in the base drive of the bottom output transistor (Fig. 11-5A). The effect of the network is shown in Fig. 11-5B. During an output transition from 1 to 0 or from 0 to 1, the output voltage in standard TTL (also high-speed and low-power TTL) will move along the lower curve as shown. With the active bypass network instead of a simple resistor, the upper curve is traced. This means the actual transition periods from low to high and from high to low are decreased, and the result is a slight increase in speed.

The *active bypass*, as it is called, is used by Motorola in its MC3100/3000 series of devices (also called MTTL III). The impedances used in the basic gate are very close to those in high-speed gates (type H). Power consumption is rated the same for both—22 mW per gate—except that the improved transfer characteristic results in less current-spiking during transitions and, thus, the overall power consumption is lower. Gate delay is improved slightly over the H-type gate.

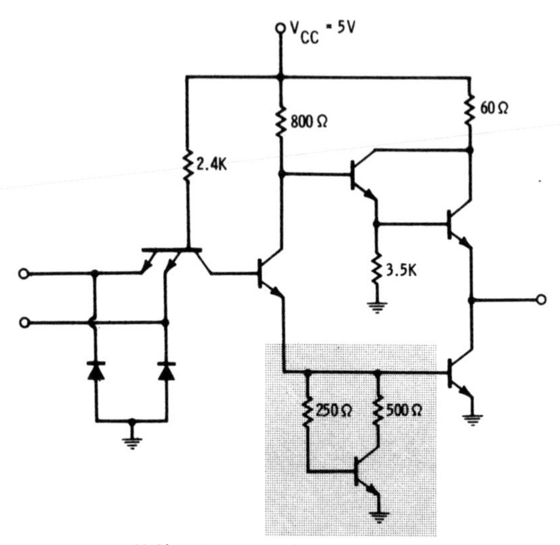

(A) Showing active bypass network.

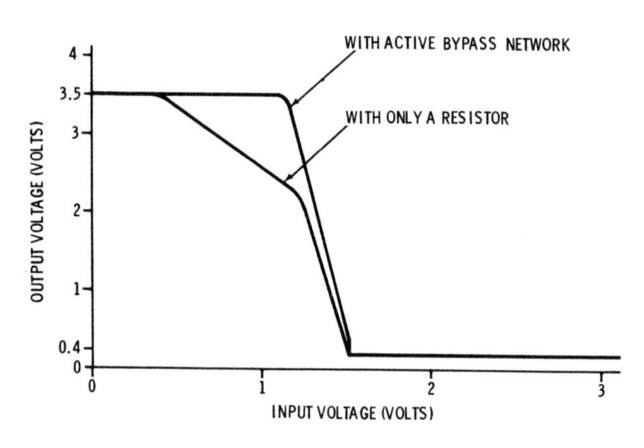

(B) Square transfer characteristic curve.

Fig. 11-5. Typical Motorola MTTL III circuit.

SCHOTTKY-CLAMPED TTL

Until the development of Schottky-clamped TTL, all TTL families operated on the principle of saturated logic. That is, transistors were generally overdriven so that their impedance

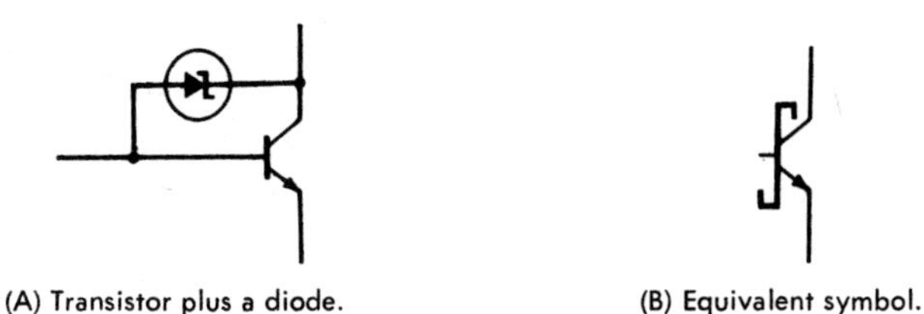

(A) Transistor plus a diode. (B) Equivalent symbol.

Fig. 11-6. Schottky-barrier diode-clamped transistor.

was as low as possible when they were on and as high as possible when they were off. Because of being overdriven, the circuits required a little extra time to change from one state to the other. A major advantage of this type operation is that it keeps the noise margin high. If the drive is reduced, so that a transistor is turned on but not thoroughly saturated, the noise immunity is also reduced.

Schottky-clamped TTL uses a recently developed component called a Schottky-barrier diode to keep transistors in TTL from saturating. The basic circuit device is an ordinary transistor with a Schottky-barrier diode connected from base to collector as shown in Fig. 11-6A. When base drive is applied to this circuit, the transistor is driven almost into saturation. At this point, the diode, which has a lower forward voltage drop than the base-collector junction of the npn transistor, takes over and diverts excess current away from the junction. The diode itself has practically no storage capacity. When base drive is removed, the transistor can follow immediately without first having to dissipate a stored charge. Thus, the switch-

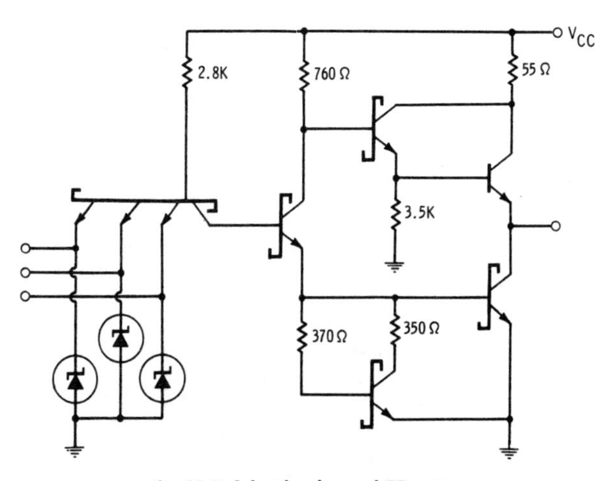

Fig. 11-7. Schottky-clamped TTL gate.

ing characteristic of the combination is significantly better than it is when just a transistor is driven into saturation. The symbol in Fig. 11-6B is used to represent the combination of diode and transistor.

Fig. 11-7 shows a Schottky-clamped TTL gate. In addition to clamped transistors, the circuit uses a Darlington-connected output circuit for the upper part of the totem pole output and the active bypass network for the lower part. The input clamping diodes are also Schottky-barrier type to reduce storage effects. Thus, every change that anybody has been able to think of has been thrown in to increase speed.

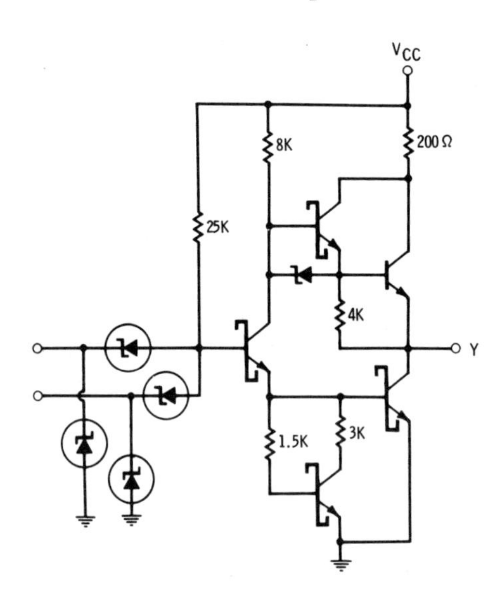

Fig. 11-8. Low-power Schottky TTL gate with totem pole output.

The result is a basic gate with a propagation delay of 3 ns. Power consumption is slightly less than the 22 mW-per-gate of high-speed TTL, but the speed is much higher. The family is called type 54S/74S circuits. Flip-flops of this family toggle reliably at 100 MHz.

LOW-POWER SCHOTTKY TTL

Because Schottky-clamped TTL is so fast, it becomes possible to trade off some of its speed and obtain a savings in power consumption. The result is low-power Schottky TTL, which has only 2-mW dissipation per gate and a propagation delay of

10 ns. The basic circuit for low-power Schottky TTL (or type 54LS/74LS) is shown in Fig. 11-8 for totem pole output and in Fig. 11-9 for open-collector output.

Low power is obtained by raising the impedances of the circuit elements. The input resistor has been increased to 25K from its nominal 1.6K in a standard TTL gate. Note also that the multiemitter input transistor (a common characteristic of TTL) has been replaced by Schottky-barrier diodes. Since

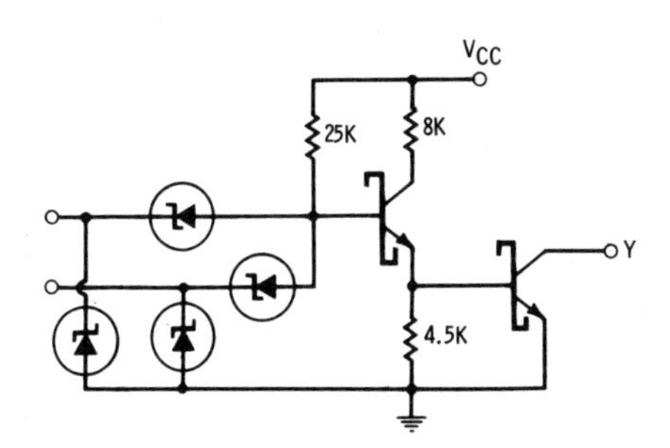

Fig. 11-9. Low-power Schottky TTL gate with open-collector output.

the diodes have so little storage, little speed, if any, is lost by this change. The input circuit, however, is similar to the input circuit for Diode Transistor Logic (DTL).

PNP INPUTS

The input circuit found on most TTL ICs is a transistor with one or more ungrounded emitters. For circuits where only one data input is required, or where the input transistor is not performing a logic function, a higher impedance input circuit has been developed. The circuit, shown in Fig. 11-10, uses a pnp transistor (with input protecting diode).

When the input is high, Q1 is off and the input to Q2 is high. When the input to Q1 is low, Q1 is on, and the input to Q2 is low. Q2 then feeds the rest of the device. When the input is

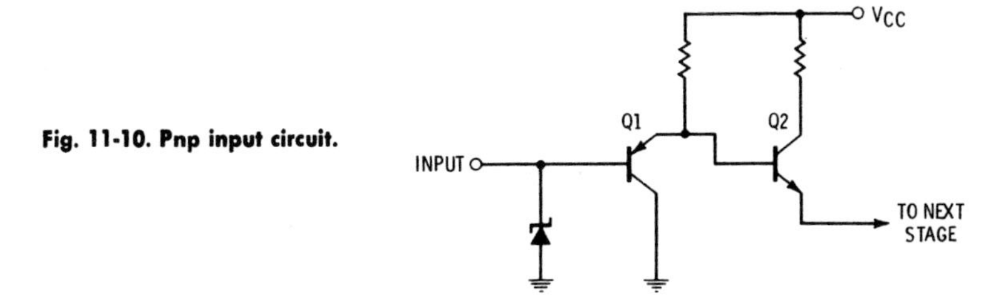

Fig. 11-10. Pnp input circuit.

high, the leakage into Q1 from the driving circuit is only about 25 μA, less than the 40 μA of a regular TTL input. When the input is low, the driving circuit must sink only about 200 μA, considerably less than the 1.6 mA of a regular TTL gate.

HIGH-NOISE IMMUNITY LOGIC

In many industrial environments electrical noise is often too high for any of the TTL families which operate with a 5-volt power supply, and 2.4 to 3 volts or so for a logic high. To provide more noise immunity, a family of higher voltage logic was developed by Teledyne Semiconductor. It is called High Noise Immunity Logic, or HiNIL, and is available in two ratings, one for operation with a 12-volt power supply and one for 15 volts. The nominal voltages for a logic high are 10 and 13 volts, respectively, which is much higher than TTL.

A typical NAND gate is shown in Fig. 11-11A. The inputs are diodes, as with DTL and Schottky TTL. In addition, a zener diode rated at 5.8 volts guarantees that only signals higher than 6.5 volts can turn on Q1. HiNIL gates are available with open collector, Fig. 11-11B, and with a passive pull-up resistor instead of an active transistor. Relatively few circuits have been developed compared to 5 volt TTL. In many cases HiNIL circuits act as interfaces to a regular TTL system.

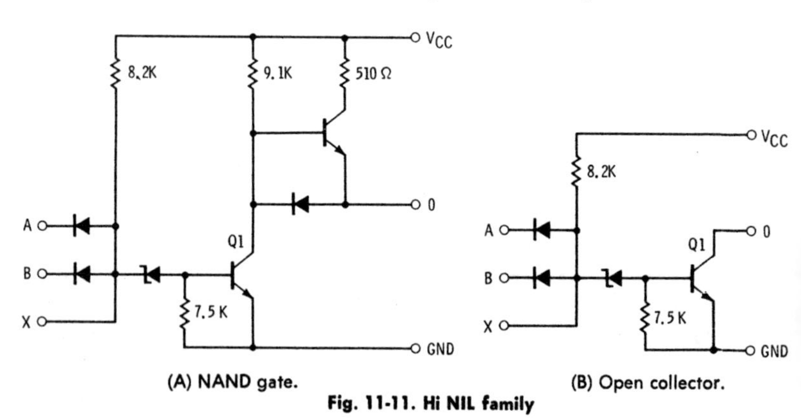

(A) NAND gate.

(B) Open collector.

Fig. 11-11. Hi NIL family

TRI-STATE LOGIC

One of the characteristics of TTL is that the output is either high or grounded. Thus, the outputs cannot be connected together, except in the open-collector configuration. But in a data transmission system, in which a single pair of wires is

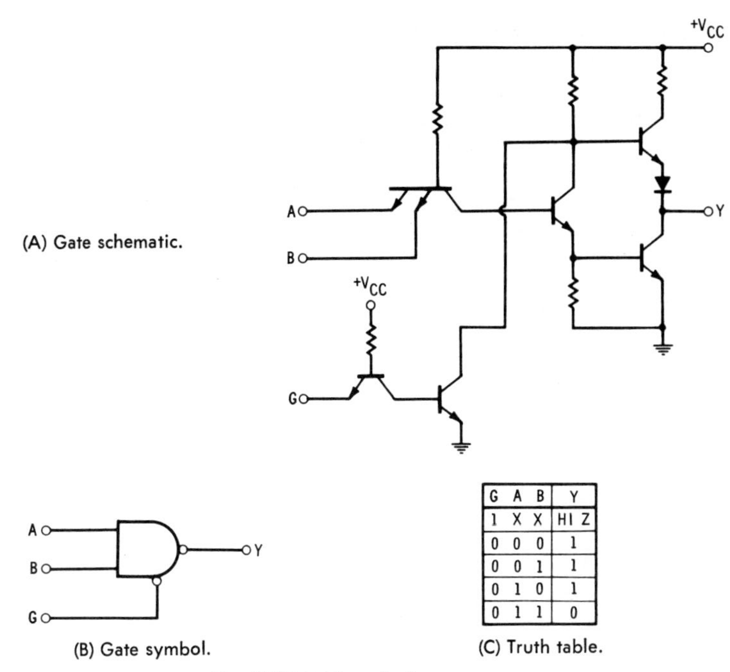

(A) Gate schematic.

(B) Gate symbol.

G	A	B	Y
1	X	X	HI Z
0	0	0	1
0	0	1	1
0	1	0	1
0	1	1	0

(C) Truth table.

Fig. 11-12. Tri-State logic gate.

used to carry data back and forth between many different stations, some way of allowing many gates to feed the same circuit is needed. To solve this problem, National Semiconductor Corporation developed what is called Tri-State Logic.

Tri-State Logic, shown in Fig. 11-12, uses extra transistors to control the output circuit. Whenever the control transistor is turned on, it turns both output transistors off. As a result, the output of a Tri-State gate has three states: low voltage, or 0; high voltage, or 1; and high impedance, or OFF. In the first two states, 0 and 1, the gate can feed data into the common line. In the third state, one of the other gates on the line can feed data into the line. The turned-off gate will not be affected. Thus, Tri-State Logic allows multistation operation, as long as two outputs are not allowed to talk at the same time. The Tri-State mode of operation has been applied to certain types of gates and devices in all TTL families.

TTL TRENDS

TTL circuits being produced today are primarily in the SSI and MSI class. Many new functions, especially in MSI, have appeared since the first edition of this book and new circuits are introduced all the time. The natural evolution of TTL would seem to be toward complete systems on a single chip, with everything—all the electronics—in one tiny package. But a number of factors are working at cross purposes to this development, including power consumption, package limitations, and alternative technologies.

When you put 100 standard TTL gates in one package, you have a device with an average power consumption of 1000 mW (1 watt). But, the semiconductor chip itself is only a small part of a small package, and the local heating can be severe.

One limit to the number of gates that can be integrated on one chip is determined by how much power they dissipate and how fast this power—heat—can be conducted away and dumped to the outside world. If the heat is not removed fast enough, the temperature can rise high enough to impair circuit operation and destroy the chip. Cooling effectiveness can be increased by using heat sinks, fans, and even liquid cooling. Heat generation, on the other hand, can be reduced by using LPTTL circuit concepts of higher impedances and by simplifying internal circuits as much as possible. However, reducing power consumption usually slows things down, which is acceptable in some applications but not in others. To summarize, the power consumption problem may limit the use of TTL to MSI complexity only and may keep it from going very far into LSI. That still, of course, leaves a tremendous field of application.

A second limitation relates to the number of connections the chip can make to the outside world. Two factors are at work here. First, a connection to the outside world requires that a relatively large pad must be metallized on the chip so that a wire can be bonded to the circuit. Space on the chip is at a premium. If you install too many connection pads, you won't have any room left to install transistors and resistors. The second factor relates to the number of pins that can be brought out of a given size package. The more complex a chip is, the more external connections it is likely to require. Dual-in-line packages (called DIP packages), with pins designed to plug into a socket, are available with 14 pins, 16 pins, and so on, up to about 80 pins. As you increase the number of pins, you increase the difficulty of inserting and removing the package from a socket, and you increase the danger of breaking a pin off. You also decrease the reliability of the system because of the increased possibility of a poor connection between the pins and the socket connections.

If a system has only a few inputs and outputs, it can be very complex internally and still fit into a package with a limited number of pins. If the system has many inputs and outputs, the requirement for many interface connections may dictate the use of less complex chips than would normally be used.

The future of TTL will also be influenced by the development of alternative technologies. The most important alternative is Metal-Oxide Semiconductors (MOS). A large variety of MOS devices have already been developed, and more are on the way. The major advantages of MOS are its low power consumption and the fact that many more transistors can be placed on a chip than in TTL technology. If LSI and VLSI devices are to become popular, it may be that only MOS will be used in these areas. The package problem with respect to the number of pins remains, however. Thus, circuit configurations, such as regular arrays of memory cells, that minimize the problem are favored. Early types of MOS were much slower than TTL, and they could not compete effectively where speed was important. Recently developed MOS families are as fast as certain types of TTL. Therefore, much greater use of MOS can be expected.

In addition, a family of CMOS circuits has been developed that duplicates many of the functions of 54/74 TTL. The same numbering system is used, with C substituted for H, LP, S, or LS, and pinouts are identical.

ECL families, mentioned previously, are still the fastest form of digital logic, and they are being used where the ultimate in speed is necessary. Speed is especially important in large systems where data should be handled as rapidly as possible to obtain maximum use of all circuits. Circuits that have been paid for, but which are seldom used because of a transportation bottleneck somewhere in the system, are very expensive. A circuit that can do a job in 100 ns is obviously working far below maximum efficiency when it is only used once an hour. When there are 10,000 such circuits in a system, the need for data handling speed becomes apparent.

System designers look first for a technology that will be able to perform the desired task properly and reliably. If two suitable technologies are found, then the designer will normally choose the least expensive way, if everything else is equal. In real life, of course, "everything else" is never exactly equal. One method will be more reliable than the other, or weigh less, or be more easily maintained, etc. Economy, nevertheless, is a vitally important consideration. TTL today is a very economical technology. For this reason alone, TTL will continue to see wide and growing use. Added to this is the availability of a great and growing variety of complex circuits and the in-

Table 11-1. Major

TTL Type	Texas Instruments Incorporated	Fairchild Semiconductor	Motorola Semiconductor Products, Inc.
Standard	Series 54/74	9000 Series 9N00/5400 Series 9N00/7400 Series 9300 Series 9600 Series 93400	MTTL (MC500/400 Series) (MC5400/7400 Series) (MC9300/8300 Series) (MC9600/8600 Series) MTTL I (MC500/400 Series) (MC4300/4000 Series) (MC5400/7400 Series)
Low-Power	Series 54L/74L	9L00 Series 93L00 Series	
High-Speed	Series 54H/74H	9H00/54H00 Series 9H00/74H00 Series	MTTL II (MC2100/2000 Series) (MC4300/4000 Series) MTTL III (MC3100/3000 Series)
Schottky	Series 54S/74S	9S00/54S00 Series 9S00/74S00 Series 93S00 Series	
Low-Power Schottky	Series 54LS/74LS		

creasing familiarity of designers with TTL systems. All these factors mean that TTL will be used in more and more systems.

FAMILIES OF TTL

This book has dealt primarily with the type 54/74 family of TTL, because this family is the largest and best known. It is manufactured by most of the leading semiconductor manufacturers. Quite a few other TTL families have been developed, of course, since each manufacturer would like to have his own special family.

All TTL families have characteristics similar to type 54/74. Sometimes, devices in one or more of the other families can be interchanged directly with type 54/74 devices. In other cases, the devices may perform exactly the same function, but the pin arrangements are different. In addition, some functions are not available in type 54/74 but are available in one or more of the other families. The total number of TTL devices in all families is very large and is growing all the time; thus,

TTL Families

National Semiconductor	Sprague Electric Company	Raytheon Company	Signetics Corporation
DM5400 DM7400 DM8000 DM8200 DM8500	Series US5400/ USS9600 Series US7400/ USN9600 Series US5400/ US7400	RAY I RAY II	54/74XX Series 8200 Series 8T
Series DM54LXX/ DM74LXX Low Power/883			
	Series US54H00 Series US74H00	RAY III	S54H N74H
			S54S/N74S 82S

a complete listing is not possible here. However, the major families are listed in Table 11-1. Some of the families have only a few devices, while others have hundreds of different circuits.

Even though the table may not show it, many of the families are available from more than one manufacturer. In addition, a number of overseas manufacturers make TTL devices in still other families, some of which are interchangeable with devices from U.S. manufacturers. U.S. manufacturers publish cross-reference guides to their own products, and D.A.T.A. (32 Lincoln Avenue, Orange, N.J. 07050) publishes guides containing reference data and cross-references to TTL on a world-wide basis.

CHAPTER 12

TTL Applications

This chapter discusses only two of the many applications of TTL logic. The basic circuit for the Up/Down Counting system was developed by Fairchild Semiconductor. The basic circuit for the Data Transmission system was developed by Texas Instruments Incorporated.

UP/DOWN COUNTING SYSTEM

Counting up or down (depending on the direction in which a part is moving) is very useful in solving some industrial and scientific problems. Fig. 12-1 shows an up/down counting system that uses a light source and photo transistors as signal inputs. An object moving from photo transistor Q2 to photo transistor Q1 causes the count shown by the display tubes to increase by 1; an object moving in the opposite direction causes the count to decrease by 1.

The only significant restriction on the system is that the objects being counted must be large enough to cover both photo transistors at the same time. Up-count information is derived from the fact that an object entering the detection area, first interrupts the light input to transistor Q2, then to both transistors Q2 and Q1, then to transistor Q1 only, and finally, to neither. Down-count information is derived from the reverse sequence.

When no object is present, transistors Q1 and Q2 are on. This allows current to flow through resistors R1 and R2 to ground, turning transistors Q3 and Q4 on. Therefore, Gates

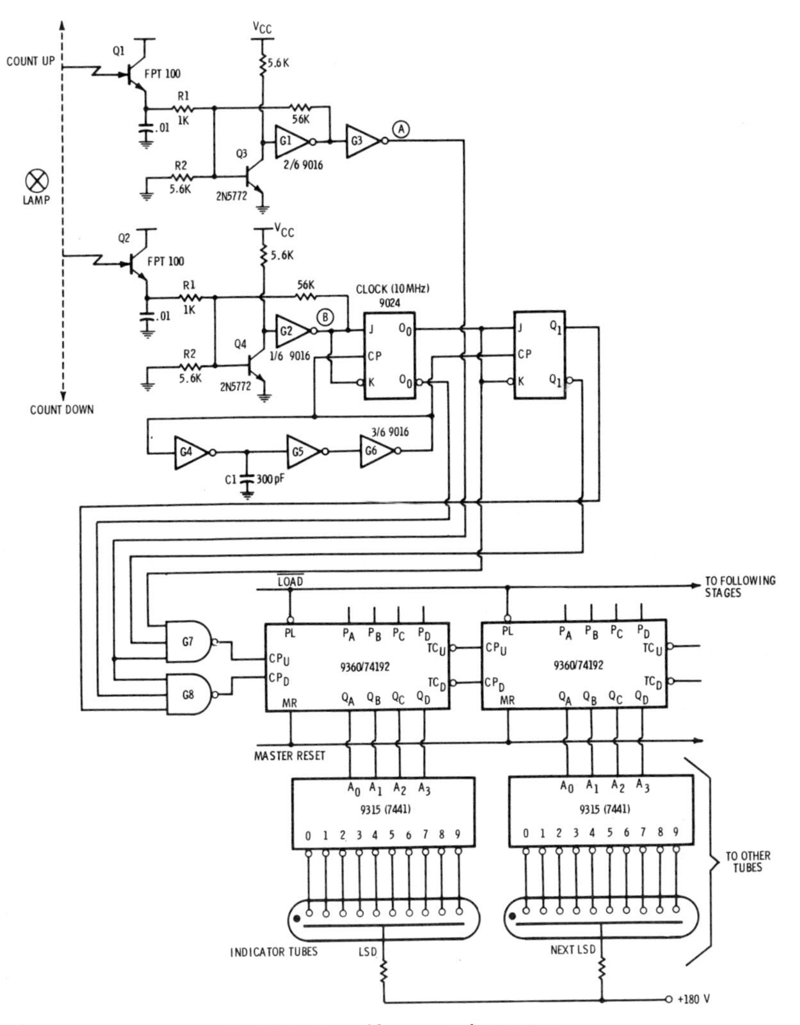

Fig. 12-1. An up/down counting system.

G1 and G2 have low inputs and high outputs; thus point B is high and point A is low. Point A thus holds the outputs of Gates G7 and G8 high.

Gates G4, G5 and G6, in combination with the capacitor C1, form a free-running clock that operates at about 10 MHz. When Gate G4 goes low, it discharges the capacitor and drives Gate G5 high and Gate G6 low. When Gate G6 is low, it drives G4 high. But when Gate G4 goes high, it must first charge up capacitor C1 before the voltage at the input of Gate G5 rises sufficiently to switch the gate low. Thus, the circuit operates as a relaxation oscillator to provide clock pulses to the two flip-flops.

The flip-flops form a 2-bit shift register. As long as point B is high, the first flip-flop holds a 1 ($Q_0 = 1$), which in turn puts a 1 into the second flip-flop. Gates G7 and G8 are held high by $Q_0 = Q_1 = 0$.

Let an object enter the detection area in the count-up direction. Transistor Q2 is covered first, which removes most of the drive current to transistor Q4 and turns it off. This puts a high at the input of Gate 2 and a low at point B. The next clock pulse, after point B goes low, puts a 0 into the first flip-flop; the next clock pulse puts a 0 into the second flip-flop. At this point, Gates G7 and G8 each have two 0s and a 1 as inputs and, therefore, are high.

The object moves further to cover transistor Q1 while transistor Q2 is still covered. This drives point A high. Gates G7 and G8 now have two 1s and one 0 as inputs.

The object next uncovers transistor Q2, which causes point B to go high, and the next clock pulse puts a 1 into the first flip-flop. At this point, Gate G7 has all 1s as inputs and goes to 0, while Gate G8 has two 1s and a 0. The negative transition on the Count-Up input to the counter causes the device to advance one count. On the next clock pulse, Gate G7 is again disabled by transistor Q1 = 0. As the object advances further, it clears transistor Q1, and point A again goes low.

When an object enters from the opposite direction, point A goes high first. As transistor Q2 is covered, point B goes low, which allows a 0 to enter the flip-flop. This condition of 0 in flip-flop 1 and 1 in flip-flop 2 opens Gate G8 for one clock pulse, which causes the counter to make a down count.

Only two decades of counting are shown but more can be added. The system can be modified to generate a signal when a preset count is reached.

DATA TRANSMISSION SYSTEM

One of the major advantages of digital systems is that they can handle information without being degraded by noise. This characteristic allows data to be transmitted long distances through noisy channels without loss of information. However, digital signals are not immune to noise; if sufficient interference occurs, they can be completely lost, just like an analog signal. But, as long as the signal-to-noise ratio is kept above a minimum, the signal can be transmitted without error.

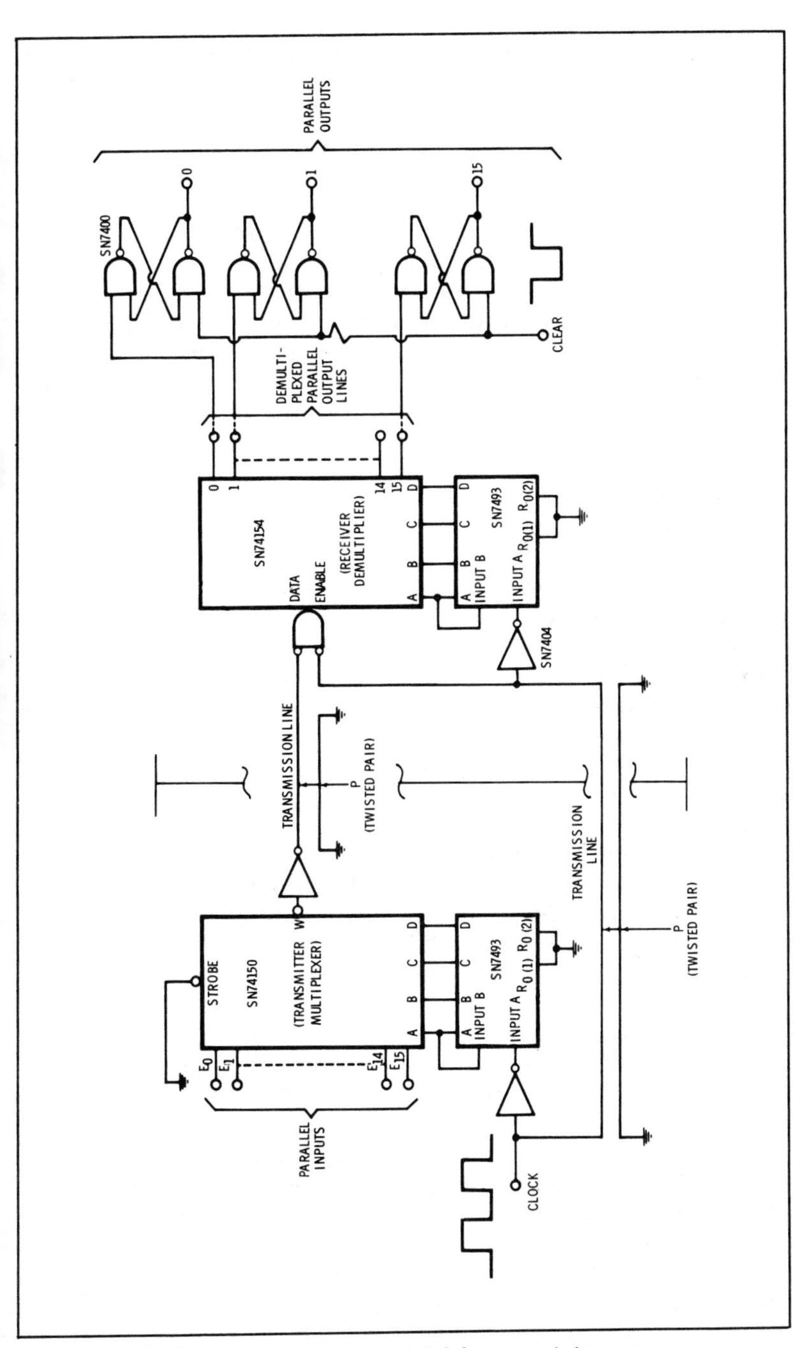

Fig. 12-2. Logic diagram for a digital data transmission system.

Fig. 12-2 shows a straightforward transmission system for digital data. The data is available at the transmitting end of the communications link in the form of 16-bit, parallel words. To keep the cost of wiring between transmitter and receiver low, the data is to be sent serially over one pair of twisted wires. To keep the electronic encoding and decoding system uncomplicated, a second pair of twisted wires is used to synchronize the operation of transmitter and receiver. For relatively short transmission links (as in a factory between a production line and a central computer), the separation of data channel from control channel is practical and economical. In longer links and in more complex systems, control and data can be transmitted over the same pair of wires—or radio channel, etc.

The 16-bit word is applied to the 16-parallel inputs of the data selector/multiplexer, type SN74150 (Fig. 12-2). With the Strobe input 0 (grounded, as shown), the multiplexer will deliver the input bits to the outputs, one at a time, under control of the address or select inputs A, B, C, and D. The address bits are obtained from a binary counter, circuit type SN7493. The counter is connected to run as a 0 to 16-bit counter. Thus, as it passes through its count sequence, it will generate the required 16 address codes for the SN74150 multiplexer.

The clock signal is obtained from an oscillator. Assuming the clock is a positive-going signal, an inverter is required at the input of the binary counter, since it operates on the negative edge of the clock pulse.

The clock signal is also fed over a second pair of transmission lines to an identical inverter at the input to a 16-bit binary counter at the receiver. The data coming out of the multiplexer appears in inverted form; therefore, an inverter is used to restore the data to its true form. It is then sent over the line to the receiver.

At the receiver, a 4-line-to-16-line decoder/demultiplexer (circuit type SN74154) acts to sort out the stream of serial bits and reconstruct the original transmitted word. When Data and Enable inputs are both low (Fig. 12-3), the SN74154 demultiplexer causes the addressed output to go low. Thus, when the address is 0000, output 0 is addressed. It will follow the Data input, going low if Data is low; otherwise, output 0 stays high.

Assume first that the two addressing circuits start out from 0000 together and stay in step throughout the operation of the system. This can be assured by resetting the counters to 0000 before every transmission. With the counters in step, both the

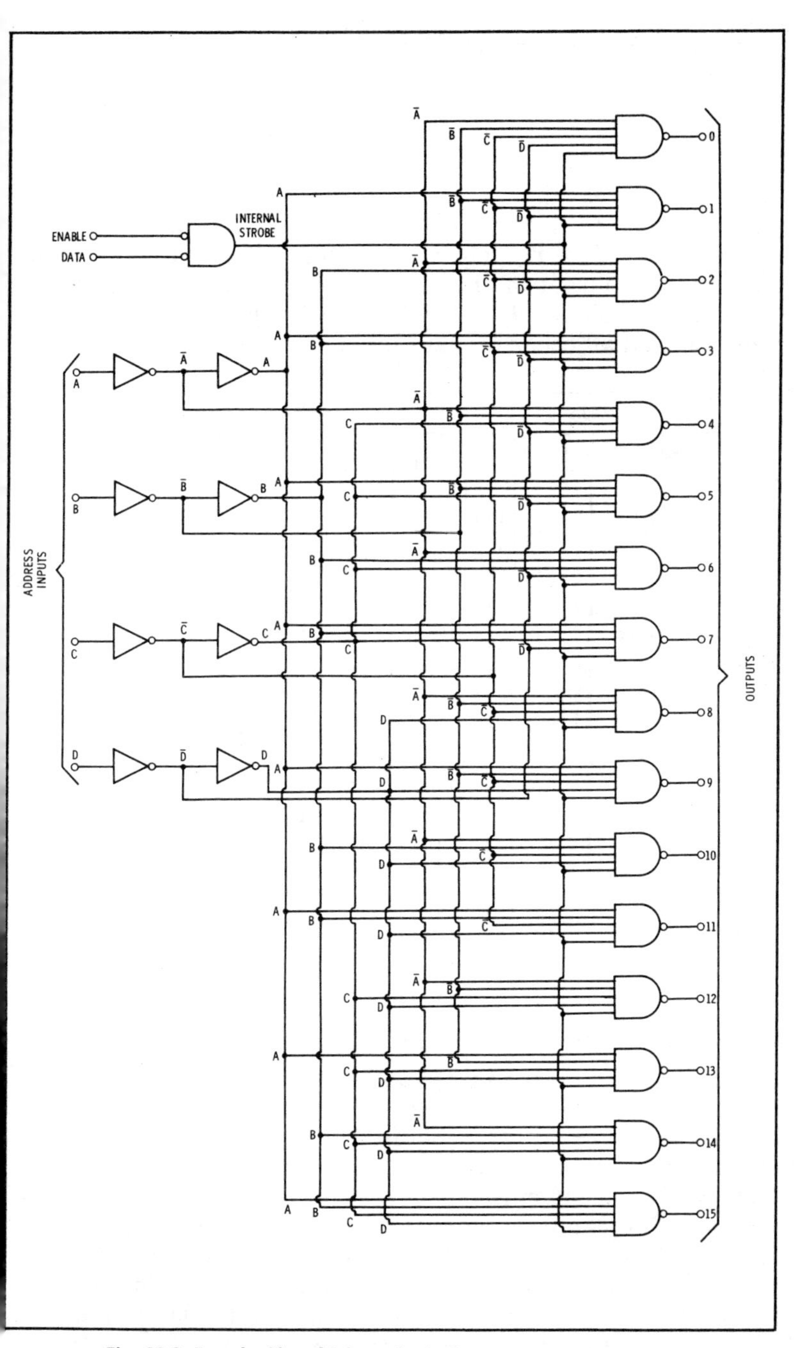

Fig. 12-3. Decoder/demultiplexer logic diagram (type SN74154).

multiplexer and the demultiplexer will always be addressing the same bit. The time delay over the transmission path is assumed to be close to zero and, therefore, negligible. The sequence of operation can be deduced from the waveforms of Fig. 12-5. As each bit (E_0 through E_{15}) of the word to be transmitted is addressed, it appears at the input of the demultiplexer. When the clock goes low, the bit appears at the output of the demultiplexer. Note that, if the bit is a 1, no change occurs in the output of the demultiplexer, since its normal or quiescent output is a 1. If the bit is a 0, the addressed output goes low, and all other bits are high.

INPUTS						OUTPUTS															
ENABLE	DATA	D	C	B	A	0	1	2	3	4	5	6	7	8	9	10	11	12	13	14	15
0	0	0	0	0	0	0	1	1	1	1	1	1	1	1	1	1	1	1	1	1	1
0	0	0	0	0	1	1	0	1	1	1	1	1	1	1	1	1	1	1	1	1	1
0	0	0	0	1	0	1	1	0	1	1	1	1	1	1	1	1	1	1	1	1	1
0	0	0	0	1	1	1	1	1	0	1	1	1	1	1	1	1	1	1	1	1	1
0	0	0	1	0	0	1	1	1	1	0	1	1	1	1	1	1	1	1	1	1	1
0	0	0	1	0	1	1	1	1	1	1	0	1	1	1	1	1	1	1	1	1	1
0	0	0	1	1	0	1	1	1	1	1	1	0	1	1	1	1	1	1	1	1	1
0	0	0	1	1	1	1	1	1	1	1	1	1	0	1	1	1	1	1	1	1	1
0	0	1	0	0	0	1	1	1	1	1	1	1	1	0	1	1	1	1	1	1	1
0	0	1	0	0	1	1	1	1	1	1	1	1	1	1	0	1	1	1	1	1	1
0	0	1	0	1	0	1	1	1	1	1	1	1	1	1	1	0	1	1	1	1	1
0	0	1	0	1	1	1	1	1	1	1	1	1	1	1	1	1	0	1	1	1	1
0	0	1	1	0	0	1	1	1	1	1	1	1	1	1	1	1	1	0	1	1	1
0	0	1	1	0	1	1	1	1	1	1	1	1	1	1	1	1	1	1	0	1	1
0	0	1	1	1	0	1	1	1	1	1	1	1	1	1	1	1	1	1	1	0	1
0	0	1	1	1	1	1	1	1	1	1	1	1	1	1	1	1	1	1	1	1	0
0	1	X	X	X	X	1	1	1	1	1	1	1	1	1	1	1	1	1	1	1	1
1	0	X	X	X	X	1	1	1	1	1	1	1	1	1	1	1	1	1	1	1	1
1	1	X	X	X	X	1	1	1	1	1	1	1	1	1	1	1	1	1	1	1	1

Fig. 12-4. Truth table for Fig. 12-3.

If the received data can be used in this format, no further processing is required. But if the word is to be "captured," each individual bit must be stored until the complete word is received. This can be accomplished with the latch circuits (Fig. 12-2). Before a word is transmitted, the latches are all set to 1 by driving the Clear line to 0. Then, as the word is received, any bit that is a 1 does not affect its associated latch, but any bit that is a 0 drives its latch to 0. Thus, the word is captured.

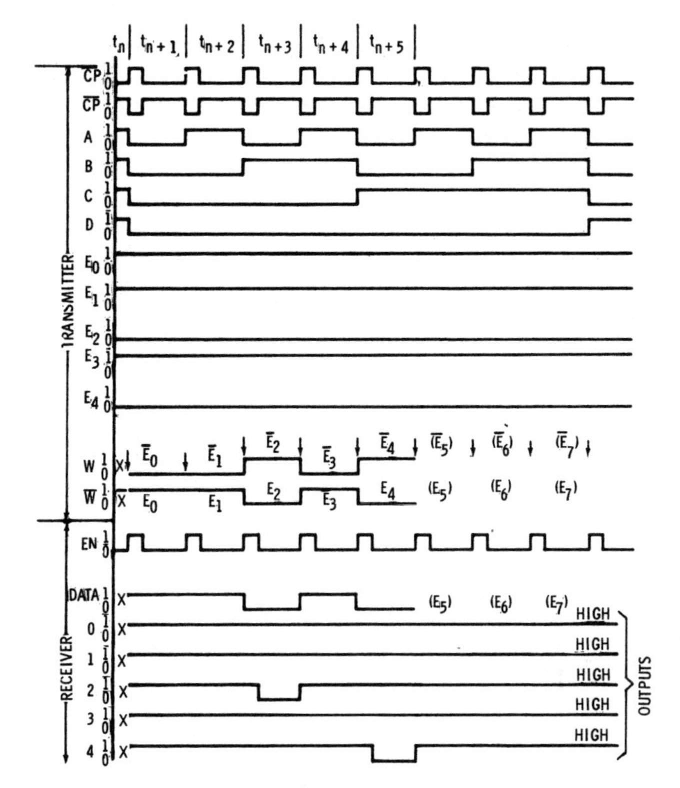

Fig. 12-5. Waveforms for Fig. 12-3.

The data transmission system described above can be modified and elaborated in many ways. Two-way transmission may be necessary; multistation operation with point-to-point dial-up may be needed, etc. Digital techniques can be applied in each case. If the transmission lines are too noisy, line drivers and receivers can be used to reduce errors.

APPENDIX A

Digital Logic Conventions

The basic symbols used in digital electronics are relatively few in number, but they must be interpreted rigidly. A gate may perform one function for positive logic and a different, but equally valid, function for negative logic. So watch out.

For the symbols shown, let a 1 be a positive voltage of about 3.5 volts, and let a 0 be zero volts. In positive logic, a signal is called "True" when it is a 1 and "False" when it is a 0. We are primarily interested in true statements, not false statements, because a true statement means that a certain set of specified conditions have been met. A false statement means only that the conditions have not been met, which is often useful but is not very precise.

The AND function is shown by the open D symbol (Fig. A-1A). When inputs A AND B are true—that is, 1—then the output is true, or a 1. If either input A or input B is not 1, then output Q is 0, or false, which means the AND function has not been satisfied. But output Q being a 0 does not tell us whether A or B is a 0 or if both are 0. The truth table lists all possible combinations of inputs and the resulting output for each con-

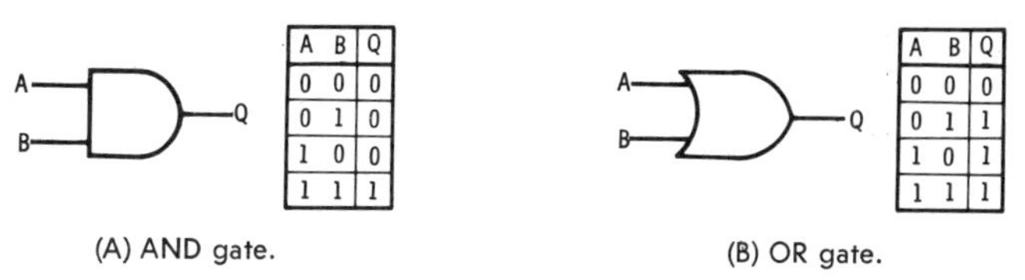

A	B	Q
0	0	0
0	1	0
1	0	0
1	1	1

(A) AND gate.

A	B	Q
0	0	0
0	1	1
1	0	1
1	1	1

(B) OR gate.

Fig. A-1. Basic logic gates and their truth tables.

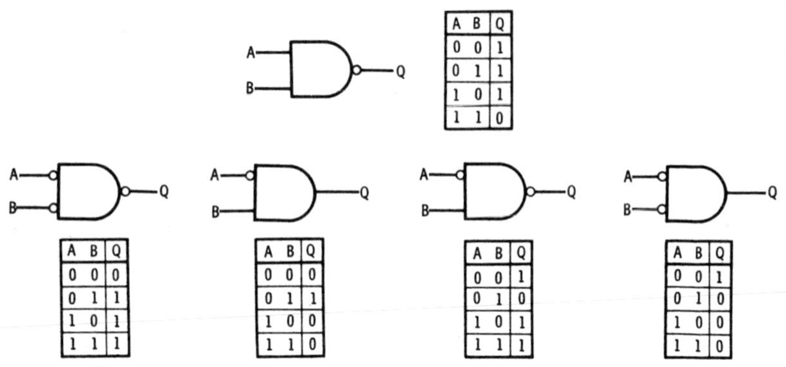

A	B	Q
0	0	1
0	1	1
1	0	1
1	1	0

A	B	Q
0	0	0
0	1	1
1	0	1
1	1	1

A	B	Q
0	0	0
0	1	1
1	0	0
1	1	0

A	B	Q
0	0	1
0	1	0
1	0	1
1	1	1

A	B	Q
0	0	1
0	1	0
1	0	0
1	1	0

Fig. A-2. Basic NAND gate and four variations, with their truth tables.

dition. Only two inputs are shown, but the same logic applies for more inputs: all must be a 1 for output Q to be a 1.

The symbol for an OR gate is similar to that for an AND gate, except the input line is curved (Fig. A-1B). Again, the truth table spells out all the states of the circuit.

The NAND symbol is an AND gate with an open circle on the output to indicate negation. Output Q is a 0 when inputs A and B are both high. When a circuit responds such that a low input is to be the true input, rather than a high input being true, an open circle is placed at the input (touching the symbol). One or more inputs may be involved. The effect on the operation of NAND and AND gates is shown in Fig. A-2.

A NOR gate is a negated or inverted OR gate. The symbol has an open circle on its output. The basic gate and four variations are shown in Fig. A-3.

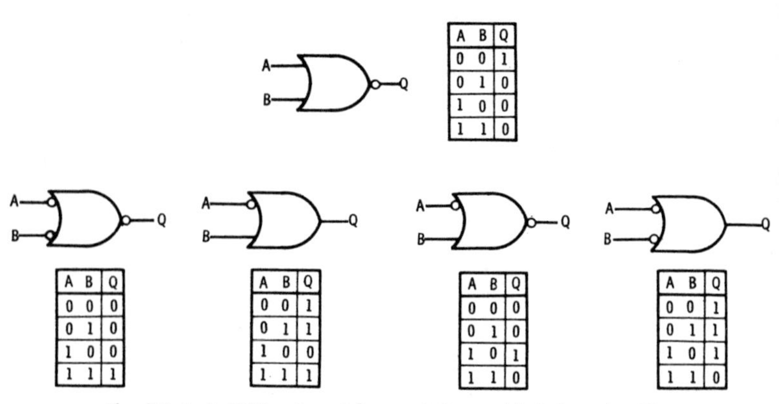

A	B	Q
0	0	1
0	1	0
1	0	0
1	1	0

A	B	Q
0	0	0
0	1	0
1	0	0
1	1	1

A	B	Q
0	0	1
0	1	1
1	0	0
1	1	1

A	B	Q
0	0	0
0	1	0
1	0	1
1	1	0

A	B	Q
0	0	1
0	1	1
1	0	1
1	1	0

Fig. A-3. Basic NOR gate and four variations, with their truth tables.

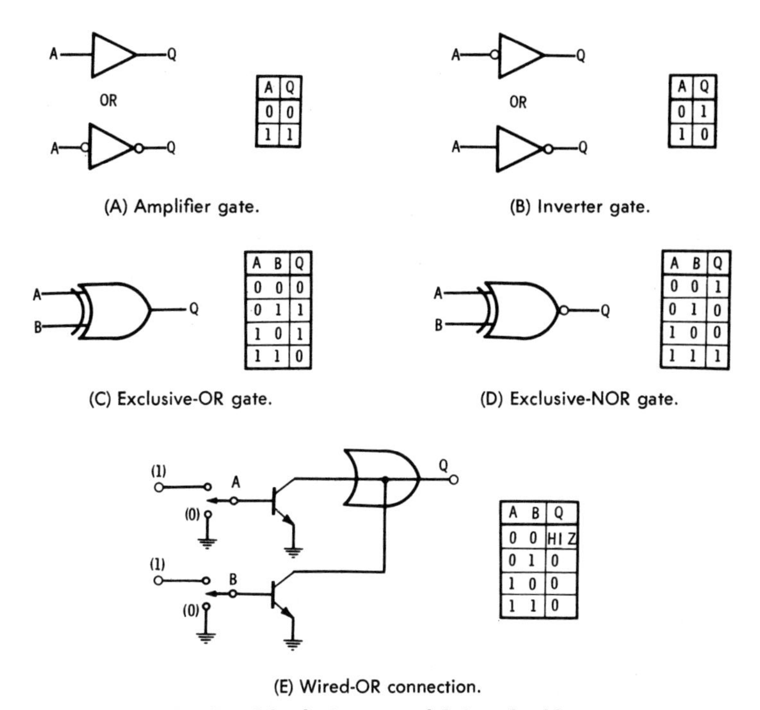

(A) Amplifier gate.

A	Q
0	0
1	1

(B) Inverter gate.

A	Q
0	1
1	0

(C) Exclusive-OR gate.

A	B	Q
0	0	0
0	1	1
1	0	1
1	1	0

(D) Exclusive-NOR gate.

A	B	Q
0	0	1
0	1	0
1	0	0
1	1	1

(E) Wired-OR connection.

A	B	Q
0	0	HI Z
0	1	0
1	0	0
1	1	0

Fig. A-4. Other logic gates and their truth tables.

Fig. A-4 shows the symbols and truth tables for amplifiers (a triangle), inverters (triangle with open circle on input or output), an exclusive-OR gate, an exclusive-NOR gate, and a wired-OR configuration.

APPENDIX B

Numbering Systems

The decimal system of numbering, counting, and performing mathematical operations is the best-known number system. Thus, it usually serves as a reference for other systems. The decimal system up to number 33 is shown in column 1 of Table B-1 (pages 162 and 163). The equivalents in natural binary are shown in column 3. Thus, decimal 4 represents the same quantity of things as binary 000100. Although not shown in Table B-1, decimal points are used similarly in both decimal and binary systems (for binary it can be called a binary point). In the decimal system, 0.1 represents 1/10 of a full digit, 0.01 represents 1/100 of a full digit, etc. In binary, 0.1 represents ½ of a full digit, 0.01 represents ¼ of a full digit, 0.001 represents ⅛, etc.

Column 4 shows the excess-3 binary number code. The system throws away the first 3 counts of natural binary and starts at binary 000011, which is actually the fourth count in straight binary. Thus, 000011 in Excess-3 binary is the equivalent of decimal 0.

Column 5 shows the "2-out-of-5" numbering code. This code uses 5 bits but uses only those combinations which have two 1s and three 0s. This code is useful in certain types of mathematical operations.

Column 6 shows binary coded decimal. Each digit requires 4 bits. Thus, 0111 is the equivalent of decimal 7, and 1000 is the equivalent of 8. To write a two-decimal-digit number requires two binary-coded-decimal groups of 4 bits each. Thus,

Table B-1. Numbering Systems

Decimal (1)	Hexadecimal (2)	Binary (Base 2) (3)	Binary Coded				Octal (Base 8) (8)
			Excess-3 (4)	2-out-of-5 (5)	Decimal (6)	Octal (7)	
0	0	0 0 0 0 0 0	0 0 0 0 1 1	0 0 0 1 1	0 0 0 0 0 0 0 0	0 0 0 0 0 0	0
1	1	0 0 0 0 0 1	0 0 0 1 0 0	0 0 1 0 1	0 0 0 0 0 0 0 1	0 0 0 0 0 1	1
2	2	0 0 0 0 1 0	0 0 0 1 0 1	0 0 1 1 0	0 0 0 0 0 0 1 0	0 0 0 0 1 0	2
3	3	0 0 0 0 1 1	0 0 0 1 1 0	0 1 0 0 1	0 0 0 0 0 0 1 1	0 0 0 0 1 1	3
4	4	0 0 0 1 0 0	0 0 0 1 1 1	0 1 0 1 0	0 0 0 0 0 1 0 0	0 0 0 1 0 0	4
5	5	0 0 0 1 0 1	0 0 1 0 0 0	0 1 1 0 0	0 0 0 0 0 1 0 1	0 0 0 1 0 1	5
6	6	0 0 0 1 1 0	0 0 1 0 0 1	1 0 0 0 1	0 0 0 0 0 1 1 0	0 0 0 1 1 0	6
7	7	0 0 0 1 1 1	0 0 1 0 1 0	1 0 0 1 0	0 0 0 0 0 1 1 1	0 0 0 1 1 1	7
8	8	0 0 1 0 0 0	0 0 1 0 1 1	1 0 1 0 0	0 0 0 0 1 0 0 0	0 0 1 0 0 0	10
9	9	0 0 1 0 0 1	0 0 1 1 0 0	1 1 0 0 0	0 0 0 0 1 0 0 1	0 0 1 0 0 1	11
10	A	0 0 1 0 1 0	0 0 1 1 0 1		0 0 0 1 0 0 0 0	0 0 1 0 1 0	12
11	B	0 0 1 0 1 1	0 0 1 1 1 0		0 0 0 1 0 0 0 1	0 0 1 0 1 1	13
12	C	0 0 1 1 0 0	0 0 1 1 1 1		0 0 0 1 0 0 1 0	0 0 1 1 0 0	14
13	D	0 0 1 1 0 1	0 1 0 0 0 0		0 0 0 1 0 0 1 1	0 0 1 1 0 1	15
14	E	0 0 1 1 1 0	0 1 0 0 0 1		0 0 0 1 0 1 0 0	0 0 1 1 1 0	16
15	F	0 0 1 1 1 1	0 1 0 0 1 0		0 0 0 1 0 1 0 1	0 0 1 1 1 1	17

16	10	0 1 0 0 0 0	0 1 0 0 1 1		0 0 0 1	0 1 1 0	0 1 0	0 0 0	20
17	11	0 1 0 0 0 1	0 1 0 1 0 0		0 0 0 1	0 1 1 1	0 1 0	0 0 1	21
18	12	0 1 0 0 1 0	0 1 0 1 0 1		0 0 0 1	1 0 0 0	0 1 0	0 1 0	22
19	13	0 1 0 0 1 1	0 1 0 1 1 0		0 0 0 1	1 0 0 1	0 1 0	0 1 1	23
20	14	0 1 0 1 0 0	0 1 0 1 1 1		0 0 1 0	0 0 0 0	0 1 0	1 0 0	24
21	15	0 1 0 1 0 1	0 1 1 0 0 0		0 0 1 0	0 0 0 1	0 1 0	1 0 1	25
22	16	0 1 0 1 1 0	0 1 1 0 0 1		0 0 1 0	0 0 1 0	0 1 0	1 1 0	26
23	17	0 1 0 1 1 1	0 1 1 0 1 0		0 0 1 0	0 0 1 1	0 1 0	1 1 1	27
24	18	0 1 1 0 0 0	0 1 1 0 1 1		0 0 1 0	0 1 0 0	0 1 1	0 0 0	30
25	19	0 1 1 0 0 1	0 1 1 1 0 0		0 0 1 0	0 1 0 1	0 1 1	0 0 1	31
26	1A	0 1 1 0 1 0	0 1 1 1 0 1		0 0 1 0	0 1 1 0	0 1 1	0 1 0	32
27	1B	0 1 1 0 1 1	0 1 1 1 1 0		0 0 1 0	0 1 1 1	0 1 1	0 1 1	33
28	1C	0 1 1 1 0 0	0 1 1 1 1 1		0 0 1 0	1 0 0 0	0 1 1	1 0 0	34
29	1D	0 1 1 1 0 1	1 0 0 0 0 0		0 0 1 0	1 0 0 1	0 1 1	1 0 1	35
30	1E	0 1 1 1 1 0	1 0 0 0 0 1		0 0 1 1	0 0 0 0	0 1 1	1 1 0	36
31	1F	0 1 1 1 1 1	1 0 0 0 1 0		0 0 1 1	0 0 0 1	0 1 1	1 1 1	37
32	20	1 0 0 0 0 0	1 0 0 0 1 1		0 0 1 1	0 0 1 0	1 0 0	0 0 0	40
33	21	1 0 0 0 0 1	1 0 0 1 0 0		0 0 1 1	0 0 1 1	1 0 0	0 0 1	41

number 12 is written as 0001 followed by 0010, which is the equivalent of 1 and 2 respectively.

The octal system, Column 7, uses only 3 bits; therefore, it can represent only 8 levels—0 through 7. The next quantity after 7 is 8, which is written as 001 followed by 000. This is written in the octal (base 8) system as 10 and is the equivalent in decimal of 8. The octal system fully utilizes its 3-bit identification scheme, whereas the binary-coded decimal system uses only 10 different codes of the 16 possible with a 4-bit word.

To take full advantage of the 4-bit code, the hexadecimal numbering system (Column 2) was developed. Since only 10 different numerals are available, the letters A, B, C, D, E, and F have been used to give single character representation for 16 different levels or quantities. At level 16, two hexadecimal characters are required. Number 16 is written as 10, while 1F is the equivalent of decimal 31.

Hexadecimal has become popular as a shorthand way of writing binary numbers. Suppose you need to write the number 28 (decimal) in binary, using one 8-bit byte, as you might want to do when programming a ROM or PROM. You would write 00011100. Using hex shorthand, you would write 1C, where 1 stands for 0001 and C for 1100. Hex is faster and mistakes are less likely.

APPENDIX C

TTL Power Supply

A simple 5.1-volt power supply can be constructed as shown in Fig. C-1. The 5.1 voltage level, which is close enough to the nominal 5.0 volts of TTL devices, will be maintained for load currents up to about 90 mA (enough to operate several flip-flops). At higher load currents, the output voltage will be determined by the voltage drop across resistor R, since the zener diode will stop conducting as the output voltage falls below 5.1 volts.

When the load current is 0, the current through the zener diode will be about 90 mA, causing a power dissipation in the diode of about 0.45 watts. Since the diode is rated for 1-watt dissipation, resistor R can be reduced to about 5 ohms. This will allow a larger load current to be drawn.

The drain on the battery can be reduced by increasing the resistance of R.

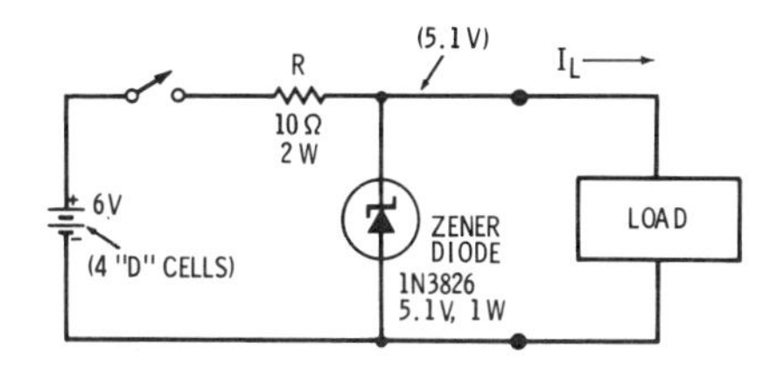

Fig. C-1. Schematic of 5-volt power supply for TTL circuits.

APPENDIX D

Guidelines for System Design*

The following represent rule-of-thumb answers to questions regarding the use of TTL circuits. These should not be adhered to on an absolute basis; rather, they should be treated as guidelines.

General Power supply	Maintain ripple $\leq$ 5%. Maintain regulation $\leq$ 5%. Rf bypass supply primary.
Decoupling	Decouple every 5 to 10 packages with rf capacitors of 0.01 to 0.1 μF.
Grounding	A ground plane is desirable, especially when the pc board contains a large number of packages. If no ground plane is used, incorporate ground bus around pc board periphery where possible. Make ground bus as wide as possible. Always return both ends of long ground bus to common point (system ground).
Gates Data input rise and fall times	Reduce as driver output impedance increases. Should be no greater than 1 μs for $Z_0 \geq$ ohms.
Unused inputs of AND and NAND gates and unused preset and clear inputs of flip-flops.	Tie directly to $+V_{CC}$ where V_{CC} is guaranteed to **always** be $\leq$ 5.5 v; or Tie to V_{CC} through resistor $\geq$ 1K ohms. Several unused inputs can be tied to one resistor; or Tie to used input of same gate if maximum fan-out of driving device will not be exceeded; or Tie to unused gate output where unused gate input is grounded.
Unused inputs of NOR gates.	Tie to used input of same gate if max fan-out of driving device will not be exceeded; or Tie to ground.
Unused gates.	Tie inputs of unused gates to ground for lowest power drain.

Increasing gate/buffer fan-out.	Parallel gates/buffers of same package.
Expanders.	Place expanders as close as possible to the gate being expanded and avoid capacitive loading of the expander nodes if switching speed is to be maintained.
Flip-Flops Preset and clear pulses.	If clock pulse is present, maintain preset or clear pulse until clock pulse goes low.
Clock pulse.	Rise and fall times should be less than 150 ns to improve noise immunity.
Input data.	In general, input data of master-slave J-K flip-flops should not be changed while the clock pulse is high. Consult data sheet for possible exceptions.
Line Driving and Receiving Single-wire interconnections.	May be used up to approximately 10" without particular precaution. A ground plane is always desirable. If longer than 10", ground plane is mandatory with wire routed as close to it as possible. Use twisted pair or coax lengths exceeding 20".
Coaxial and twisted pair cables.	Design around approximately 100 ohms characteristic impedance. Higher impedances increase crosstalk while lower impedances are difficult to drive. a. coaxial cable of 93 ohms impedance (such as Microdot 293-3913) is recommended; b. for twisted pair, Nos. 26 or 28 wire with thin insulation twisted about 30 turns/foot work well.
Transmission-line ground.	Ensure that transmission-line ground returns are carried through at both transmitting and receiving ends.
Resistive pull-up.	Use 500 to 1000 ohms resistive pull-up at **receiving** end of long cables for added noise margin and more rapid rise times.
Line termination.	Reverse terminate with 27 to 47 ohms at **driving** end in series with the line to prevent negative overshoot.
Gates as line drivers.	Drive into only one transmission-line terminated with one gate input. Adverse effects from multiple loads include: a. erroneous signals due to line reflections; b. long delay times; c. excessive driver loading.
Gates as line receivers.	Use only one gate input to terminate line. Follow unused input rules for receiver gates.
Flip-flops as line drivers.	Generally unsatisfactory due to the possibility of collector commutation from reflected signals.
Decoupling.	Always decouple driving/receiving devices in addition to normal decoupling. Use 0.1 μF rf capacitors located at V_{CC} and ground pins.

*Courtesy Texas Instruments Incorporated

APPENDIX E

Glossary

A

Analog-to-Digital Converter—A device for converting a voltage level that is the measure of some physical condition into a digital word. (An 8-bit ADC generates an 8-bit word; a 12-bit ADC generates a 12-bit word. The encoding is more precise as more bits are used.)

Asynchronous—Clearing a circuit to all zeros or presetting to some condition independently of the clock.

B

Bit—A bit is one character of a digital word. It can be either a 1 or a 0. The position of the bit in the word usually determines its significance. The first bit is often a sign bit, with 0 representing a plus sign and a 1 representing a minus sign.

Blanking Input—A control input for decoding circuits.

Boolean Equation—Mathematical expression of logic relationships. The Boolean equation $F = A \cdot B$ means function "F" is true when "A" is true AND "B" is true. (Thus, F will be a 1 if both A and $B = 1$; for all other combinations of values for A and B, F will be a 0.)

Buffer—A device which has sufficient fan-out to drive all the internal gates while presenting only a unit load (or less) to the driving source. Sometimes, one or more of the inputs—for example, the clock signal of a shift register or counter—is required to drive a number of gates. To prevent these multiple tasks from putting too large a load on the driving source, the input signal is fed to a buffer stage—often an inverter.

Byte—A byte is a group of bits.

C

Clear—A circuit is said to be cleared when it is set to all 0s.

Clear Input—The Clear Input generates the Clear function.

Clock—Also called Clock Pulse and Clock Signal. It can be derived from a crystal oscillator, a multivibrator, or other type of oscillator. Most digital systems use a clock pulse as a pacing signal. When the clock goes high, the gates and other elements respond as the circuit requires. When the clock goes low, the gates may go to a new state. On the next high clock pulse, the gates respond again, going to a new state if required. The clock signal must repeat often enough to allow the system to complete its task in a reasonable time, but it must not occur so fast that circuits cannot respond properly before the next transition occurs.

D

Digital-to-Analog Converter—A device for converting a digital word into an analog voltage level.

DIP—Abbreviation for dual-in-line package, it is usually mentioned as a DIP package. Its connection pins extend down from the body of the IC package in two parallel rows.

Duty Cycle—The ratio of on-time to total cycle time is the duty cycle:

$$\text{Duty cycle} = \frac{\text{On time}}{\text{On time} + \text{Off time}}$$

E

Enable—An input which, when true, allows the circuit to function.

F

Fan-Out—The number of additional gates one gate can drive. A typical TTL gate has a fan-out of 10 unit loads. If a gate is required to drive more than its maximum fan-out, a buffer gate can be used as one or more of the loads to increase the fan-out.

Flatpack—An IC package. Its connection pins come straight out from the sides of the IC package, giving a flat, pancake structure.

G

Gate—The simplest logic circuit is called a gate. Its output voltage will be high or low depending on the state of the inputs and the type of gate.

I

IC—Abbreviation for integrated circuit. It is usually a monolithic circuit.

Inhibit—An input which, when true, prevents the circuit from functioning.

Input Buffer—See Buffer.

Input Clamping—Use of input clamping diodes to prevent ringing. They allow the input signal to go positive but act as a low-impedance short circuit when the signal goes negative; thus, they effectively clamp the input at 0 voltage or above.

Input Gating—Input gates keep a circuit from responding unless a special input condition has been satisfied. A clock, strobe, or other control signal may be used to activate the input gate.

Inverter—A gate in which the output signal is the inversion of the input signal.

L

Least Significant Bit—The bit in a number that is the least important or having the least weight.

LSI—Abbreviation for large-scale integration. A chip containing more than 100 gates.

M

Monolithic—In electronics, this refers to a circuit built on one chip of silicon.

Most Significant Bit—The bit in a number that is the most important or that has the most weight.

MSI—Abbreviation for medium-scale integration. A chip having from 10 to 100 gates.

Multiplexing—The process of combining the data from a number of sources into one stream of data. The reverse process of sorting out multiplexed data is called demultiplexing.

N

Negative-Edge Gating—The circuit responds as the control signal goes from high to low.

Negative Logic—See Positive Logic.

O

Open-Collector Output—A TTL gate with only one output transistor instead of the traditional 2-transistor totem pole output.

P

Parallel Data—All the bits in a word are available simultaneously on a parallel front.

Positive-Edge Gating—The circuit responds as the control signal goes from low to high. Thereafter, the circuit is quiescent until the clock first goes low, then high again.

Positive Logic—A positive voltage (2.0 to 3.6 volts in TTL) is a true signal, and a zero or negative voltage is a false signal (a not-true signal). In negative logic, the more negative of two voltages is true, and the more positive is false (not-true), even if both voltages are negative.

Preset—A procedure for loading a circuit, such as a counter, with certain data prior to going into operation. The circuit will then start from the preset condition.

Propagation Delay—The time required for a circuit to go to the state demanded by the inputs. Alternatively, the time required for a signal to travel from one point in a circuit (or signal channel) to another point.

Pull Up/Pull Down—When an open-collector output stage is in its high-impedance state, it is generating the equivalent of a high logic level, except that it cannot supply a positive voltage to a load. By connecting a resistor between the output collector and the usual +5-volt supply, the collector voltage is pulled up to a positive voltage when the transistor is off or in its high impedance state. When the transistor is on, the collector voltage falls to the saturation voltage of the transistor (nominally about 0.4 volt). A pull-down resistor, on the other hand, is used to pull a circuit to ground in the absence of a driving signal.

Q

Quiescent Dissipation—The power consumed by a device when it is at rest.

R

Reset—Setting a flip-flop to the Q = 0 state. Also applies when any circuit is placed or driven to its normal starting condition.

Ringing—When a circuit is driven from low to high or high to low, stored energy may cause the signal level to oscillate briefly between the high and low levels, much as a bell rings for a short time when it is struck.

Ripple Through—When two binary numbers are added, the two least significant bits can produce a carry bit that must be added to the next two least significant bits, which in turn may produce a carry that will affect the next two bits, etc. The correct output cannot be obtained until all the carrys have rippled through.

S

Serial Data—The data is available as a series of bits occurring one after the other in a single file.

Set—Placing a flip-flop in the Q =-1 state.

SSI—Abbreviation for small-scale integration. A chip containing up to about 10 or 12 gates.

Substrate—The silicon chip on which transistors and resistors are formed or deposited.

Synchronous—Running a circuit that is normally driven by a clock at a constant frequency synchronous with the clock.

T

Tri-State Gate—A special gating circuit that can be driven to one of three states: 0, 1, or high impedance, which is the equivalent of OFF.

Truth Table—A table showing the various combinations of input conditions and the logically possible response of a circuit.

U

Unit Load—Each input of a standard TTL gate is called a unit load. When an input circuit requires more current than a standard unit load, it is rated at 2 or 3 unit loads. If the input circuit requires less current than a standard unit load, it may be rated as a fractional unit load. Data sheets for every TTL device in all families will show the loads they present to driving circuits. A gate should not be asked to drive more unit loads than its maximum rating.

V

VLSI—Abbreviation for very large-scale integration. A chip containing more than 1000 gates.

W

Word—A digital word is composed of a group of bits—and often a group of bytes. Digital words can be any length, but they are usually multiples of 2: 8, 12, 16, 24, 36, 64 bits, etc.

Z

Zero Suppression—Suppressing unnecessary zeros in a number register. The zeros may lead or trail the significant figures of the number.

APPENDIX F

TTL Devices

Devices in the following lists are all TTL ICs. Many duplications exist from family to family but pinouts will generally be different. Some TTL families are no longer being added to and some families and/or devices are no longer being manufactured. Other families are still being added to and devices are available from multiple sources.

Many devices are available both in military and commercial versions. In the lists, an open star indicates that the specific device is or was available in a military version; a box indicates that it is available in the commercial version.

Here are some common abbreviations used in the following IC lists:

ALU: arithmetic logic unit
A-O: AND-OR
A-O-I: AND-OR-inverter
BCD: binary-coded decimal
FF: flip-flop
H & L: high and low
Hex: six
I: inverter
MV: multivibrator
NI: noninverting
N/2: divide by 2
OC: open collector output
PPU: passive pull-up
SAR: successive approximation register
SR: set-reset
SR SL: shift right, shift left
Syn: synchronous
TP: totem pole
U/D: up/down
1-K: 1024 bits
2-In: 2-input
2-W: 2-wide
3-S: three state or tri-state
4-B: four-bit, for example
4-K: 4096 bits

TELEDYNE HiNIL—HIGH NOISE IMMUNITY LOGIC

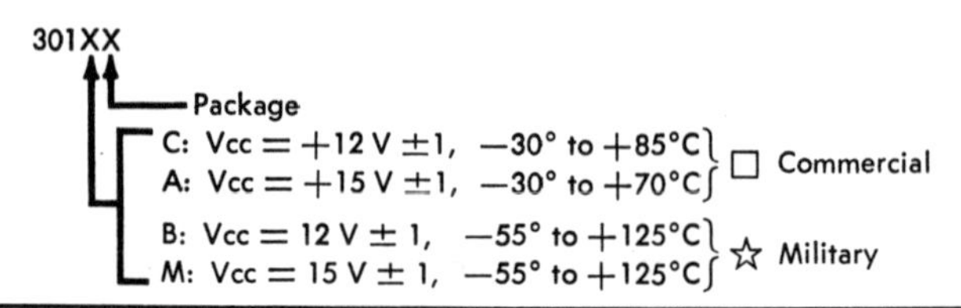

3XX	Description
301	Dual 5-In power NAND
302	Quad 2-In Power NAND OC
303	Quad 2-In Power NAND PPU
311	Master-Slave Flip-Flop
312	Dual JK or SR Flip-Flop
313	Dual JK Master-Slave Flip-Flop
321	Quad 2-In NAND
322	Dual 5-In NAND
323	Quad 2-In NAND OC
324	Quad 2-In NAND PPU
325	2, 2, 3, 3-In NAND
326	2, 2, 3, 3-In NAND PPU
331	Dual 5-In Expander
332	Hex Inverter OC
333	Hex Inverter PPU
334	Hex Inverter OC
335	Hex Inverter PPU
341	Dual 2-In A-O-I
342	Dual Monostable MV
343	4-Bit Comparator
344	Expandable AND-NOR
347	Dual Retriggerable Monostable MV
350	8-Bit Multiplexer
351	Dual 4-Bit Multiplexer
361	Dual Input Interface
362	Dual Output Interface
363	Quad Output Interface
367	Quad Schmitt Trigger/Line Receiver
368	Quad Schmitt Trigger/Line Receiver OC
370	Quad D FF PPU
371	Decade Counter PPU
372	Hexadecimal Counter PPU
375	4-Bit Shift Register
380	BCD to Decade Decoder/Line Driver OC
381	BCD to Decade Decoder OC
382	BCD to Decade Decoder Gas Discharge Tube
383	BCD to 7-Segment Decoder/Driver

MOTOROLA MC500/400; MC550/450 SERIES

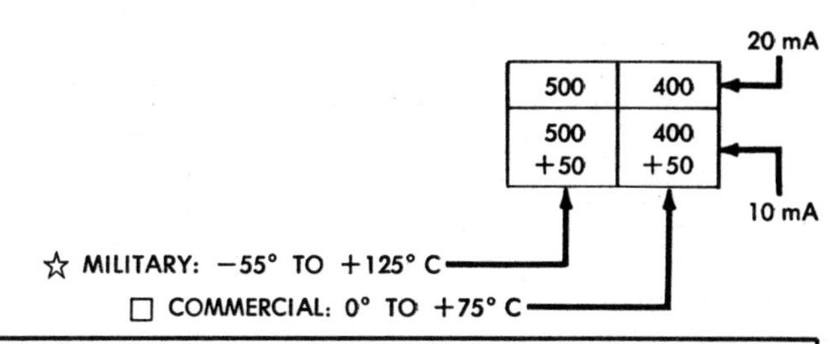

4XX	4XX +50	Description	4XX 20 mA	4XX +50 10 mA
400	450	Dual 4-Input NAND	☆ □	☆ □
401	451	Expandable 2-2-2-3 A-O-I	☆ □	☆ □
402	452	8-Input NAND	☆ □	☆ □
403	453	2-Wide 3-Input A-O-I with Complement	☆ □	☆ □
404	454	Expandable 3-W 3-In A-O-I	☆ □	☆ □
405	455	Expandable 2-W 4-In A-O-I	☆ □	☆ □
406	456	Expandable 8-In NAND	☆ □	☆ □
407	457	Line Driver	☆ □	☆ □
408	458	Quad 2-In NAND	☆ □	☆ □
409	459	4-W 3-2-2-3 Expander for A-O-I	☆ □	☆ □
410	460	Dual 4-In Expander for A-O-I	☆ □	☆ □
411	461	Dual 4-In Expander for NAND	☆ □	☆ □
412	462	Triple 3-In NAND	☆ □	☆ □
413	463	Set Reset Flip-Flop	☆ □	☆ □
414	464	Gated Set Reset Flip-Flop	☆ □	☆ □
415	465	AND JK Flip-Flop	☆ □	☆ □
416	466	OR JK Flip-Flop	☆ □	☆ □
417	467	AND JK Flip-Flop	☆ □	☆ □
418	468	D Flip-Flop	☆ □	☆ □
419	469	Triple 2-In Bus Driver	☆ □	☆ □
420	470	Expandable Dual 2-W 2-In A-O-I	☆ □	☆ □
421	471	A-C Coupled RS Flip-Flop	☆ □	☆ □
422	472	Dual D Flip-Flop	☆ □	☆ □
423	473	Dual JK Flip-Flop	☆ □	☆ □
424	474	Dual JK Flip-Flop	☆ □	☆ □
425	475	Hex Inverter	☆ □	☆ □
426	476	Dual 3-In Pulse Shaper/Delay AND	☆ □	☆ □
427	477	OR Expandable Dual 4-In AND	☆ □	☆ □
428	478	Dual 2-W 2-3-In OR Expander	☆ □	☆ □
429	479	Hex Inverter	☆ □	☆ □

MOTOROLA MC660 SERIES

(−30° TO +75°C)
(AVAILABLE ON SPECIAL ORDER FOR −55° TO +125°C)

6XX	Description
660	Dual Expandable 4-In NAND
661	Dual Expandable 4-In NAND
662	Dual Expandable Line Driver
663	Dual JK Flip-Flop
664	Master-Slave Set-Reset Flip-Flop
665	Triple Level Translator
666	Triple Level Translator
667	Dual Monostable Multivibrator
668	Quad 2-In NAND
669	Dual 4-In Expander
670	Triple 3-In NAND
671	Triple 3-In NAND
672	Quad 2-In NAND
673	Dual 2-In A-O-I
674	Dual 2-In A-O-I
675	Dual Pulse Stretcher
676	BCD to Decimal Decoder/Driver
677	Hex Inverter with Strobe
678	Hex Inverter with Strobe
679	Dual Lamp Driver
679B	Dual Lamp Driver
680	Hex Inverter
681	Hex Inverter Open Collector
682	Quad Latch
683	Quad 2-In X-OR
684	Decade Counter
685	Binary Counter
686	4-Bit Shift Register
688	Dual JK Flip-Flop
689	Hex Inverter (HV)
690	Hex Inverter
696	Dual Interface, Line Driver/Receiver

MOTOROLA MC2100/2000; MC2150/2050 SERIES

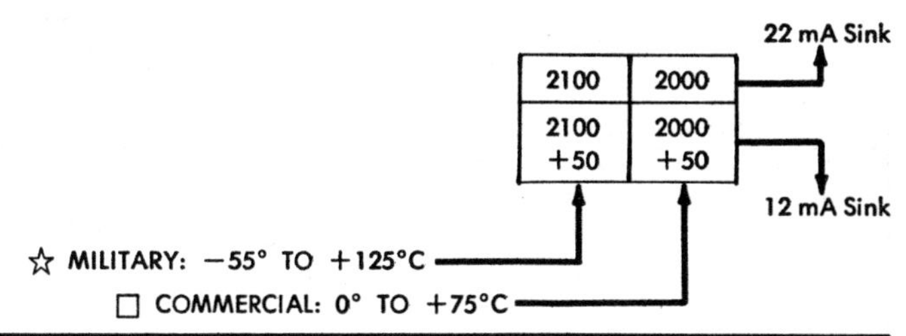

20XX	20XX +50	Description	20XX 22 mA	20XX +50 12 mA
2000	2050	Expandable 2-W 4-In A-O-I	☆ □	☆ □
2001	2051	Quad 2-In NAND	☆ □	☆ □
2002	2052	4-W 3-2-2-3-In Expander	☆ □	☆ □
2003	2053	Dual 4-In NAND	☆ □	☆ □
2004	2054	Expandable 4-W 2-2-2-3-In A-O-I	☆ □	☆ □
2005	2055	8-In NAND	☆ □	☆ □
2006	2056	Dual 4-In Expander	☆ □	☆ □
2007	2057	Triple 3-In NAND	☆ □	☆ □
2008	2058	Hex Inverter	□	□
2009	2059	AND JK Flip-Flop	☆ □	☆ □
2010	2060	OR JK Flip-Flop	☆ □	☆ □
2011	2061	Expandable 8-In NAND	☆ □	☆ □
2012	2062	Expandable 3-W 3-In A-O-I	☆ □	☆ □
2013	2063	Expandable Dual 2-W 2-In A-O-I	☆ □	☆ □
2023	2073	Dual JK Flip-Flop	☆ □	☆ □
2024	2074	Dual JK Flip-Flop	☆ □	☆ □
2025	2075	AND JK Flip-Flop	☆ □	☆ □
2026	2076	OR JK Flip-Flop	☆ □	☆ □
2028	2078	OR JK Filip-Flop	☆ □	☆ □

ADVANCED MICRO DEVICES Am25 SERIES

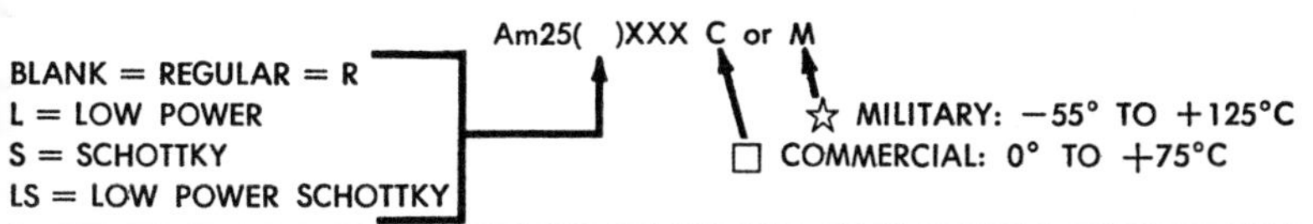

25XXX	Description	R	L	S	LS
2501	4-B Binary Syn U/D Counter	☆			
2502	8-B SAR	☆	☆		
2503	8-B SAR	☆	☆		
2504	12-B SAR	☆	☆		
2505	4-B × 2-B 2s Complement Multiplier	☆	☆	☆ □	

ADVANCED MICRO DEVICES Am25 SERIES *cont*

25XXX	Description	R	L	S	LS
2506	4-B ALU	☆	☆		
2507	6-B Register			☆ □	☆
2508	4-B Register			☆ □	☆ □
2509	Quad 2-In Shift Register			☆ □	☆ □
2510	4-B 4-Way Shifter 3-State			☆ □	
2514	8 × 1 Serial/Parallel 2s Complement Multiplier				☆ □
2515	4-B Serial/Parallel Adder Subtractor				☆
2518	4-B Register TP & 3-S			☆ □	
2522	8-B Serial/Parallel Register				☆
2523	8-B Shift/Storage Register				☆ □
25138	1 of 8 Decoder/Demultiplexer				☆ □
25139	Dual 1 of 4 Decoder				☆
25151	8-In Multiplexer				☆ □
25153	Dual 4-In Multiplexer				☆ □
25157	Quad 2-In Multiplexer				☆ □
25158	Quad 2-In Multiplexer Inverting				☆ □
25160	Syn BCD Decade Counter				☆ □
25161	Syn 4-B Binary Counter				☆ □
25162	Syn BCD Decade Counter				☆ □
25163	Syn 4-B Binary Counter				☆ □
25174	6-B Register				☆ □
25175	Quad Register				☆ □
25181	4-B ALU				☆ □
25190	Syn BCD Decade U/D Counter				☆ □
25191	Syn 4-B Binary U/D Counter				☆ □
25194A	4-B Register SR SL Parallel Load				☆ □
25195A	4-B Shift Register				☆ □
25251	8-In Multiplexer 3-S				☆ □
25253	Dual 4-In Multiplexer 3-S				☆ □
25257	Quad 2-In Multiplexer 3-S NI				☆ □
25258	Quad 2-In Multiplexer 3-S I				☆ □
25299	8-B Shift Register				☆
25373	Octal Transparent Latch				☆
25374	Octal D Register				☆
25377	Octal D Register				☆
25381	4-B ALU				☆
25517	4-B ALU				☆
25526	4-B Register				☆
25537	1 of 10 Decoder 3-S				☆
25538	1 of 8 Decoder 3-S				☆
25539	Dual 1 of 4 Decoder 3-S				☆
25540	Octal Bus Buffer				☆
25541	Octal Bus Inverter				☆
25568	4-B U/D Counter 3-S				☆
25569	4-B U/D Counter 3-S				☆

ADVANCED MICRO DEVICES Am26 SERIES

Am26( )XXX C or M

BLANK = REGULAR = R
L = LOW POWER
S = SCHOTTKY
LS = LOW POWER SCHOTTKY

☆ MILITARY: −55° TO +125°C
□ COMMERCIAL: 0° TO +75°C

26XX	Description	R	L	S	LS
2602	Dual Retriggerable Resettable Mono MV			☆ □	
2610	Quad Bus Transceiver OC I			☆ □	
2611	Quad Bus Transceiver OC NI			☆ □	
2612	Quad Bus Transceiver OC			☆ □	
2612A	Quad Bus Transceiver OC			☆ □	

ADVANCED MICRO DEVICES Am27 SERIES

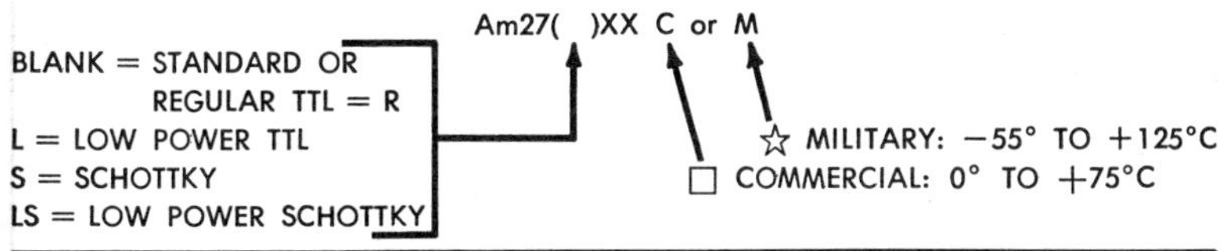

27XX	Description	R	L	S	LS
2700	256-B RAM 3-S				☆ □
2701	256-B RAM OC				☆ □
2702	64-B RAM OC			☆ □	
2703	64-B RAM 3-S			☆ □	
2708	32-Words × 8-B PROM OC			☆ □	☆ □
2709	32-Words × 8-B PROM 3-S			☆ □	☆ □
2710	256-W × 8-B PROM OC			☆ □	☆ □
2711	256-W × 4-B PROM 3-S			☆ □	☆ □
2780	1024-W × 8-B ROM OC			☆ □	
2781	1024-W × 8-B ROM 3-S			☆ □	

ADVANCED MICRO DEVICES Am29 SERIES

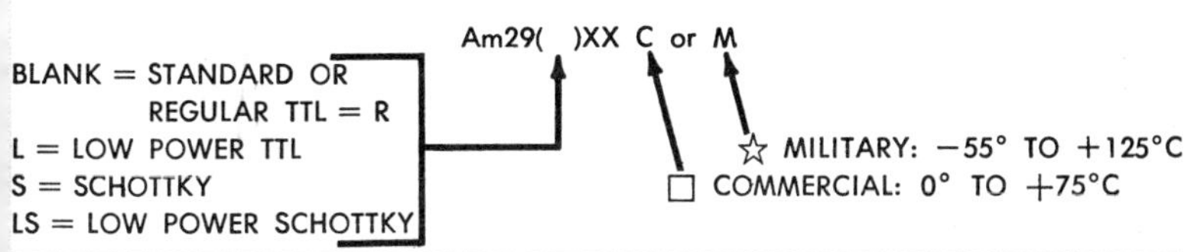

29XX	Description	R	L	S	LS
2901	4-B Microprocessor Slice				☆ □
2902	Look Ahead Carry Generator				☆ □
2905	Quad 2-In Bus Transceiver OC				☆ □
2906	Quad 2-In Bus Transceiver OC				☆ □
2907	Quad 2-In Bus Transceiver OC				☆ □

ADVANCED MICRO DEVICES Am29 SERIES *cont*

29XX	Description	R	L	S	LS
2909	4-B Microprogram Sequencer				☆ □
2911	4-B Microprogram Sequencer				☆ □
2915	Quad 2-In Bus Transceiver OC				☆ □
2916	Quad 2-In Bus Transceiver OC				☆ □
2917	Quad 2-In Bus Transceiver OC				☆ □

MOTOROLA 3000 SERIES

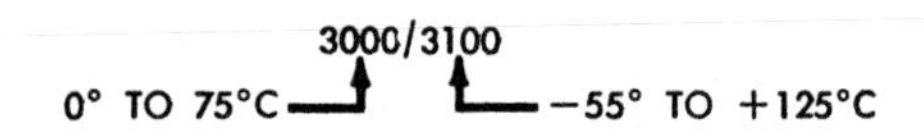

30XX	Description
3000	Quad 2-In NAND
3001	Quad 2-In AND
3002	Quad 2-In NOR
3003	Quad 2-In OR
3004	Quad 2-In NAND OC
3005	Triple 3-In NAND
3006	Triple 3-In AND
3007	Triple 3-In NAND OC
3008	Hex Inverter
3009	Hex Inverter
3010	Dual 4-In NAND
3011	Dual 4-In AND
3012	Dual 4-In NAND OC
3015	8-In NAND
3016	8-In NAND
3018	3-2-2-3-In AND-OR Expander
3019	Triple 3-In Expander
3020	Expandable Dual 2-W 2-In A-O-I
3021	Quad 2-In X-OR
3022	Quad 2-In X-NOR
3023	Dual 2-W 2-In A-O-I
3024	Dual 4-In NAND Buffer
3025	Dual 4-In NAND Power Gate
3026	Dual 4-In Power AND
3028	Dual 3-In 3-Out AND Line Driver
3029	Dual 3-In 3-Out NAND Line Driver
3030	Dual 4-In Expander for A-O-I
3031	Expandable 4-W A-O-I
3032	Expandable 4-W 2-In A-O-I
3033	4-W 2-In A-O-I

MOTOROLA 3000 SERIES *cont*

30XX	Description
3034	Expandable 2-W 4-In A-O-I
3050	AND JK Flip-Flop
3051	AND JK Flip-Flop
3052	AND JK Flip-Flop
3053	Double Edge, T, D MS Flip-Flop
3054	OR-In JK Flip-Flop
3055	AND-In JK Flip-Flop
3060	Dual D Flip-Flop
3061	Dual JK Flip-Flop
3062	Dual JK Flip-Flop
3063	Dual JK Flip-Flop

INTEL 3000 SERIES

3XXX	Description
3101	64-Bit RAM
3101A	64-Bit RAM High Speed
3104	16-Bit CAM
3106	256-Bit RAM
3106A	256-Bit RAM High Speed
3107	256-Bit RAM OC
3107A	256-Bit RAM OC High Speed
3205	1 of 8 Binary Decoder
3207A	Quad Bipolar to MOS Interface
3207A-1	Quad Bipolar to MOS Interface
3208A	Hex Sense Amplifier (For MOS)
3301A	1-K ROM
3304A	4-K ROM
3404	8-Bit Latch High Speed
3408A	Hex Sense Amp and Latch
3601	1-K EPROM

MOTOROLA 4000 SERIES

4000/4300

0° TO 75°C (4000) — −55° TO +125°C (4300)

40XX	Description
4000	Dual 4-Channel Data Selector
4001	BCD/Binary/BCD Converter
4002	Dual Data Distributor
4004	16-Bit RAM OC (40 mA)
4005	16-Bit RAM OC (20 mA)
4006	1 of 8 Decoder
4007	Dual 1 of 4 Decoder
4008	8 Bit Parity Tree
4010	Dual 4-Bit Parity Tree
4012	4-Bit Shift Register

MOTOROLA 4000 SERIES *cont*

40XX	Description
4015	Quad D Flip-Flop
4016	Programmable Decade Counter
4017	Programmable Modulo 5 Counter
4018	Programmable Hexadecimal Counter
4019	Dual Programmable Modulo 4 Counter
4021	Dual 4-Bit Comparator OC
4022	Dual 4-Bit Comparator
4023	4-Bit Divide by 2 and 6 Counter
4024	Dual Voltage Controlled MV
4026	4-Bit Binary Full Adder
4027	4-Bit Binary Full Adder
4028	Adder Dependent Carry
4029	Adder Dependent Carry
4030	Adder Independent Carry
4031	Adder Independent Carry
4032	Carry Decoder
4035	Quad Latch OC
4037	Quad Latch
4038	1 of 8 Decoder H & L (ROM)
4039	7-Segment Character Generator (ROM)
4040	Binary 2 of 8 Decoder (ROM)
4041	Single Error Hamming Code Detector and Generator (ROM)
4042	Quad Predriver
4043	Dual Line Selector
4044	Phase-Frequency Detector
4048	1 of 8 Decoder
4050	4-Bit Counter Latch Decoder
4051	4-Bit Counter Latch Decoder
4062	Dual Majority Logic Gate
4064	64-Bit RAM
4067	Binary to BCD Converter OC
4068	Binary to BCD Converter OC
4069	Hollerith to ASCII Converter OC
4070	Hollerith to ASCII Converter OC

TEXAS INSTRUMENTS 54/74 FAMILY

54/74( )XXX

☆ MILITARY: −55° TO +125°C
□ COMMERCIAL: 0° TO +70°C

BLANK = REGULAR = R
H = HIGH SPEED
LP = LOW POWER
S = SCHOTTKY
LC = LOW POWER SCHOTTKY
C = CMOS

XXX	Description	R	H	LP	S	LS	C
00	Quad 2-In NAND	☆ □	☆ □	☆ □	☆ □	☆ □	☆ □
01	Quad 2-In NAND OC	☆ □	☆ □			☆ □	
02	Quad 2-In NOR	☆ □		☆ □	☆ □	☆ □	□
03	Quad 2-In NAND OC	☆ □		☆ □	☆ □	☆ □	
04	Hex Inverter	☆ □	☆ □	☆ □	☆ □	☆ □	□
05	Hex Inverter OC	☆ □	☆ □		☆ □	☆ □	
06	Hex Inverter/Driver OC (30 V)	☆ □					
07	Hex Buffer OC (30 V)	☆ □					
08	Quad 2-In AND	☆ □			☆ □	☆ □	
09	Quad 2-In AND OC	☆ □			☆ □	☆ □	
10	Triple 3-In NAND	☆ □	☆ □	☆ □	☆ □	☆ □	□
11	Triple 3-In AND		☆ □		☆ □	☆ □	
12	Triple 3-In NAND OC	☆ □				☆ □	
13	Dual 4-In NAND Schmitt Trigger	☆ □				☆ □	□
14	Hex Schmitt Trigger I	☆ □				☆ □	□
15	Triple 3-In AND OC		☆ □		☆ □	☆ □	
16	Hex Inverter/Driver OC (15 V)	☆ □					
17	Hex Buffer/Driver OC (15 V)	☆ □					
20	Dual 4-In NAND	☆ □	☆ □	☆ □	☆ □	☆ □	□
21	Dual 4-In AND		☆ □			☆ □	

TEXAS INSTRUMENTS 54/74 FAMILY *cont*

XXX	Description	R	H	LP	S	LS	C
22	Dual 4-In NAND OC	☆ □	☆ □		☆ □	☆ □	
23	Dual 4-In NOR	☆ □					
25	Dual 4-In NOR	☆ □					
26	Quad 2-In NAND OC (15 V)	☆ □				☆ □	
27	Triple 3-In NOR	☆ □				☆ □	
28	Quad 2-In NOR	☆ □				☆ □	
30	8-In NAND	☆ □	☆ □	☆ □	☆ □	☆ □	□
32	Quad 2-In OR	☆ □			☆ □	☆ □	□
33	Quad 2-In NOR OC	☆ □				☆ □	
37	Quad 2-In NAND Buffer	☆ □			☆ □	☆ □	
38	Quad 2-In NAND Buffer OC	☆ □			☆ □	☆ □	
39	Dual 4-In AND Buffer						
40	Dual 4-In NAND Buffer	☆ □	☆ □		☆ □	☆ □	
41	BCD to Decimal Decoder/Driver						
41A	BCD to Decimal Decoder/Driver	☆ □					
42	1 of 10 Decoder	☆ □		☆ □	☆ □	☆ □	□
42A	1 of 10 Decoder			☆ □			
43	1 of 10 Decoder			☆ □			
43A	1 of 10 Decoder	☆ □					
44	1 of 10 Decoder			☆ □			
44A	1 of 10 Decoder	☆ □					
45	BCD to Decimal Decoder/Driver	☆ □					
46	BCD to 7-Segment Decoder/Driver OC			☆ □			
46A	BCD to 7-Segment Decoder/Driver OC	☆ □					
47	BCD to 7-Segment Decoder/Driver OC			☆ □		☆ □	
47A	BCD to 7-Segment Decoder/Driver OC	☆ □					
48	BCD to 7-Segment Decoder/Driver	☆ □				☆ □	□
49	BCD to 7-Segment Decoder/Driver OC	☆				☆ □	

50	Dual 2-W 2-In A-O-I	☆ □	☆ □				
51	Dual 2-W 2-In A-O-I	☆ □	☆ □	☆ □	☆ □	☆ □	
51	3-3-In and 2-2-In A-O-I						
52	2-2-2-3-In A-O		☆ □				
53	Expandable 4-W (2-2-2-2) A-O-I	☆ □	☆ □				
54	2-2-2-2-In A-O-I	☆ □	☆ □	☆ □		☆ □	
54	2-2-2-3-In A-O-I		☆ □				
54	3-2-2-3-In A-O-I			☆ □		☆ □	
55	2-W 4-In A-O-I		☆ □	☆ □	☆ □	☆ □	
55	2-W 4-In A-O-I Expandable						
60	Dual 4-In Expander	☆ □	☆ □				
61	Triple 3-In Expander		☆ □				
62	4-W (3-2-2-3) A-O Expander		☆ □				
64	4-2-3-2-In A-O-I				☆ □		
65	4-2-3-2-In A-O-I OC				☆ □		
70	AND JK Flip-Flop	☆ □					
71	AND-OR JK Master/Slave Flip-Flop		☆ □	☆ □			
71	AND RS Master-Slave Flip-Flop						
72	AND JK Master-Slave Flip-Flop	☆ □	☆ □	☆ □			
73	Dual JK Flip Flop	☆ □	☆ □	☆ □		☆ □	□
74	Dual D Flip-Flop	☆ □	☆ □	☆ □	☆ □	☆ □	□
75	4-B Bistable Latch	☆ □		☆ □		☆ □	
76	Dual JK Flip-Flop	☆ □	☆ □			☆ □	□
77	4-B Bistable Latch	☆		☆ □		☆	
78	Dual JK Flip-Flop		☆ □	☆ □		☆ □	
79	Dual D Flip-Flop						
80	Gated Full Adder	☆ □					
81A	16-B RAM	☆ □					
82	2-B Binary Full Adder	☆ □					

TEXAS INSTRUMENTS 54/74 FAMILY *cont*

XXX	Description	R	H	LP	S	LS	C
83	4-B Binary Full Adder						□
83A	4-B Binary Full Adder	☆ □				☆ □	
84A	16-B RAM	☆ □					
85	4-B Magnitude Comparator	☆ □		☆ □	☆ □	☆ □	□
86	Quad 2-In X-OR	☆ □		☆ □	☆ □	☆ □	□
87	4-B True/Complement Zero/One		☆ □				
88	256-B ROM						
88A	256-B ROM OC	☆ □					
89	64-B RAM CC	□				☆ □	□
90	Decade Counter			☆ □		☆ □	
90A	Decade Counter	☆ □					
91	8-B Shift Register			☆ □		☆ □	
91A	8-Bit Shift Register	☆ □					
92	Divide by 12 (N/2 & N/6) Counter					☆ □	
92A	Divide by 12 (N/2 & N/6) Counter	☆ □					
93	4-B Binary Counter			☆ □		☆ □	
93A	4-B Binary Counter	☆ □					
94	4-B Shift Register	☆ □					
95	4-B Shift Register			☆ □			□
95A	4-B Shift Register	☆ □					
95B	4-B Shift Register					☆ □	
96	5-B Shift Register	☆ □		☆ □		☆ □	
97	6-B Binary Rate Multiplier	☆ □					
98	4-B Data Selector/Storage Register			☆ □			□
99	4-B Shift Register			☆ □			
100	8-B Bistable Latch	☆ □					
101	JK Master-Slave Flip-Flop		☆ □				

102	JK Master-Slave Flip-Flop		☆ □				
103	Dual JK Master-Slave Flip-Flop		☆ □				
104	JK Master-Slave Flip-Flop	□					
105	JK Master-Slave Flip-Flop	□					
106	Dual JK Flip-Flop		☆ □				
107	Dual JK Flip-Flop	☆ □				☆ □	□
108	Dual JK Flip-Flop		☆ □				
109	Dual JK Flip-Flop	☆ □				☆ □	
110	JK Flip-Flop	☆ □					
111	Dual JK Flip-Flop	☆ □					
112	Dual JK Flip-Flop				☆ □	☆ □	
113	Dual JK Flip-Flop				☆ □	☆ □	
114	Dual JK Flip-Flop				☆ □	☆ □	
115	AND JK Flip-Flop		☆ □				
116	Dual 4-B Latch	☆ □					
117	AND JK Flip-Flop		☆ □				
118	Double Edge Master-Slave D Flip-Flop		☆ □				
119	Dual JK Flip-Flop						
120	Dual Pulse Synchronizer/Driver	☆ □					
121	Mono MV	☆ □		☆ □			
122	Retriggerable Mono MV	☆ □		☆ □		☆ □	
123	Dual Retriggerable One-Shot MV	☆ □		☆ □		☆ □	□
124	Dual Voltage-Controlled Osc				☆ □	☆ □	
125	Quad Bus Buffer 3-S	☆ □				☆ □	
126	Quad Bus Buffer 3-S	☆ □				☆ □	
128	Quad 2-In NOR Line Driver (54128: 75-Ohm Line; 74128: 50-Ohm Line)	☆ □					
132	Quad 2-In NAND Schmitt Trigger	☆ □			☆ □	☆ □	
133	13-In NAND				☆ □		
134	12-In NAND 3-S				☆ □		
135	Quad X-OR/X-NOR				☆ □		

TEXAS INSTRUMENTS 54/74 FAMILY *cont*

XXX	Description	R	H	LP	S	LS	C
136	Quad 2-In X-OR OC	☆ □				☆ □	
138	3-Line to 8-Line Decoder 3-S				☆ □	☆ □	
139	Dual 2-Line to 4-Line Decoder				☆ □	☆ □	
140	Dual 4-In NAND 50-Ohm Line Driver				☆ □		
141	BCD to Decimal Decoder/Driver	□					
142	BCD Counter/Latch/BCD Decoder/Driver	□					
143	4-B Counter/Latch/7-Segment LED-Lamp Driver	☆ □					
144	4-B Counter/Latch/7-Segment LED-Lamp Dr. OC	☆ □					
145	BCD to Decimal Decoder/Driver	☆ □				☆ □	
147	Decimal to BCD Priority Encoder	☆ □					
148	8-Line to Octal Priority Encoder	☆ □					
150	1 of 16 Data Selector (Multiplexer)	☆ □					
151	1 of 8 Data Selector (Multiplexer)				☆ □	☆ □	□
151A	1 of 8 Data Selector (Multiplexer)	☆ □					
152	1 of 8 Data Selector (Multiplexer)					☆	
152A	1 of 8 Data Selector (Multiplexer)	☆					
153	1 of 4 Data Selector (Multiplexer)	☆ □		☆ □	☆ □	☆ □	
154	1 of 16 Decoder/Demultiplexer	☆ □		☆ □		☆ □	□
155	Dual 1 of 4 Decoder/Demultiplexer	☆ □				☆ □	
156	Dual 1 of 4 Decoder/Demultiplexer/OC	☆ □				☆ □	
157	Quad 1 of 2 Data Selector (Multiplexer)	☆ □		☆ □	☆ □	☆ □	□
158	Quad 1 of 2 Data Selector (Multiplexer) I				☆ □	☆ □	
159	1 of 16 Decoder/Demultiplexer OC	☆ □					
160	Decade Counter	☆ □				☆ □	□
161	4-B Binary Counter	☆ □				☆ □	□
162	Decade Counter	☆ □			☆ □	☆ □	□
163	4-B Binary Counter	☆ □			☆ □	☆ □	□

164	8-B Shift Register	☆ □			☆ □	☆ □	□
165	8-B Shift Register	☆ □					□
166	8-B Shift Register	☆ □					
167	Syn Decade Rate Multiplier	☆ □					
168	Syn U/D Decade Counter				☆ □	☆ □	
169	Syn 4-B Binary U/D Counter				☆ □	☆ □	
170	4-B × 4-B Register File OC	☆ □				☆ □	
172	16-B Register File 3-S	□					
173	4-B D Registers 3-S	☆ □					□
174	Hex D Flip-Flop	☆ □			☆ □	☆ □	□
175	Quad D Flip-Flop	☆ □			☆ □	☆ □	□
176	Decade/Bi-Quinary Counter/Latch	☆ □					
177	4-B Binary Counter/Latch	☆ □					
178	4-B Shift Register	☆ □					
179	4-B Shift Register	☆ □					
180	9-B Odd-Even Parity Generator/Checker	☆ □					
181	4-B Arithmetic Logic Unit	☆ □			☆ □	☆ □	
182	4 Level Look-Ahead Carry Generator	☆ □			☆ □		
183	Dual Carry-Save Full Adder		☆ □				
184	BCD to Binary Converter	☆ □					
185A	Binary to BCD Converter	☆ □					
186	512-B Prom OC	☆ □					
187	1024 ROM OC	☆ □					
188	256-B PROM OC						
188A	256-B PROM OC	□					
189	64-B RAM 3-S				☆ □	☆ □	
190	Syn U/D Decade Counter	☆ □				☆ □	
191	Syn U/D 4-B Binary Counter	☆ □				☆ □	
192	Syn U/D Decade Counter	☆ □		☆ □		☆ □	□
193	Syn U/D 4-B Binary Counter	☆ □		☆ □		☆ □	□

TEXAS INSTRUMENTS 54/74 FAMILY *cont*

XXX	Description	R	H	LP	S	LS	C
194	4-B Shift Register	☆ □			☆ □		□
194A	4-B Shift Register					☆ □	
195	4-Bit Shift Register	☆ □			☆ □		□
195A	4-B Shift Register					☆ □	
196	Decade/Bi-Quinary Counter/Latch	☆ □				☆ □	
197	4-B Binary Counter/Latch	☆ □				☆ □	
198	8-B Shift Register	☆ □					
199	8-B Shift Register	☆ □					
200	256-RAM 3-S	□			☆ □		□
201	256-B RAM 3-S				□		
206	256-B RAM OC				☆ □		
221	Dual Mono MV with Schmitt Trigger In	☆ □				☆ □	□
240	Octal Inverter Buffer 3-S					☆ □	
241	Octal Buffer 3-S					☆ □	
242	Quad Bus Transceiver					☆ □	
243	Quad Bus Transceiver					☆ □	
244	Octal Buffer 3-S					☆ □	
245	Octal Bus Transceiver					☆ □	
246	BCD to 7-Segment Decoder/Driver OC (30 V)	☆ □					
247	BCD to 7-Segment Decoder/Driver OC (15 V)	☆ □				☆ □	
248	BCD to 7-Segment Decoder/Driver	☆ □				☆ □	
249	BCD to 7-Segment Decoder/Driver OC	☆ □				☆ □	
251	1 of 8 Data Selector (Multiplexer) 3-S	☆ □			☆ □	☆ □	
253	1 of 4 Data Selector (Multiplexer) 3-S					☆ □	
256	Dual 4-B Latch OC					☆ □	
257	Quad 1 of 2 Data Selector (Multiplexer) 3-S				☆ □	☆ □	
258	Quad 1 of 2 Data Selector (Multiplexer) I 3-S				☆ □	☆ □	

259	8-B Addressable Latch OC					☆	□
260	Dual 5-In NOR			☆	□	☆	□
261	2-B × 4-B Parallel Binary Multiplier					☆	□
265	Dual Amp/I + Dual 2-In AND/NAND	☆	□				
266	Quad 2-In X-NOR OC					☆	□
270	2048-B ROM OC (512-W × 4-B)			☆	□		
271	2048-B ROM OC (256-B × 8-B)				□		
273	Octal D Flip-Flop		□			☆	□
274	4-B × 4-B Binary Multiplier 3-S				□		
275	7-B Slice Wallace Tree 3-S			☆	□		
278	4-B Priority Encoder	☆	□				
279	Quad S-R Latch	☆	□			☆	□
280	9-B Odd-Even.Parity Generator/Checker	☆	□		□		
281	4-B Parallel Binary Accumulator			☆	□		
283	4-B Binary Full Adder	☆	□			☆	□
284	4-B × 4-B Parallel Binary Multiplier	☆	□				
285	4-B × 4-B Parallel Binary Multiplier	☆	□				
287	1024-B PROM 3-S				□		
288	256-B PROM OC			☆	□		
289	64-B RAM OC			☆	□	☆	□
290	Decade Counter	☆	□			☆	□
293	4-B Binary Counter	☆	□			☆	□
295	4-B Shift Register 3-S						
295A	4-B Shift Register 3-S					☆	□
298	Quad 2-In Multiplexer/Store	☆	□			☆	□
299	8-B Shift Register/Store				□	☆	□
301	256-B RAM OC				□		
323	8-B Shift/Storage Register					☆	□
351	Dual 1 of 8 Data Selector 3-S		□				
363	Octal Latch for MOS 3-S					☆	□
364	Octal D Flip-Flop for MOS 3-S					☆	□

TEXAS INSTRUMENTS 54/74 FAMILY *cont*

XXX	Description	R	H	LP	S	LS	C
365	Hex Bus Driver 3-S	☆ □				☆ □	
366	Hex Bus Driver I 3-S	☆ □				☆ □	
367	Hex Bus Driver 3-S	☆ □				☆ □	
368	Hex Bus Driver I 3-S	☆ □				☆ □	
370	2048 ROM 3-S (512-W × 4-B) 3-S				☆ □		
371	2048-B ROM 3-S (256-B × 8-B)				□		
373	Octal Latch 3-S					☆ □	
374	Octal D Flip-Flop 3-S	☆ □				☆ □	
375	Quad Latch					☆ □	
377	Octal D Flip-Flop					☆ □	
378	Hex D Flip-Flop					☆ □	
379	Quad D Flip-Flop					☆ □	
381	4-B Binary Arithmetic Logic Unit				□		
386	Quad X-OR					☆ □	
387	1024 PROM OC				□		
390	Dual Decade/Bi-Quinary Counter	☆ □				☆ □	
393	Dual 4-B Binary Counter	☆ □				☆ □	
395	4-B Shift Register 3-S					☆ □	
398	Quad 2-Port Register					☆ □	
399	Quad 2-Port Register					☆ □	
406	1 of 8 Decoder	☆ □					
408	8-B Parity Tree	☆ □					
416	Modulo N Decade Counter	☆ □					
417	Modulo N Decade Counter	☆ □					
418	Modulo N 4-B Binary Counter	☆ □					
419	Modulo N 4-B Binary Counter	☆ □					
445	BCD to Decimal Decoder TV					☆ □	
450	Counter Latch Decoder	☆ □					

452	Dual Decade Counter	☆	□					
453	Dual 4-B Binary Counter	☆	□					
454	Dual Decade U/D Counter	☆	□					
455	Dual Binary U/D Counter	☆	□					
456	NBCD Adder	☆	□					
460	Bus Transfer Switch	☆	□					
468	Dual MOS to TTL Level Translator 3-S	☆	□					
490	Dual Decade Counter	☆	□			☆	□	
568	BCD Decade U/D Counter 3-S					☆	□	
569	4-B Binary U/D Counter 3-S					☆	□	
571A	AND-OR JK Flip-Flop			☆	□			
572A	AND JK Flip-Flop			☆	□			
670	4-B × 4-B Register File 3-S					☆	□	
901	Hex TTL Buffer I							□
902	Hex TTL Buffer							□
903	Hex PMOS Buffer I							□
904	Hex PMOS Buffer							□
911	Display Controller, 4-Digit, 3-S							□
912	Display Controller, 6-Digit, 3-S							□
913	Display Controller, 4-Digit							□

NATIONAL SEMICONDUCTOR MC70/80 SERIES

DM70/80( )XXX

☆ MILITARY: −55° +125°C
□ COMMERCIAL: 0° TO +70°C

BLANK = REGULAR = R
L = LOW POWER
LS = LOW POWER SCHOTTKY

8XXX	Description	R	L	LS
8006	Quad 2-In NAND		□	
8090	Quad Inverter + Dual 2-In NAND Buffer	☆ □		
8091	Quad 2-In NAND Buffer	☆ □		
8092	Dual 5-In NAND	☆ □		
8093	Quad Buffer 3-S	☆ □		
8094	Quad Buffer 3-S	☆ □		
8095	Hex Buffer 3-S	☆ □	☆ □	
8096	Hex Inverter 3-S	☆ □	☆ □	
8097	Hex Buffer 3-S	☆ □	☆ □	
8098	Hex Inverter 3-S	☆ □	☆ □	
8099	Quad 2-In NAND Buffer	☆ □		
8121	8-Channel Multiplexer 3-S	☆ □		
8122	Quad 2-In Multiplexer		☆ □	
8123	Quad 2-In Multiplexer 3-S	☆ □	☆ □	
8130	10-Bit Comparator	☆ □		
8131	6-Bit Unified Bus Comparator	☆ □		
8136	6-Bit Comparator	☆ □		
8160	6-Bit Comparator	☆ □		
8195	Octal Buffer 3-S			☆ □
8196	Octal Buffer 3-S			☆ □
8197	Octal Buffer 3-S			☆ □
8198	Octal Buffer 3-S			☆ □
8200	4-Bit Comparator	☆ □		
8210	8-Channel Digital Switch	☆ □		
8211	8-Channel Digital Switch	☆ □		
8214	Dual 4 Line to 1 Line Multiplexer 3-S	☆ □		
8219	16 Line to 1 Line Multiplexer 3-S	☆ □		
8220	Parity Generator Checker	☆ □		
8223	1 Line to 8 Line Demultiplexer	☆ □		
8230	Dual 2/4 Demultiplexer 3-S	☆ □		
8280	Presettable Decade Counter			
8281	Presettable Binary Counter			
8288	Presettable Divide by 12 Counter			
8511	Dual Gated D Flip-Flop	☆ □	☆ □	
8512	Dual Flip-Flop Master/Slave JK/D	☆ □	☆ □	
8520	Modulo N Divider (N = 2 to 15)	☆ □		
8531	ROM 16K 3-S	□		
8542	Quad I/O Registers 3-S	☆ □		
8544	Quad Switch Debouncers	☆ □		
8546	8-B Universal I/O Shift Registers	☆ □		

NATIONAL SEMICONDUCTOR MC70/80 SERIES *cont*

8XXX	Description	R	L	LS
8550	6-B Shift Registers	□		
8551	Quad D Flip-Flop 3-S	☆ □	☆ □	
8552	Decade Counter/Latch 3-S	☆ □	☆ □	
8553	8-Bit Latch 3-S	☆ □		
8554	Binary Counter/Latch 3-S	☆ □	☆ □	
8555	Programmable Decade Counter 3-S	☆ □		
8556	Programmable Decade Counter 3-S	☆ □		
8560	U/D Decade Counter	☆ □		
8563	U/D Binary Counter	☆ □		
8568	64-B Edge Triggered Register	☆ □		
8570	8-Bit Shift Register	☆ □		
8573	1-K PROM	☆ □		
8574	1-K PROM 3-S	☆ □		
8575	Programmed Logic Array	☆ □		
8576	Programmed Logic Array	☆ □		
8577	256-B PROM	☆ □		
8578	256-B PROM 3-S	☆ □		
8581	16-K ROM 3-S	□		
8582	256-Bit RAM OC			
8590	8-Bit Shift Register	☆ □		
8595	4-K ROM	☆ □		
8596	4-K ROM 3-S	☆ □		
8597	1-K ROM 3-S	☆ □		
8598	256-Bit ROM 3-S	☆ □		
8599	64-Bit RAM	☆ □		
8602	Dual Monostable MV			
8613	Quad D Flip-Flop	☆ □	☆ □	
8624	Magnitude Comparator (A ≈ B) 3-S		☆ □	
8625	7-Segment to BCD Decoder 3-S		☆ □	
8670	8-Bit Shift Register		☆ □	
8675	Presettable Decade Counter		☆ □	
8676	Presettable Binary Counter		☆ □	
8678	7 By 9 Character Generator	☆ □		
8679	7 By 9 Character Generator	☆ □		
8690	8-B Shift Register		☆ □	
8693	Binary Ripple Counter			☆ □
8695	4-K ROM			
8696	4-K ROM 3-S			
8697	1-K ROM 3-S		☆ □	
8699	64-Bit RAM 3-5		☆ □	
8795	4-K ROM	☆ □		
8796	4-K ROM 3-S	☆ □		
8800	Dual Voltage Translator			
8806	MOS to TTL Translator			
8810	Quad 2-In TTL-MOS Translator			

NATIONAL SEMICONDUCTOR MC70/80 SERIES *cont*

8XXX	Description	R	L	LS
8811	Quad 2-In TTL-MOS Translator			
8812	Hex TTL-MOS Inverter			
8819	Quad 2-In TTL-MOS AND			
8820	Dual Line Receiver			
8820A	Dual Line Receiver			
8822	Dual Line Receiver			
8830	Dual Differential Line Driver			
8831	Line Driver 3-S			
8832	Line Driver 3-S			
8833	Quad Transceiver 3-S			
8834	Quad Transceiver 3-S			
8835	Quad Transceiver 3-S			
8836	Quad NOR Unified Bus Receiver			
8837	Hex Unified Bus Receiver			
8838	Quad Unified Bus Transceiver			
8839	Quad Transceiver 3-S			
8853	Dual Retriggerable MV	☆ □		
8875A	4-Bit Multiplier 3-S	☆ □		
8875B	4-Bit Multiplier 3-S	☆ □		
8880	High Voltage 7-Segment Decoder/ Driver			
8884A	High Voltage Cathode Decoder/Driver			
8885	MOS to High Voltage Cathode Buffer			
8898	BCD to Binary Converter 3-S	□		
8899	Binary to BCD Converter 3-S	□		

SIGNETICS 8200 SERIES

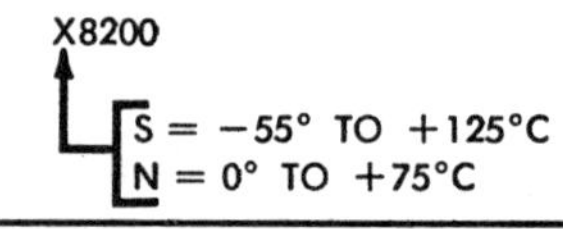

82XX	Description
8200	Dual 5-Bit Buffer Register
8201	Dual 5-Bit Buffer Register (Inverted Inputs)
8202	10-Bit Buffer Register
8203	10-Bit Buffer Register (Inverted Inputs)
8204	2-K ROM
8205	4-K ROM
8206	256-Bit RAM 3-S
8207	256-Bit RAM OC
8212	High Speed Multiport (8 × 4) RAM
8216	256-Bit RAM 3-S
8217	256-Bit RAM OC
8220	8-Bit CAM
8221	64-Bit High Speed RAM
8223	256-Bit PROM
8224	256-Bit ROM

SIGNETICS 8200 SERIES *cont*

82XX	Description
8225	256-Bit RAM
8226	1-K PROM
8228	4-K ROM
8229	1-K PROM
8230	8-In Multiplexer
8231	8-In Multiplexer
8232	8-In Multiplexer
8233	2-In 4-Bit Multiplexer
8234	2-In 4-Bit Multiplexer
8235	2-In 4-Bit Multiplexer
8241	Quad X-OR
8242	Quad X-NOR
8243	8-Bit Position Scaler
8250	Binary to Octal Decoder
8251	BCD to Decimal Decoder
8252	BCD to Decimal Decoder
8260	Arithmetic Logic Element
8261	Fast Carry Extender
8262	9-Bit Parity Generator/Checker
8263	3-In 4-Bit Multiplexer
8264	3-In 4-Bit Multiplexer
8266	2-In 4-Bit Multiplexer
8267	2-In 4-Bit Multiplexer OC
8268	Gated Full Adder
8269	4-Bit Comparator
8270	4-Bit Shift Register
8271	4-Bit Shift Register
8273	10-Bit Shift Register
8274	10-Bit Shift Register
8275	Quad Latch
8276	8-Bit Shift Register
8277	Dual 8-Bit Shift Register
8280	Presettable Decade Counter
8281	Presettable Binary Counter
8282	4-Bit BCD Arithmetic Unit
8283	4-Bit BCD Adder
8284	Binary Up/Down Counter
8285	Decade Up/Down Counter
8288	Divide by 12 Counter
8290	Presettable High Speed Decade Counter
8291	Presettable High Speed Binary Counter
8292	Presettable LP Decade Counter
8293	Presettable LP Binary Counter
82112	High Speed 8 × 4-Bit RAM Multiport
82123	256-Bit PROM 3-S

SIGNETICS 8T00 SERIES

8TXX	Description
8T01	Nixie Decoder/Driver
8T04	7-Segment Decoder/Driver (L)
8T05	7-Segment Decoder/Driver (H)
8T06	7-Segment Decoder/Driver (H)
8T09	Quad Bus Driver
8T10	Quad D Flip-Flop
8T13	Dual Line Receiver
8T14	Triple Line Receiver/Schmitt Trigger
8T15	Dual Line Driver
8T16	Dual Line Receiver
8T18	Dual Interface Gate (HV to TTL)
8T20	Monostable Multivibrator
8T22	Retriggerable Monostable Multivibrator
8T23	Dual Line Receiver
8T24	Triple Line Receiver
8T25	Dual MOS Sense Amplifier
8T26	Dual Bus Driver/Receiver
8T28	Quad Noninverting Bus Transceiver 3-S
8T30	Dual TTL to MOS Transceiver
8T31	8-Bit Bidirectional Input/Output Port
8T32	Interface Vector (IV) Byte
8T33	Interface Vector (IV) Byte)
8T34	Quad Bus Transceiver
8T37	Hex Buffer/Schmitt Trigger
8T38	Quad Bus Transceiver OC
8T51	CC 7-Seg LED Decoder/Driver (Source 5 mA)
8T54	CC 7-Seg LED Decoder/Driver (Sink 200 mA)
8T59	CC 7-Seg LED Decoder/Driver (Source 50 mA)
8T71	CC 7-Seg LED Decoder/Driver W/L (Source 5 mA)
8T74	CC 7-Seg LED Decoder/Driver W/L (Sink 20 mA)
8T75	CC 7-Seg LED Decoder/Driver W/L (Source 20 mA)
8T79	CC 7-Seg LED Decoder/Driver W/L (Source 50 mA)
8T80	Quad Interface Gate (TTL to HV)
8T90	Hex Interface Buffer (TTL to Hv)
8T93	High Speed Hex Inverter (pnp Input)
8T94	High Speed Hex Inverter (pnp Input) OC
8T95	High Speed Hex Buffer 3-S (pnp Input)
8T96	High Speed Hex Buffer Inverter 3-S (pnp Input)
8T97	High Speed Hex Buffer 3-S (pnp Input)
8T98	High Speed Hex Buffer Inverter 3-S (pnp Input)

SIGNETICS 8T00 SERIES *cont*

8TXX	Description
8T100	Quad Differential Line Driver (5 V)
8T101	Quad Differential Line Driver
8T110	Quad Differential Line Receiver (5 V)
8T111	Quad Differential Line Receiver
8T125	Octal Transceiver I
8T126	Quad Transceiver
8T127	Quad Transceiver
8T128	Quad Transceiver
8T129	Quad Transceiver
8T363	Dual Zero Crossing Detector
8T380	Quad Bus Receiver W/Hysteresis

SIGNETICS 8HXX SERIES

8HXX	Description
8H10	Triple 3-In NAND
8H16	Dual 4-In NAND
8H20	Dual JK Flip-Flop
8H21	Dual JK Flip-Flop
8H22	Dual JK Flip-Flop
8H70	Dual JK Flip-Flop
8H80	Quad 2-In NAND
8H90	Hex Inverter

FAIRCHILD SEMICONDUCTOR 9000 SERIES

9XXX XC or XM

☐ COMMERCIAL: 0° TO +75°C ☆ MILITARY: −55° TO +125°C

9XXX	Description	M	C
9000	JK Master-Slave Flip-Flop	☆	☐
9001	JK Master-Slave Flip-Flop	☆	☐
9002	Quad 2-In NAND	☆	☐
9003	Triple 3-In NAND	☆	☐
9004	Dual 4-In NAND	☆	☐
9005	Dual A-O-I/Expander	☆	☐
9006	Dual 4-In Expander	☆	☐
9007	8-In NAND	☆	☐
9008	2-2-2-3 A-O-I	☆	☐
9009	Dual 4-In NAND Buffer	☆	☐
9012	Quad 2-In NAND OC	☆	☐
9014	Quad X-OR	☆	☐
9015	2-2-2-4 NOR	☆	☐
9016	Hex Inverter	☆	☐
9017	Hex Inverter OC	☆	☐

FAIRCHILD SEMICONDUCTOR 9000 SERIES *cont*

9XXX	Description	M	C
9020	Dual JK Flip-Flop	☆	□
9022	Dual JK Master-Slave Flip-Flop	☆	□
9024	Dual JK Flip-Flop	☆	□
9033	See 93433		
9034	See 93434		
9035	See 93435		

FAIRCHILD SEMICONDUCTOR 9300 SERIES

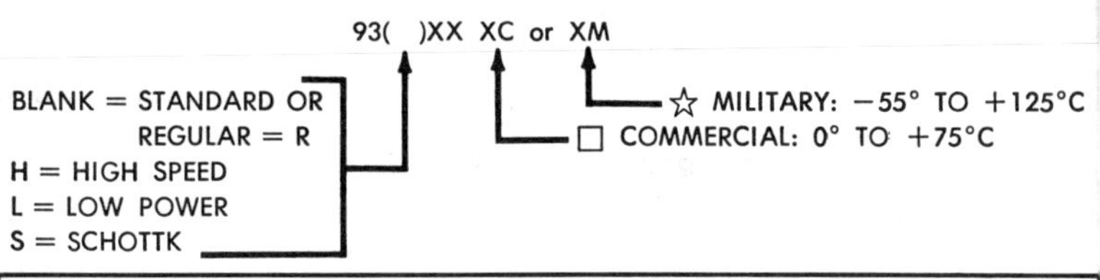

93XXX	Description	R	H	L	S
9300	4-B Shift Register	☆ □	☆ □	☆ □	□
9301	1 of 10 Decoder	☆ □		☆ □	
9302	1 of 10 Decoder OC	☆ □			
9304	Dual Full Adder	☆ □			
9305	Variable Modulo Counter	☆ □			□
9306	Presettable Decade U/D Counter				
9307	7-Segment Decoder	☆ □			
9308	Dual 4-B Latch	☆ □		☆ □	
9309	Dual 4-In Multiplexer	☆ □		☆ □	
9310	Decade Counter	☆ □		☆ □	☆ □
9311	1 of 16 Decoder	☆ □		☆ □	
9312	8-In Multiplexer	☆ □		☆ □	
9313	8-In Multiplexer OC	☆ □			□
9314	4-B Latch	☆ □		☆ □	
9315	1 of 10 Decoder Driver	☆ □			
9316	4-B Binary Counter	☆ □		☆ □	☆ □
9317B	7-Segment Decoder Driver (20 V/40 mA)	☆ □			
9317C	7-Segment Decoder Driver (30 V/20 mA)	☆ □			
9318	8-In Priority Encoder	☆ □		☆ □	
9321	Dual 1 of 4 Decoder	☆ □		☆ □	
9322	Quad 2-In Multiplexer	☆ □		☆ □	
9324	5-B Comparator	☆ □		☆ □	
9328	Dual 8-B Shift Register	☆ □		☆ □	
9334	8-B Addressable Latch	☆ □			
9338	8-B Multiport Register	☆ □			
9339	8-B Multiport Register	☆ □			□
9340	4-B Arithmetic Logic Unit	☆ □			
9341	4-B Arithmetic Logic Unit	☆ □			☆ □
9342	Look-Ahead Carry Generator	☆ □			□
9343	2s Complement Multiplier				□

FAIRCHILD SEMICONDUCTOR 9300 SERIES *cont*

93XXX	Description	R	H	L	S
9344	4-B × 2-B Multiplier	☆ □			
9345	1 of 10 Decoder	☆ □			
9348	12-In Parity Generator/Checker	☆ □			☆ □
9350	Decade Counter	□			
9352	BCD to Decimal Decoder	☆ □			
9353	Excess-3 to Decimal Decoder	☆ □			
9354	Excess-3 Gray to Decimal Decoder	☆ □			
9356	Binary Counter	□			
9357A	BCD to 7-Segment Decoder Driver OC (30 V)	☆ □			
9357B	BCD to 7-Segment Decoder Driver OC (15 V)	☆ □			
9358	BCD to 7-Segment Decoder	☆ □			
9359	BCD to 7-Segment Decoder	☆ □			
9360	U/D Decade Counter	☆ □			
9362	9-B Parity Checker/Generator				□
9366	U/D Binary Counter	☆ □			
9368	7-Segment Decoder/Driver/Latch (H)	□			
9370	7-Segment Decoder/Driver/Latch (L)	□			
9372	4-B Shift Register		☆ □		
9374	7-Segment Decoder/Driver/Latch (L)	□			
9375	4-B Latch	☆ □			
9377	4-B Latch	☆ □			
9380	Full Adder	☆ □			
9382	2-B Full Adder	☆ □			
9383	4-B Full Adder	☆ □			
9386	Quad X-NOR/Complement	☆ □			
9387	4-B True/Complement	☆ □			
9390	Decade Counter	☆ □			
9391	8-B Shift Register	☆ □			
9392	Divide by 12 Counter	☆ □			
9393	Binary Counter	☆ □			
9394	4-B Shift Register	☆ □			
9395	4-B Right/Left Shift Register	☆ □			
9396	5-B Shift Register	☆ □			
93137	1 of 8 Decoder				□
93138	1 of 8 Decoder/Demultiplexer	□			
93139	Dual 1 of 4 Decoder/Demultiplexer	□			
93141	BCD to Decimal Decoder/Driver	□			
93145	1 of 10 Decoder/Driver				
93150	16-In Multiplexer	☆ □			
93151	8-In Multiplexer	☆ □			
93152	8-In Multiplexer	☆ □			
93153	Dual 4-In Multiplexer	☆ □			
93164	8-B Serial to Parallel Converter	☆ □			
93165	8-B Parallel to Serial Converter	☆ □			
93176	BCD Decoder Counter	□			

FAIRCHILD SEMICONDUCTOR 9300 SERIES *cont*

93XXX	Description	R	H	L	S
93177	Binary Counter	□			
93178	4-B Shift Register	□			
93179	4-B Shift Register	□			
93180	8-B Parity Generator/Checker	☆ □			
93183	Dual Full Adder	☆ □			
93190	U/D Decade Counter	☆ □			
93191	U/D Binary Counter	☆ □			
93196	Decade Counter	☆ □			
93197	Binary Counter	☆ □			
93198	8-B Shift Register	☆ □			

FAIRCHILD SEMICONDUCTOR 934XX SERIES (MEMORY DEVICES)

934XX	Description	R
93400	256-B RAM	□
93400B	256-B RAM	□
93401	Decoder/Driver for 934000	□
93402	16-B CAM	□
93403	64-B RAM	□
93406	1024-B ROM	□
93407	16-B R/W Memory	☆ □
93410	256-B RAM	☆ □
93410A	256-B RAM	□
93415	1024-B R/W Memory	□
93433	16-B RAM	☆ □
93434	256-B ROM	☆ □
93435	64-B RAM	□

FAIRCHILD SEMICONDUCTOR 9400 SERIES (SCHOTTKY)

(−55°C TO +125°C)

94XX	Description
9401	Cyclic Redundancy Check Generator/Checker
9403	First In First Out Memory
9404	Data Path Switch
9405	Arithmetic Logic Register Stack
9406	Program Stack
9407	Data Access Register
9410	16 × 4-B RAM 3-S

FAIRCHILD SEMICONDUCTOR 9600 SERIES

96XX	Description	R	H	L	S
9600	One-Shot MV	☆ □			
9601	One-Shot MV	☆ □			
9602	Dual One-Shot MV	☆ □		☆ □	□
9603	One-Shot MV	☆ □			
μA9614	Dual Line Driver	☆ □			
μA9615	Dual Line Receiver	☆ □			
μA9616	EIA Line Driver	□			
μA9617	EIA Line Receiver	□			
μA9620	Dual Line Receiver	☆ □			
μA9621	Dual Line Driver	☆ □			
μA9622	Dual Line Receiver	☆ □			
μA9624	Dual TTL to MOS Interface	☆ □			
μA9625	Dual MOS to TTL Interface	☆ □			
μA9644	Dual High Voltage High Current Driver	☆ □			

APPENDIX G

Pin Assignments

Pin assignments for most of the ICs in the preceding list are given in this appendix. In some cases the pin functions were not available. The identification scheme in general follows the same scheme used by the manufacturer, but there are some exceptions. An effort has been made to identify dual circuit functions, which was not always done by the manufacturer. Abbreviations are used because of the need for conciseness. In some cases the arrangement and operation of an IC can readily be determined from the pin assignments. In other cases, the operation can only be determined only by using the manufacturer's data sheets. Once the IC's function is understood, the pin assignments serve as a quick reference to inputs and outputs.

Many of the abbreviations are common to most of the ICs: Ys and Qs for outputs, but Os are also used. Many abbreviations are special. A list of special abbreviations is given at the end of the pin assignments.

TELEDYNE HiNIL HIGH NOISE IMMUNITY LOGIC

	1	2	3	4	5	6	7	8	9	10	11	12	13	14	15	16
301	Y1	A1	B1	C1	D1	E1	X1	GND	X2	E2	D2	C2	B2	A2	Y2	V_{CC}
302	Y4	B4	A4	Y2	X2	B2	A2	GND	Y3	A3	B3	Y1	X1	A1	B1	V_{CC}
303	SAME AS 302															
311	A1	A2	A3	T1	B1	B2	B3	GND	NC	$\overline{Q}$	$\overline{S}$	$\overline{R}$	Q	T2	NC	V_{CC}
312	$\overline{R1}$	$\overline{Q1}$	K1	T1	J1	Q1	$\overline{S1}$	GND	S2	Q2	J2	T2	K2	$\overline{Q2}$	$\overline{R2}$	V_{CC}
313	SAME AS 312															
321	SAME AS 302															
322	Y1	X1	A1	B1	C1	D1	E1	GND	E2	D2	C2	B2	A2	X2	Y2	V_{CC}
323	SAME AS 302															
324	SAME AS 302															
325	Y3	B3	A3	Y1	C1	B1	A1	GND	Y4	A4	B4	Y2	A2	B2	C2	V_{CC}
326	SAME AS 325															
331	R1	O1	A1	B1	C1	D1	E1	GND	A2	B2	C2	D2	E2	O2	R2	V_{CC}
332	A5	B5	Y5	A3	Y3	A1	YI	GND	Y2	A2	Y4	A4	Y6	A6	B6	V_{CC}
333	SAME AS 332															
334	1	A6	Y6	A5	Y5	AY	Y4	GND	Y3	A3	Y2	A2	Y1	A1	B12	V_{CC}
335	SAME AS 334															
341	Y1	A1	B1	X1	C1	D1	XX1	GND	XX2	C2	D2	X2	A2	B2	Y2	V_{CC}
342	RI1	Q1	CX1	CX1	Q1	A1	X1	GND	X2	A2	Q2	CX2	CX2	Q2	RI2	V_{CC}

343	A2	B2	A1	B1	A > B	A < B	A = B	GND	ST	[2]	[3]	A8	B8	A4	B4	V_{CC}
344	Y1	OX1	C1	D1	B1	A1	X1	GND	X21	A2	B2	C2	D2	X22	Y2	V_{CC}
347	B1	A1	$\overline{R1}$	R/C1	NC	$\overline{Q1}$	Q1	GND	$\overline{Q2}$	Q2	NC	R/C2	$\overline{R2}$	A2	B2	V_{CC}
350	D3	D2	D1	D0	Y	$\overline{Y}$	$\overline{E}$	GND	S2	S1	S0	D7	D6	D5	D4	V_{CC}
351	A3	A2	A1	A0	YA	YB	$\overline{EA}$	GND	$\overline{EB}$	S1	S0	B3	B2	B1	BO	V_{CC}
361	[4]	[5]	YI	A1	B1	NC	NC	GND	NC	NC	A2	B2	Y2	[6]	[7]	V_{CC}
362	NC	Y1	[8]	[9]	[10]	[11]	NC	GND	NC	[12]	[13]	[14]	[15]	Y2	NC	V_{CC}
363								SAME AS 302								
367	PU	D1	A1	O1	O2	A2	D2	GND	INH	D3	A3	O3	O4	A4	D4	V_{CC}
368								SAME AS 367								
370	CK	Q1	Q1	D1	D2	Q2	$\overline{Q2}$	GND	NC	$\overline{Q3}$	Q3	D3	D4	Q4	Q4	V_{CC}
371	R	CK1	NC	S4	Q4	S8	Q8	GND	C0	S1	Q1	S2	Q2	NC	CK2	V_{CC}
372								SAME AS 371								
375	CK	P2	Q2	$\overline{PE}$	P3	$\overline{Q3}$	Q3	GND	$\overline{MR}$	P0	J	$\overline{K}$	Q0	P1	Q1	V_{CC}
380	A1	A2	A4	A8	O9	O8	O7	GND	O6	O5	O4	O3	O2	O1	O0	V_{CC}
381								SAME AS 380								
382								SAME AS 380								
383	B	C	LT	[16]	RB1	D	A	GND	e	d	c	b	a	g	f	V_{CC}

[1]B3456
[2]A = BI_n
[3]A > BI_n
[4]TTL V_{CC1}
[5]RTL V_{CC1}
[6]RTL V_{CC2}
[7]TTL V_{CC2}
[8]RTL B1
[9]TTL A1
[10]RTL A1
[11]TTL B1
[12]TTL B2
[13]RTL A2
[14]TTL A2
[15]RTL B2
[16]B1/RB

MOTOROLA MC500/400; MC550/450

MC	1	2	3	4	5	6	7	8	9	10	11	12	13	14
400	B1	C1	D1	V_{CC}	A2	B2	C2	NC	D2	GND	Y2	Y1	A1	NC
401	B1	A2	B2	V_{CC}	A3	B3	A4	B4	C4	GND	Y	COL	EM	A1
402	A	B	C	V_{CC}	D	E	F	NC	G	GND	NC	Y	H	NC
403	A2	B2	C2	V_{CC}	A3	B3	C3	NC	NC	GND	Y23	Y1	A1	B1
404	A1	B1	C1	V_{CC}	A2	B2	C2	A3	B3	GND	C3	Y	COL	EM
405	B1	C1	D1	V_{CC}	A2	B2	C2	D2	COL	GND	NC	Y	EM	A1
406	B	C	D	V_{CC}	E	F	G	H	BAS	GND	NC	Y	COL	A
407	B1	C1	D1	V_{CC}	A2	B2	C2	NC	D2	GND	Y2	Y1	A1	NC
408	A1	B1	Y1	V_{CC}	A2	B2	Y2	A3	B3	GND	Y3	A4	B4	Y4
409	C1	A2	B2	V_{CC}	A3	B3	A4	B4	C4	GND	COL	EM	A1	B1
410	B1	C1	D1	V_{CC}	A2	B2	C2	D2	EM2	GND	CO2	CO1	EM1	A1
411	B1	C1	D1	NC	A2	B2	C2	D2	BA2	GND	CO2	CO1	BA1	A1
412	A1	B1	C1	V_{CC}	Y1	A2	B2	C2	Y2	GND	A3	B3	C3	Y3
413	NC	$\overline{R1}$	$\overline{R2}$	V_{CC}	$\overline{S1}$	$\overline{S2}$	NC	NC	$\overline{S3}$	GND	Q	$\overline{Q}$	$\overline{R3}$	NC

414	S2	S3	CK	V_{CC}	$\overline{SD}$	R1	R2	NC	R3	GND	Q	$\overline{Q}$	$\overline{RD}$	S1
415	K2	K1	CK	V_{CC}	J1	J2	J3	$\overline{S}$	$\overline{P}$	GND	Q	$\overline{Q}$	$\overline{R}$	K3
416	K2	K1	CK	V_{CC}	J1	J2	L1	L2	$\overline{S}$	GND	Q	$\overline{Q}$	M2	M1
417	K3	R	CK	V_{CC}	JK	S	K1	K2	K3	GND	Q	$\overline{Q}$	J1	J2
418	A1	S	CK	V_{CC}	E	R	A2	B2	C2	GND	Q	$\overline{Q}$	B1	C1
419	YI	A1	B1	V_{CC}	A2	B2	Y2	5K	5K	GND	Y3	A3	B3	5K
420	B1	C1	D1	V_{CC}	A2	B2	E2	CO2	C2	GND	D2	Y2	Y1	A1
421	NC	$\overline{RC}$	$\overline{CR}$	V_{CC}	$\overline{CS}$	$\overline{SC}$	NC	NC	$\overline{SD}$	GND	Q	$\overline{Q}$	$\overline{RD}$	NC
422	CK1	D1	$\overline{R1}$	V_{CC}	$\overline{R2}$	D2	CK2	$\overline{S2}$	Q2	GND	$\overline{Q2}$	$\overline{Q1}$	Q1	$\overline{S1}$
423	K1	J1	$\overline{CK1}$	V_{CC}	$\overline{CK2}$	J2	K2	$\overline{S2}$	Q2	GND	$\overline{Q2}$	$\overline{Q1}$	Q1	$\overline{S1}$
424	K1	J2	$\overline{CK}$	V_{CC}	$\overline{RI2}$	J2	K2	$\overline{S2}$	Q2	GND	$\overline{Q2}$	$\overline{Q1}$	Q1	$\overline{S1}$
425	Y6	Y1	A1	V_{CC}	A2	Y2	Y3	A3	Y4	GND	A4	A5	Y5	A6
426	A1	BA1	RE1	V_{CC}	RE2	BA2	A2	B2	C2	GND	Y2	Y1	B1	C2
427	A1	B1	C1	V_{CC}	A2	B2	C2	D2	BA2	GND	Y2	Y1	BA1	D1

MOTOROLA MHTL SERIES MC660

MC	1	2	3	4	5	6	7	8	9	10	11	12	13	14
660	A1	B1	EX1	C1	D1	Y1	GND	Y2	A2	B2	EX2	C2	D2	V_{CC}
661							SAME AS MC660							
662							SAME AS MC660							
663	$\overline{Q1}$	K1	$\overline{R1}$	$\overline{CK1}$	J1	Q1	GND	Q2	J2	$\overline{CK2}$	R2	K2	$\overline{Q2}$	V_{CC}
664	NC	$\overline{CK}$	S1	S2	$\overline{R}$	Q	GND	NC	$\overline{Q}$	$\overline{S}$	R1	R2	NC	V_{CC}
665	A1	EX1	Y1	1	EX2	A2	GND	Y2	1	Y3	A3	1	1	V_{CC}
666	EX1	A1	Y2	B2	A2	EX2	GND	A3	EX3	B3	Y3	Y1	B1	V_{CC}
667	T1	Q1	CEX1	RI1	CEX1	$\overline{Q1}$	GND	$\overline{Q2}$	CEX2	RI2	CEX2	Q2	T2	V_{CC}
668	A1	B1	Y1	A2	B2	Y2	GND	Y3	A3	B3	Y4	A4	B4	V_{CC}
669	NC	A1	B1	Y1	C1	D1	GND	NC	A2	B2	Y2	C2	D2	NC
670	A3	B3	A1	B1	C1	Y1	GND	Y2	A2	B2	C2	Y3	C3	V_{CC}
671							SAME AS MC670							
672							SAME AS MC668							
673	A1	B1	EX1	C1	D1	Y1	GND	Y2	D2	C2	EX2	B2	A2	V_{CC}
674							SAME AS MC673							

[1]See data sheets.

MOTOROLA MC2100/2000; MC2150/2050

MC	1	2	3	4	5	6	7	8	9	10	11	12	13	14
2000	B1	C1	D1	V_{CC}	A2	B2	C2	D2	COL	GND	NC	Y	EM	A1
2001	A1	B1	Y1	V_{CC}	A2	B2	Y2	A3	B3	GND	Y3	A4	B4	Y4
2002	C1	A2	B2	V_{CC}	A3	B3	A4	B4	C4	GND	COO	EMO	A1	B1
2003	B1	C1	D1	V_{CC}	A2	B2	C2	NC	D2	GND	Y2	Y1	A1	NC
2004	B1	A2	B2	V_{CC}	A3	B3	A4	B4	C4	GND	Y	COL	EM	A1
2005	A	B	C	V_{CC}	D	E	F	NC	G	GND	NC	Y	H	NC
2006	B1	C1	D1	V_{CC}	A2	B2	C2	D2	EM2	GND	CO2	CO1	EM1	A1
2007	A1	B1	C1	V_{CC}	Y1	A2	B2	C2	Y2	GND	A3	B3	C3	Y3
2008	Y6	Y1	A1	V_{CC}	A2	Y2	Y3	A3	Y4	GND	A4	A5	Y5	A6
2009	K2	K1	CK	V_{CC}	J1	J2	J3	$\overline{S}$	$\overline{P}$	GND	Q	$\overline{Q}$	$\overline{R}$	K3
2010	K2	K1	$\overline{CK}$	V_{CC}	J1	J2	L1	L2	$\overline{S}$	GND	Q	$\overline{Q}$	M2	M1
2011	A	B	C	V_{CC}	D	E	F	G	BA	GND	NC	Y	C0	H
2012	A1	B1	C1	V_{CC}	A2	B2	C2	A3	B3	GND	C3	Y	COL	EM
2013	B1	C1	D1	V_{CC}	A2	B2	EM2	CO2	C2	GND	D2	Y2	Y1	A1
2023	K1	J1	$\overline{CK1}$	V_{CC}	$\overline{CK2}$	J2	K2	$\overline{S2}$	Q2	GND	$\overline{Q2}$	$\overline{Q1}$	Q1	$\overline{S1}$
2024	K1	J1	$\overline{CK}$	V_{CC}	$\overline{R}$	J2	K2	$\overline{S2}$	Q2	GND	$\overline{Q2}$	$\overline{Q1}$	Q1	$\overline{S1}$
2025	K2	K1	CK	V_{CC}	J1	J2	J3	$\overline{S}$	$\overline{P}$	GND	Q	$\overline{Q}$	$\overline{R}$	K3
2026	K2	K1	$\overline{CK}$	V_{CC}	J1	J2	L1	L2	$\overline{S}$	GND	Q	$\overline{Q}$	M2	M1
2028	K1	K2	CK	V_{CC}	JK2	J2	J1	$\overline{S1}$	$\overline{S2}$	GND	Q	$\overline{Q}$	$\overline{R}$	JK1

ADVANCED MICRO DEVICES Am 2500

AM	1 13	2 14	3 15	4 16	5 17	6 18	7 19	8 20	9 21	10 22	11 23	12 24
2500												
2501	CP P1	$\overline{CD}$ P0	Q0 PE	Q1 V_{CC}	Q2	Q3	TC	GND	CE	CE	P3	P2
2502	$\overline{E}$ Q6	$\overline{CC}$ Q7	Q0 $\overline{Q7}$	Q1 V_{CC}	Q2	Q3	D	GND	CP	$\overline{S}$	Q4	Q5
2503	$\overline{E}$ Q6	$\overline{CC}$ Q7	Q0 Q7	Q1 V_{CC}	Q2	Q3	D	GND	CP	$\overline{S}$	Q4	Q5
2504	$\overline{E}$ CP	D0 $\overline{S}$	$\overline{CC}$ NC	Q0 Q6	Q1 Q7	Q2 Q8	Q3 Q9	Q4 Q10	Q5 $\overline{Q11}$	NC NC	D Q11	GND V_{CC}
2505	X4 C_n4	C_n S4	X3 S5	X2 K3	X1 K2	X0 K1	X — 1 K0	S0 $\overline{P}$	S1 Y1	S2 Y0	S3 Y — 1	GND V_{CC}
2506	$\overline{B0}$ $\overline{Q3}$	A0 E	S3 $\overline{P}$	S2 C_{n+4}	S1 $\overline{G}$	S0 $\overline{B3}$	C_n $\overline{A3}$	M B2	$\overline{Q0}$ $\overline{A2}$	$\overline{Q1}$ $\overline{B1}$	$\overline{Q2}$ $\overline{A1}$	GND V_{CC}
2507	$\overline{E}$ D4	Q0 D5	D0 Q5	D1 V_{CC}	Q1	D2	Q2	GND	CK	Q3	D3	Q4
2508	E D3	$\overline{Q0}$ $\overline{Q3}$	Q0 Q3	D0 V_{CC}	D1	$\overline{Q1}$	Q1	GND	CK	Q2	$\overline{Q2}$	D2

2509	S D3B	Q0 D3A	D0A Q3	D0B V_{CC}	D1B	D1A	Q1	GND	CK	Q2	D2A	D2B
2510	$\overline{I\text{-}3}$ $\overline{OE}$	I-2 Y1	I-1 Y0	I0 V_{CC}	I1	I2	I3	GND	S1	S0	Y3	Y2
2514	$\overline{CR}$ X5	X3 X4	X2 Y	X1 V_{CC}	X0	S	CK	GND	M	K	X7	X6
2515	CK S3	$\Sigma 1$ B3	S1 A3	B1 A4	A1 B4	A2 S4	B2 $\Sigma 4$	S2 V_{CC}	$\Sigma 2$	GND	CR	$\Sigma 3$
2518	D0 Q3′	Q0 Q3	Q0′ D3	D1 V_{CC}	Q1	Q1′	$\overline{OE}$	GND	CK	Q2′	Q2	D2
2522	$\overline{E}$ DY0	S/P DY2	DA DY4	DY7 DY6	DY5 DB	DY3 $\overline{SE}$	DY1 S	$\overline{OE}$ V_{CC}	CR	GND	CK	Q0
2523	S0 B/QB	$\overline{G1}$ D/QD	$\overline{G2}$ F/QF	G/QG H/QH	E/QE QH1	C/QC SL	A/QA S1	QA1 V_{CC}	CR	GND	SR	CK

ADVANCED MICRO DEVICES Am 2600

Am	1	2	3	4	5	6	7	8	9	10	11	12	13	14	15	16
2602	1CX	[1]	$\overline{1CD}$	1A1	1A2	1Q	$\overline{1Q}$	GND	$\overline{2Q}$	2Q	$\overline{2A2}$	2A1	$\overline{2CD}$	[2]	2CX	V_{CC}
2610	GND1	$\overline{B0}$	Z0	IZ	I1	Z1	$\overline{B1}$	GND 2	$\overline{B2}$	Z2	I2	$\overline{E}$	I3	Z3	$\overline{B3}$	V_{CC}
2611	GND1	$\overline{B0}$	Z0	$\overline{IZ}$	I1	Z1	$\overline{B1}$	GND 2	$\overline{B2}$	Z2	$\overline{I2}$	$\overline{E}$	$\overline{I3}$	Z3	$\overline{B3}$	V_{CC}
2612	$\overline{B0}$	I0	Z0	$\overline{BI}$	I1	Z1	$\overline{E1}$	GND	$\overline{E2}$	Z2	I2	$\overline{B2}$	Z3	I3	$\overline{B3}$	V_{CC}

[1] 1CXR [2] 2CXR

ADVANCED MICRO DEVICES Am 2700

	1	2	3	4	5	6	7	8	9	10	11	12
Am	**13**	**14**	**15**	**16**	**17**	**18**	**19**	**20**	**21**	**22**	**23**	**24**
2700	A1 D1	A0 A3	CS1 A2	CS2 V_{CC}	CS3	D0	A4	GND	A5	A6	A7	WE
2701	SAME AS Am 2700											
2702	A0 A3	$\overline{CS}$ A2	$\overline{WE}$ A1	D0 V_{CC}	$\overline{O0}$	D1	$\overline{O1}$	GND	$\overline{O2}$	D2	$\overline{O3}$	D3
2703	SAME AS Am 2702											
2708	O0 A3	O1 A4	O2 $\overline{CS}$	03 V_{CC}	O4	O5	O6	GND	O7	A0	A1	A2
2709	SAME AS Am 2708											
2710	A6 $\overline{CS1}$	A5 CS2	A4 A7	A3 V_{CC}	A0	A1	A2	GND	O3	Q2	O1	O0
2711	SAME AS Am 2710											
2780	A7 O4	A6 O5	A5 O6	A4 Q7	A3 O8	A2 E4	A1 E3	A0 $\overline{E2}$	O1 $\overline{E1}$	O2 A9	O3 A8	GND V_{CC}
2781	SAME AS Am 2780											

Am	1 13	2 14	3 15	4 16	5 17	6 18	7 19	8 20	9 21	10 22	11 23	12 24
2901	A3 I1	A2 I2	A1 CP	A0 Q3	I6 B0	I8 B1	I7 B2	RAM3 B3	RAM0	V_{CC}	F = 0	I0
(2901)	Q0 [1]	D3 OVR	D2 P	D1 Y0	D0 Y1	I3 Y2	I5 Y3	I4 $\overline{OE}$	C_n	GND	F3	$\overline{G}$ (PINS 21–40)
2902	Q1 C_n	P1 G2	G0 P2	P0 V_{CC}	G3	P3	P	GND	[2]	G	[3]	[4]
2905	$\overline{RLE}$ S	R0 R2	B0 B2	A0 A2	BUS0 BUS2	GND1 GND2	BUS1 BUS3	A1 A3	B1 B3	R1 R3	$\overline{BE}$ DRCP	OE V_{CC}
2906	$\overline{RLE}$ S	R0 R2	B0 B2	A0 A2	BUS0 BUS2	GND1 GND2	BUS1 BUS3	A1 A3	B1 B3	R1 R3	$\overline{BE}$ DRCP	ODD V_{CC}
2907	$\overline{RLE}$ A2	R0 BUS3	A0 GND2	BUS0 BUS3	GND1 A3	BUS1 R3	A1 DRCP	R1 V_{CC}	BE	ODD	OE	R2
2909	$\overline{RE}$ D0	R3 GND	R2 [5]	R1 S0	R0 S1	OR3 Y0	D3 Y1	OR2 Y2	D2	O41	D1	OR0
(2909)	Y3	$\overline{OE}$	C_n	[1]	$\overline{FE}$	[6]	CP	V_{CC}				(PINS 21–28)
2911	CP Y1	V_{CC} Y2	$\overline{RE}$ Y3	D3 $\overline{OE}$	D2 C_n	D1 [1]	D0 $\overline{FB}$	GND PUP	[5]	S0	S1	Y0
2915						SAME AS 2905						
2916						SAME AS 2906						
2917						SAME AS 2907						

[1]Cn + 4 [2]Cn + z [3]Cn + y [4]Cn + x [5]$\overline{Zero}$ [6]PUSH/POP

MOTOROLA 3000 SERIES

	1	2	3	4	5	6	7	8	9	10	11	12	13	14
3000	A1	B1	Y1	A2	B2	Y2	GND	Y3	A3	B3	Y4	A4	B4	V_{CC}
3001							SAME AS 3000							
3002							SAME AS 3000							
3003							SAME AS 3000							
3004							SAME AS 3000							
3005	A1	B1	A2	B2	C2	Y2	GND	Y3	A3	B3	C3	Y1	C1	V_{CC}
3006							SAME AS 3005							
3007							SAME AS 3005							
3010	A1	B1	NC	C1	D1	Y1	GND	Y2	A2	B2	NC	C2	D2	V_{CC}
3011							SAME AS 3010							
3012							SAME AS 3010							
3015	A	B	C	D	NC	NC	GND	Y	NC	E	F	G	H	V_{CC}
3020	D1	A2	B2	C2	D2	Y2	GND	Y1	A1	B1	EM1	CO1	C1	V_{CC}

3021							SAME AS 3000							
3022							SAME AS 3000							
3025							SAME AS 3010							
3026							SAME AS 3010							
3028	A1	B1	C1	75	75	Y1	GND	Y2	75	75	A2	B2	C2	V_{CC}
3029							SAME AS 3028							
3030	B1	C1	D1	A2	B2	C2	GND	D2	CO2	EM2	EM1	CO1	A1	V_{CC}
3050	JK	J1	J2	J3	R	$\overline{Q}$	GND	Q	S	K1	K2	K3	CK	V_{CC}
3051	JK	J1	J2	J3	$\overline{R}$	$\overline{Q}$	GND	Q	$\overline{S}$	K1	K2	K3	$\overline{CK}$	V_{CC}
3052	JK	$\overline{S}$	K1	J1	$\overline{J3}$	Q	GND	$\overline{Q}$	CK	$\overline{K3}$	K2	J2	$\overline{R}$	V_{CC}
3060	$\overline{R1}$	D1	CK1	$\overline{S1}$	Q1	$\overline{Q1}$	GND	$\overline{Q2}$	Q2	$\overline{S2}$	CK2	D2	$\overline{R2}$	V_{CC}
3061	$\overline{R12}$	K1	J1	$\overline{S1}$	Q1	$\overline{Q1}$	GND	$\overline{Q2}$	Q2	$\overline{S2}$	J2	K2	$\overline{CK}$	V_{CC}
3062	$\overline{CK1}$	K1	J1	$\overline{S1}$	Q1	$\overline{Q1}$	GND	$\overline{Q2}$	Q2	$\overline{S2}$	J2	K2	$\overline{CK2}$	V_{CC}

INTEL 3000 SERIES

	1	2	3	4	5	6	7	8	9	10	11	12
	13	14	15	16	17	18	19	20	21	22	23	24
3101	A0 A3	$\overline{CS}$ A2	$\overline{WE}$ A1	D1 V_{CC}	01	D2	$\overline{O2}$	GND	$\overline{O3}$	D3	$\overline{O4}$	D4
3101A						SAME AS 3101						
3104	$\overline{WE}$ $\overline{O0}$	$\overline{D3}$ $\overline{O2}$	$\overline{D2}$ $\overline{O3}$	$\overline{D1}$ $\overline{A0}$	$\overline{D0}$ $\overline{A1}$	M3 $\overline{A2}$	M2 $\overline{A3}$	M1 $\overline{E0}$	M0	$\overline{M0}$	$\overline{O1}$	GND
3106	A1 Din	A0 A3	CS1 A2	CS2 V_{CC}	CS3	$\overline{Dout}$	A4	GND	A5	A6	A7	WE
3106A						SAME AS 3106						
3107						SAME AS 3106						
3107A						SAME AS 3106						
3205	A0 $\overline{O2}$	A1 $\overline{O1}$	A2 $\overline{O0}$	$\overline{E1}$ V_{CC}	$\overline{E2}$	E3	$\overline{O7}$	GND	$\overline{O6}$	$\overline{O5}$	$\overline{O4}$	$\overline{O3}$
3207A	V_{SS} E4	O1 D4	D1 O4	E1 V_{CC}	E2	D2	O2	GND	V_{BB}	O3	D3	E3
3207A-1						SAME AS 3207A						
3208A	NC O4	REF O3	S1 O2	S2 O1	S3 $\overline{E1}$	S4 V_{CC}	S5	S6	GND	$\overline{E2}$	O6	O5
3301A	A6 $\overline{CS1}$	A5 $\overline{CS2}$	A4 A7	A3 V_{CC}	A0	A1	A2	GND	$\overline{O4}$	$\overline{O3}$	$\overline{O2}$	$\overline{O1}$
3304A	A7 O4	A6 O5	A5 O6	A4 O7	A3 O8	A2 CS4	A1 CS3	A0 $\overline{CS2}$	O1 $\overline{CS1}$	O2 V_{CC2}	O3 A8	GND V_{CC1}

3404	D1 $\overline{O6}$	$\overline{O1}$ D6	D2 $\overline{W2}$	$\overline{O2}$ V_{CC}	D3	$\overline{O3}$	$\overline{W1}$	GND	$\overline{O4}$	D4	$\overline{O5}$	D5
3408A	$\overline{W}$ O4	REF O3	S1 O2	S2 O1	S3 $\overline{E1}$	S4 V_{CC}	S5	S6	GND	$\overline{E2}$	O6	O5
3601	A6 $\overline{CS1}$	A5 $\overline{CS2}$	A4 A7	A3 V_{CC}	A0	A1	A2	GND	O4	O3	O2	O1

MOTOROLA 4000 SERIES

MC	1	2	3	4	5	6	7	8	9	10	11	12	13	14	15	16
4004	X3	X2	X1	V_{CC}	Y1	Y2	Y3	Y4	W0	GND	S0	S1	W1	X4		
4005	SAME AS MC4004															
4006	Q7	Q6	Q5	Q4	A	B	GND	$\overline{E}$	C	Q0	Q1	Q2	Q3	V_{CC}		
4007	1Q3	1Q2	1Q1	1Q0	$\overline{1E}$	1A	1B	GND	2B	2A	$\overline{2E}$	2Q0	2Q1	2Q2	2Q3	V_{CC}
4008	A1	A2	A3	2A	2B	Y2	GND	Y1	A4	A5	A6	A7	A0	V_{CC}		
4010	1A0	1A1	NC	1A2	1A3	Y1	GND	Y2	2A0	2A1	NC	2A2	2A3	V_{CC}		
4012	MC	Q4	D4	Q3	D3	Q2	GND	D2	Q1	DS	D1	$\overline{CK}$	$\overline{ST}$	V_{CC}		
4015	D2	D1	$\overline{R}$	$\overline{S1}$	$\overline{S2}$	Q1	Q2	GND	Q3	Q4	$\overline{S3}$	$\overline{S4}$	CK	D4	D3	V_{CC}
4038	A0	Y6	Y7	Y5	Y4	A1	E1	GND	E2	$\overline{L}$/H	Y3	Y2	Y0	Y1	A2	V_{CC}
4039	A0					A1	E1	GND	E2	A3					A2	V_{CC}
4040	A0	Y6	Y7	Y5	Y4	A1	E1	GND	E2	A3	Y3	Y2	Y0	Y1	A2	V_{CC}
4041	A0					A1	E1	GND	E2	A3					A2	V_{CC}

TEXAS INSTRUMENTS 54/74 FAMILY

	1	2	3	4	5	6	7	8	9	10	11	12
54/74	**13**	**14**	**15**	**16**	**17**	**18**	**19**	**20**	**21**	**22**	**23**	**24**
00	1A 4B	1B V_{CC}	1Y	2A	2B	2Y	GND	3Y	3A	3B	4Y	4A
01	1Y 4Y	1A V_{CC}	1B	2Y	2A	2B	GND	3A	3B	3Y	4A	4B
02						SAME AS 7401						
03						SAME AS 7400						
04	1A 6A	1Y V_{CC}	2A	2Y	3A	3Y	GND	4Y	4A	5Y	5A	6Y
05						SAME AS 7404						
06						SAME AS 7404						
07						SAME AS 7404						
08						SAME AS 7400						
09						SAME AS 7400						
10	1A 1C	1B V_{CC}	2A	2B	2C	2Y	GND	3Y	3A	3B	3C	1Y
11						SAME AS 7410						
12						SAME AS 7410						
13	1A 2D	1B V_{CC}	NC	1C	1D	1Y	GND	2Y	2A	2B	NC	2C
14						SAME AS 7404						
15						SAME AS 7410						

16	SAME AS 7404											
17	SAME AS 7404											
20	SAME AS 7413											
21	SAME AS 7413											
22	SAME AS 7413											
23	1X 2C	1A 2D	1B 1X	ST1 V_{CC}	1C	1D	1Y	GND	2Y	2A	2B	ST2
25	1A 2D	1B V_{CC}	ST1	1C	1D	1Y	GND	2Y	2A	2B	ST2	2C
26	SAME AS 7400											
27	SAME AS 7410											
28	SAME AS 7401											
30	A NC	B V_{CC}	C	D	E	F	GND	Y	NC	NC	G	H
32	SAME AS 7400											
33	SAME AS 7401											
37	SAME AS 7400											
38	SAME AS 7400											
39	SAME AS 7401											
40	SAME AS 7413											
41A	Y8 Y4	Y9 Y5	A Y1	D Y0	V_{CC}	B	C	Y2	Y3	Y7	Y6	GND
42	Y0 C	Y1 B	Y2 A	Y3 V_{CC}	Y4	Y5	Y6	GND	Y7	Y8	Y9	D

TEXAS INSTRUMENTS 54/74 FAMILY *cont*

	1	2	3	4	5	6	7	8	9	10	11	12
54/74	**13**	**14**	**15**	**16**	**17**	**18**	**19**	**20**	**21**	**22**	**23**	**24**
43						SAME AS 7442						
44						SAME AS 7442						
45						SAME AS 7442						
46	B a	C g	LT f	BI/RBO V_{CC}	RBI	D	A	GND	e	d	c	b
47						SAME AS 7446						
48						SAME AS 7446						
49	B f	C V_{CC}	$\overline{BI}$	D	A	e	GND	d	c	d	a	g
50	A2 B2	A1 V_{CC}	B1	C1	D1	Y1	GND	Y2	C2	D2	X2	$\overline{X2}$
51[1]	A2 B2	A1 V_{CC}	B1	C1	D1	YI	GND	Y2	C2	D2	NC	NC
52[2]	A I	B V_{CC}	C	D	E	NC	GND	Y	X	F	G	H
53	A B	C V_{CC}	D	E	F	NC	GND	Y	G	H	X	$\overline{X}$
54[3]	A B	C V_{CC}	D	E	F	NC	GND	Y	G	H	NC	NC
55[4]	A H	B V_{CC}	C	D	X	NC	GND	Y	$\overline{X}$	E	F	G

60	1A 1D	1B V_{CC}	1C	2A	2B	2C	GND	2D	$\overline{2X}$	2X	$\overline{1X}$	1X
61	1A 3C	1B V_{CC}	1C	2A	2B	2C	GND	2X	1X	3X	3A	3B
62	A J	B V_{CC}	C	D	E	$\overline{X}$	GND	X	F	G	H	I
64	A D	E V_{CC}	F	G	H	I	GND	Y	J	K	B	C
65	SAME AS 7464											
70	NC PR	CR V_{CC}	J1	J2	$\overline{J}$	$\overline{Q}$	GND	Q	$\overline{K}$	K1	K2	CK
(H)71	J1A CK	J1B V_{CC}	J2A	J2B	$\overline{SD}$	Q	GND	Q	K1A	K1B	K2A	K2B
72	NC PR	RR V_{CC}	J1	J2	J3	$\overline{Q}$	GND	Q	K3	K1	K2	CK
73	1CK $\overline{1Q}$	1CR 1J	1K	V_{CC}	2CK	2CR	2J	$\overline{2Q}$	2Q	2K	GND	1Q
74	1CR 2CR	1D V_{CC}	1CK	1PR	IQ	IQ	GND	$\overline{2Q}$	2Q	2PR	2CK	2D
75	$\overline{1Q}$ CKA	1D $\overline{2Q}$	2D 2Q	CKB 1Q	V_{CC}	3D	4D	4Q	$\overline{4Q}$	3Q	$\overline{3Q}$	GND
76	1CK GND	1PR $\overline{1Q}$	1CR 1Q	1J 1K	V_{CC}	2CK	2PR	2CR	2J	$\overline{2Q}$	2Q	2K
77	D1 Q2	D2 Q1	CKB	V_{CC}	D3	D4	NC	Q4	Q3	NC	GND	CKA

TEXAS INSTRUMENTS 54/74 FAMILY *cont*

	1	2	3	4	5	6	7	8	9	10	11	12
54/74	**13**	**14**	**15**	**16**	**17**	**18**	**19**	**20**	**21**	**22**	**23**	**24**
78	K1 $\overline{SD1}$	Q1 V_{CC}	$\overline{Q1}$	J1	$\overline{Q2}$	Q2	GND	K2	$\overline{CK}$	$\overline{SD2}$	J2	$\overline{RD}$
80	B* B2	BC V_{CC}	C_N	δ	Σ	Σ	GND	A1	A2	A*	AC	B1
81	X3 W1	X2 X4	X1	V_{CC}	Y1	Y2	Y3	Y4	W0	GND	S0	S1
82	$\Sigma 1$ B2	A1 A2	B1	V_{CC}	CIN	GN	CN	CN	CN	C2	GND	$\Sigma 2$
83	A4 CO	$\Sigma 3$ C4	A3 $\Sigma 4$	B3 B4	V_{CC}	$\Sigma 2$	B2	A2	$\Sigma 1$	A1	B1	GND
84	X4 S0	X3 S1	X2 W1B	X1 W1A	V_{CC}	Y1	YZ	Y3	Y4	W0B	W0A	GND
85	B3 A2	$A < BI$ B2	$A = BI$ A3	$A > BI$ V_{CC}	$A > B0$	$A = B0$	$A < B0$	GND	B0	A0	B1	A1
86						SAME AS 7400						
87	C A4	A1 V_{CC}	Y1	NC	A2	Y2	GND	B	Y3	A3	NC	Y4
88	B0 A3	B1 A4	B2 CS	B3 V_{CC}	B4	B5	B6	GND	B7	A0	A1	A2
89	A0 A3	CE A2	RE A1	D1 V_{CC}	S1	D2	S2	GND	S3	D3	S4	D4

90	1B NC	R01 1A	R02	NC	V_{CC}	R91	R92	QC	QB	GND	QD	QA
91	NC QH	NC QH	NC	NC	V_{CC}	NC	NC	NC	CK	GND	B	A
92	B NC	NC A	NC	NC	V_{CC}	R01	R02	QD	QC	GND	QB	QA
93	R01 QA	R02 A	NC	V_{CC}	NC	NC	NC	B	QB	QC	GND	QD
94	1A 2C	1B 2B	1C P2E	1D 2A	V_{CC}	PE1	SI	CK	O	CR	2D	GND
95	SI QA	B A	C	V_{CC}	D	MC	CK1	CK2	QD	QC	GND	QB
96	CK QC	A QB	B QA	C CR	V_{CC}	D	E	PE	SI	QE	QD	GND
97	B CK	E C	F D	A V_{CC}	Z	Y	EO	GND	CK	S	EI	V/C
98	A2 QC	A1 QB	B1 QA	B2 V_{CC}	C1	C2	D2	GND	WS	CK	QD	D1
99	A GND	J QB	B QA	C K	V_{CC}	D	MC	CK1	CK2	QD	$\overline{QD}$	QC
100	NC NC	1D1 NC	1D2 2D3	1Q2 2D4	1Q1 2Q4	NC 2Q3	GND 1Q3	2Q1 1Q4	2Q2 1D4	2D2 1D3	2D1 E1G	E2G V_{CC}
101	J1A CK	J1B V_{CC}	J2A	J2B	PR	Q	GND	$\overline{Q}$	K1A	K1B	K2A	K2B
102	NC PR	CR V_{CC}	J1	J2	J3	$\overline{Q}$	GND	Q	K1	K2	K3	CK

TEXAS INSTRUMENTS 54/74 FAMILY *cont*

	1	2	3	4	5	6	7	8	9	10	11	12
54/74	**13**	**14**	**15**	**16**	**17**	**18**	**19**	**20**	**21**	**22**	**23**	**24**
103	1CK $\overline{1Q}$	1CR 1J	1K	V_{CC}	2CK	2CR	2J	$\overline{2Q}$	2Q	2K	GND	1Q
104	JK $\overline{CR}$	$\overline{SD}$ V_{CC}	K1	J1	J2	Q	GND	$\overline{Q}$	CK	K2	K3	J3
105	JK $\overline{CR}$	$\overline{S}$ V_{CC}	K2	J1	$\overline{J2}$	Q	GND	$\overline{Q}$	CK	$\overline{K2}$	K3	J3
106	1CK GND	1PR $\overline{1Q}$	1CR 1Q	1J 1K	V_{CC}	2CK	2PR	2CR	2J	$\overline{2Q}$	2Q	2K
107	1J 1CR	$\overline{1Q}$ V_{CC}	1Q	1K	2Q	$\overline{2Q}$	GND	2J	2CK	2CR	2K	1CK
108	1K 1PR	1Q V_{CC}	$\overline{1Q}$	1J	$\overline{2Q}$	2Q	GND	2K	CK	2PR	2J	CR
109	1CR $\overline{2K}$	1J 2J	1K 2CR	1CK V_{CC}	1PR	1Q	$\overline{1Q}$	GND	$\overline{2Q}$	2Q	2PR	2CK
110	NC PR	CR V_{CC}	J1	J2	J3	$\overline{Q}$	GND	Q	K1	K2	K3	CK
113	1CK 2CK	1K V_{CC}	1J	1PR	1Q	$\overline{1Q}$	GND	$\overline{2Q}$	2Q	2PR	2J	2K
114	CR CK	1K V_{CC}	1J	1PR	1Q	$\overline{1Q}$	GND	$\overline{2Q}$	2Q	2PR	2J	2K
116	1CR 2CR	$\overline{1G1}$ $\overline{2G1}$	$\overline{2G2}$ $\overline{2G2}$	1D1 2D1	1Q1 2Q1	1D2 2D2	1Q2 2Q2	1D3 2D3	1Q3 2Q3	1D4 2D4	1Q4 2Q4	GND V_{CC}

120	1M 2S1	1S1 2S2	1S2 2M	1R V_{CC}	1C	1Y	$\overline{1Y}$	GND	$\overline{2Y}$	2Y	2C	2R
121	$\overline{Q}$ NC	NC V_{CC}	A1	A2	B	Q	GND	NC	R_{in}	C_{ex}	6	NC
122	A1 6	A2 V_{CC}	B1	B2	CR	$\overline{Q}$	GND	Q	R_{in}	NC	C_{ex}	NC
123	1A 1Q	1B 1Ce	1CR 8	$\overline{1Q}$ V_{CC}	2Q	2Ce	7	GND	2A	2B	2CR	$\overline{2Q}$
124	FC2 2CX	FC1 2RN	1RN 10	1CX V_{CC}	1CX	$\overline{1G}$	1Y	9	GND	2Y	$\overline{2G}$	2CX
125	1C 4C	1A V_{CC}	1Y	2C	2A	2Y	GND	3Y	3A	3C	4Y	4A
126	SAME AS 74125											
128	SAME AS 7401											
132	SAME AS 54/7400											
133	A K	B L	C M	D V_{CC}	E	F	G	GND	Y	H	I	J
134	A K	B L	C OC	D V_{CC}	E	F	G	GND	Y	H	I	J
135	1A 4Y	1B 4A	1Y 4B	1,2C V_{CC}	2A	2B	2Y	GND	3Y	3A	3B	3,4C
136	SAME AS 54/7400											
138	A Y2	B Y1	C Y0	G2A V_{CC}	G2B	G1	Y7	GND	Y6	Y5	Y4	Y3

TEXAS INSTRUMENTS 54/74 FAMILY *cont*

	1	2	3	4	5	6	7	8	9	10	11	12
54/74	13	14	15	16	17	18	19	20	21	22	23	24
139	1G	1A	1B	1Y0	1Y1	1Y2	1Y3	GND	2Y3	2Y2	2Y1	2Y0
	2B	2A	2G	V_{CC}								
140	1A	1B	NC	1C	ID	1Y	GND	2Y	2A	2B	NC	2C
	2D	V_{CC}										
141	O8	O9	A	D	V_{CC}	B	C	O2	O3	O7	O6	GND
	O4	O5	O1	O0								
142	CR	O7	O6	O4	O5	O3	O2	GND	O1	O0	O8	O9
	LS	$\overline{QD}$	CK	V_{CC}								
143	SCE	CK	CR	RBI	BI	RBO	DPI	dp	d	f	e	GND
	g	c	a	b	QA	QB	QC	QD	LS	MXC	PCE	V_{CC}
144	SAME AS 54/74143											
145	O0	O1	O2	O3	O4	O5	O6	GND	O7	O8	O9	D
	C	B	A	V_{CC}								
147	4	5	6	7	8	QC	QB	GND	QA	9	1	2
	3	QD	NC	V_{CC}								
148	4	5	6	7	E1	A2	A1	GND	A0	O	1	2
	3	GS	EO	V_{CC}								
150	7	6	5	4	3	2	1	O	ST	W	D	GND
	C	B	A	15	14	13	12	11	10	9	8	V_{CC}
151	3	2	1	O	Y	W	ST	GND	C	B	A	7
	6	5	4	V_{CC}								

152	4 5	3 V_{CC}	2	1	0	W	GND	C	B	A	7	6
153	ST1 2C3	B A	1C3 ST2	1C2 V_{CC}	1C1	1C0	1Y	GND	2Y	2C0	2C1	2C2
154	O0 O11	O1 O12	O2 O13	O3 O14	O4 O15	O5 G1	O6 G2	O7 D	O8 C	O9 B	O10 A	GND V_{CC}
155	D1 A	ST1 ST2	B D2	1Y3 V_{CC}	1Y2	1Y1	1Y0	GND	2Y0	2Y1	2Y2	2Y3
156	SAME AS 54/74155											
157	S 4B	1A 4A	1B ST	1Y V_{CC}	2A	2B	2Y	GND	3Y	3B	3A	4Y
158	SAME AS 54/74157											
159	SAME AS 54/74154											
160	CR QB	CK QA	A CO	B V_{CC}	C	D	EP	GND	L	ET	QD	QC
161	SAME AS 54/74160											
162	SAME AS 54/74160											
163	SAME AS 54/74160											
164	A QH	B V_{CC}	QA	QB	QC	QD	GND	CK	CR	QE	QF	QG
165	S/L C	CK D	E CKI	F V_{CC}	G	H	$\overline{QH}$	GND	QH	SI	A	B
166	SI QH	A H	B S/L	C V_{CC}	D	CKI	CK	GND	CR	E	F	G

TEXAS INSTRUMENTS 54/74 FAMILY *cont*

 54/74	1 13	2 14	3 15	4 16	5 17	6 18	7 19	8 20	9 21	10 22	11 23	12 24
167	NC CR	C A	D B	11 V_{CC}	Z	Y	EO	GND	CK	ST	EI	U/C
168	U/$\overline{D}$ QB	CK QA	A RC0	B V_{CC}	C	D	$\overline{EP}$	GND	$\overline{L}$	$\overline{ET}$	QD	QC
169						SAME AS 54/74168						
171	D2 WB	D3 WA	D4 D1	B V_{CC}	A	Q4	Q3	GND	Q2	Q1	GR	GW
172	1W1 2QA	1W0 1QA	1GW 1GR	1DB 2GR	2DB 12	CK 13	1R2 14	1R1 2GW	1R0 2DA	1QB 1DA	2QB 1W2	GND V_{CC}
173	M 2D	N 1D	1Q CR	2Q V_{CC}	3Q	4Q	CK	GND	G1	G2	4D	3D
174	CR 5D	1Q 6D	1D 6Q	2D V_{CC}	2Q	3D	3Q	GND	CK	4Q	4D	5Q
175	CR 4D	$\overline{1Q}$ $\overline{4Q}$	1Q 4Q	1D V_{CC}	2D	2Q	2Q	GND	CK	3Q	3Q	3D
176	C/L CR	QC V_{CC}	C	A	QA	CK2	GND	CK1	QB	B	D	QD
177						SAME AS 54/74176						
178	B C	A V_{CC}	SI	QA	CK	QB	GND	QC	L	QD	SH	D
179	CR SH	B D	A C	SI V_{CC}	QA	CK	QB	GND	QC	L	QD	QD

180	G F	H V_{CC}	EVI	ODI	ΣEO	ΣOO	GND	A	B	C	D	E
181	B0 F3	A0 A = B	S3 P	S2 15	S1 G	S0 B3	C_n A3	M B2	F0 A2	F1 B1	F2 A1	GND V_{CC}
182	G1 C_n	P1 G2	G0 P2	P0 V_{CC}	G3	P3	16	GND	17	G	18	19
183	1A 2A	NC V_{CC}	1B	$1C_n$	20	1Σ	GND	2Σ	NC	21	$2C_n$	2B
184	Y1 D	Y2 E	Y3 G	Y4 V_{CC}	Y5	Y6	Y7	GND	Y8	A	B	C
185	SAME AS 54/74184											
186	NC GN2	NC Y9	A Y8	B Y7	C Y6	ME1 Y5	ME2 Y4	D Y3	E Y2	F Y1	GN1 GN2	NC V_{CC}
187	G ME1	F ME2	E H	D V_{CC}	A	B	C	GND	Y4	Y3	Y2	Y1
188	SAME AS 54/7488											
189	A1 A4	$\overline{CE}$ A3	R/$\overline{W}$ A2	D1 V_{CC}	$\overline{Y1}$	D2	$\overline{Y2}$	GND	$\overline{Y3}$	D3	$\overline{Y4}$	D4
190	B RCK	QB CK	QA A	G V_{CC}	D/U	QC	QD	GND	D	C	L	M/M
191	SAME AS 54/74190											
192	B BO	QB CR	QA A	CD V_{CC}	CU	QC	QD	GND	D	C	L	CO
193	SAME AS 54/74192											

TEXAS INSTRUMENTS 54/74 FAMILY *cont*

54/74	1 13	2 14	3 15	4 16	5 17	6 18	7 19	8 20	9 21	10 22	11 23	12 24
194	CR QC	1 QB	A QA	B V_{CC}	C	D	2	GND	S0	S1	CK	QD
195	CR QC	J QB	$\overline{K}$ QA	A V_{CC}	B	C	D	GND	S/L	CK	$\overline{QD}$	QD
196	C/L CR	QC V_{CC}	C	A	QA	CK2	GND	CK1	QB	B	D	QD
197	SAME AS 54/74196											
198	S0 CR	22 QE	A E	QA QF	B F	QB QG	C G	QC QH	D H	QD 23	CK S1	GND V_{CC}
199	$\overline{K}$ CK	J CR	A QE	QA E	B QF	QB F	C QG	QC G	D QH	QD H	CKI S/L	GND V_{CC}
200	A DI	B H	ME1 C	ME2 V_{CC}	ME3	Y	D	GND	E	F	G	WE
201	A0 DI	A1 A7	$\overline{CE1}$ A2	CE2 V_{CC}	CE3	Y	A3	GND	A4	A5	A6	R/W
206	A DI	B H	ME1 C	ME2 V_{CC}	ME3	Y	D	GND	E	F	G	WE
221	1A $\overline{1Q}$	1B 1CX	1CR 25	$\overline{1Q}$ V_{CC}	2Q	2CX	24	GND	2A	2B	2CR	$\overline{2Q}$
246	SAME AS 7446A											
247	SAME AS 7447A											

248	SAME AS 7448											
249	B a	C g	LT f	26 V_{CC}	RBI	D	A	GND	e	d	c	b
251	D3 D6	D2 D5	D1 D4	D0 V_{CC}	Y	W	ST	GND	C	B	A	D7
253	SAME AS 54/74153											
257	S 4B	1A 4A	1B OE	1Y V_{CC}	2A	2B	2Y	GND	3Y	3B	3A	4Y
258	SAME AS 54/74257											
260	C1 D1	B1 V_{CC}	A1	A2	Y1	YZ	GND	E2	D2	C2	B2	E1
261	B3 B0	B4 B1	G B2	M2 V_{CC}	$\overline{Q4}$	Q3	Q2	GND	Q1	Q0	M0	M1
265	1A $\overline{4Y}$	1W 4W	$\overline{1Y}$ 4A	2A V_{CC}	2B	2W	$\overline{2Y}$	GND	$\overline{3Y}$	3W	3A	3B
266	1A 4B	1B V_{CC}	1Y	2Y	2A	2B	GND	3A	3B	3Y	4Y	4A
270	A6 $\overline{CS}$	A5 A8	A4 A7	A3 V_{CC}	A0	A1	A2	GND	Y4	Y3	Y2	Y1
271	A0 Y7	A1 Y8	A2 $\overline{CS1}$	A3 $\overline{CS2}$	A4 A5	Y1 A6	Y2 A7	Y3 V_{CC}	Y4	GND	Y5	Y6
273	$\overline{CR}$ 5D	1Q 6D	1D 6Q	2D 7Q	2Q 7D	3Q 8D	3D 8Q	4D V_{CC}	4Q	GND	CK	5Q

TEXAS INSTRUMENTS 54/74 FAMILY *cont*

	1	2	3	4	5	6	7	8	9	10	11	12
54/74	**13**	**14**	**15**	**16**	**17**	**18**	**19**	**20**	**21**	**22**	**23**	**24**
274[27]	A_n n6	A_{n1} n7	A_{n2} $\overline{G1}$	A_{n3} $\overline{G2}$	B_n B_{n1}	n B_{n2}	n1 B_{n3}	n2 V_{CC}	n3	GND	n4	n5
275	2_n $\overline{G}$	2_n 2_n	2_n 2_n	2_n V_{CC}	$C2_n$	$C2_n$	2_n	GND	n00	$C2_n1$	n10	n20
278	ST D2	D3 V_{CC}	D4	P0	P1	Y4	GND	Y3	Y2	Y1	NC	D1
279	$\overline{1R}$ 4Q	$\overline{1S1}$ 4R	$\overline{1S2}$ 4S	1Q V_{CC}	$\overline{2R}$	$\overline{2S}$	2Q	GND	3Q	$\overline{3R}$	$\overline{3S1}$	$\overline{3S2}$
280	G F	H V_{CC}	NC	I	ΣEV	ΣOD	GND	A	B	C	D	E
281	A1 F3	A2 F2	RS1 F1	RS0 F0	RC M	LI S2	A3 S1	C_n S0	G RI	C_n4 CK	P A0	GND V_{CC}
283	Σ2 Σ3	B2 A3	A2 B3	Σ1 V_{CC}	A1	B1	CO	GND	C4	Σ4	B4	A4
284	2C GB	2B GA	2A 2D	1D V_{CC}	1A	1B	1C	GND	Y7	Y6	Y5	Y4
285	2C GB	2B GA	2A 2D	1D V_{CC}	1A	1B	1C	GND	Y3	Y2	Y1	Y0
287	A6 $\overline{CS1}$	A5 $\overline{CS2}$	A4 A7	A3 V_{CC}	A0	A1	A2	GND	Y4	Y3	Y2	Y1
289	A0 A3	$\overline{CE}$ A2	R/W A1	D1 V_{CC}	$\overline{Y1}$	D2	$\overline{Y2}$	GND	$\overline{Y3}$	D3	$\overline{Y4}$	D4

290	R91 R02	NC V_{CC}	R92	QC	QB	NC	GND	QD	QA	A	B	RO1
293	NC RO2	NC V_{CC}	NC	QC	OB	NC	GND	QD	QA	A	B	RO1
295	SI QA	A V_{CC}	B	C	D	MC	GND	G	$\overline{CK}$	QD	QC	QB
298	B2 QC	A2 QB	A1 QA	B1 V_{CC}	C2	D2	D1	GND	C1	WS	$\overline{CK}$	QD
299	SO B/Q	$\overline{G1}$ D/Q	$\overline{G2}$ F/Q	G/Q H/Q	E/Q QH′	C/Q SL	A/Q S1	QA′ V_{CC}	$\overline{CR}$	GND	SR	CK
301	A1 DI	A0 A3	$\overline{CE1}$ A2	$\overline{CE2}$ V_{CC}	$\overline{CE3}$	$\overline{DO}$	A4	GND	A5	A6	A7	$\overline{WE}$
351	1Y D5	$\overline{G}$ D4	A 2D3	B 2D2	C 2D1	1D0 2D0	1D1 $\overline{2Y}$	1D2 V_{CC}	1D3	GND	D7	D6
365	$\overline{G1}$ 6Y	1A 6A	1Y $\overline{G2}$	2A V_{CC}	2Y	3A	3Y	GND	4Y	4A	5Y	5A
366	SAME AS 74365											
367	28 6Y	1A 6A	1Y $\overline{G5,6}$	2A V_{CC}	2Y	3A	3Y	GND	4Y	4A	5Y	5A
368	SAME AS 74367											
370	SAME AS 74270											
371	SAME AS 74271											
381	A1 G	B1 P	A0 C_n	D0 B3	S0 A3	S1 B2	S2 A2	F0 V_{CC}	F1	GND	F2	F3

TEXAS INSTRUMENTS 54/74 FAMILY *cont*

	1	2	3	4	5	6	7	8	9	10	11	12
54/74	**13**	**14**	**15**	**16**	**17**	**18**	**19**	**20**	**21**	**22**	**23**	**24**
386	1A 4B	1B V_{CC}	1Y	2Y	2A	2B	GND	3A	3B	3Y	4Y	4A
387					SAME AS 74287							
390	[29] 2QA	CR1 2CR	1QA [32]	[30] V_{CC}	1QB	1QC	1QD	GND	2QD	2QC	2QB	[31]
393	$\overline{1CK}$ $\overline{2CK}$	1CR V_{CC}	1QA	1QB	1QC	1QD	GND	2QD	2QC	2QB	2QA	2CR
395	CR QC	SI QB	A QA	B V_{CC}	C	D	L/S	GND	$\overline{OC}$	$\overline{CK}$	QD′	QD
670	D2 WB	D3 WA	D4 D1	RB V_{CC}	RA	Q4	Q3	GND	Q2	Q1	$\overline{GR}$	$\overline{GW}$

[1]Not 54L/74L51
[2]Not 54H/74H52
[3]Not 54L/7454 (and LS)
[4]Not 54L/74L55 (and LS)
[5]$\overline{C_{n+1}}$
[6]R_{ext}/C_{ext}
[7]$2R_{ext}/C_{ext}$
[8]$1R_{ext}/C_{ext}$
[9]$\approx$GND
[10]$\sim V_{CC}$
[11]Set to 9
[12]2W/R0
[13]2W/R1
[14]2W/R2
[15]C_{n+4}
[16]P_{out}
[17]C_{n+z}
[18]C_{n+y}
[19]C_{n+x}
[20]$1C_{n+1}$
[21]$2C_{n+1}$
[22]Shift Right, Serial Input
[23]Shift Left, Serial Input
[24]2RX/CX
[25]1RX/CX
[26]BI/RBO
[27]$A_n = A2^n$; $A_{n1} = A2^{n+1}$; etc.
[28]$\overline{G1,2,3,4}$
[29]$\overline{CKA1}$
[30]$\overline{1CKB}$
[31]$\overline{2CKB}$
[32]$\overline{2CKA}$

	1	2	3	4	5	6	7	8	9	10	11	12
DM	**13**	**14**	**15**	**16**	**17**	**18**	**19**	**20**	**21**	**22**	**23**	**24**
8090	A1 A5	B1 Y6	Y1 A6	A2 V_{CC}	Y2	A3	Y3	GND	Y4	A4	B4	Y5
8091	Y1 B4	A1 Y4	B1	V_{CC}	A2	B2	Y2	Y3	A3	B3	GND	A4
8092	A1 Y2	B1 V_{CC}	C1	D1	E1	Y1	GND	A2	B2	C2	D2	E2
8093	C1 C4	D1 V_{CC}	Y1	C2	D2	Y2	GND	Y3	D3	C3	Y4	D4
8094	SAME AS DM 8093											
8095	D1 Y6	A1 A6	Y1 D2	A2 V_{CC}	Y2	A3	Y3	GND	Y4	A4	Y5	A5
8096	SAME AS DM8095											
8097	D14 Y6	A1 A6	Y1 D56	A2 V_{CC}	Y2	A3	Y3	GND	Y4	A4	Y5	A5
8098	SAME AS DM8097											
8121	D3 D6	D2 D5	D1 D4	D0 V_{CC}	Y	W	S	GND	C	B	A	D7
8122	SAME AS DM8123											
8123	S 2C	1A 1C	2A E	ZA V_{CC}	1B	2B	ZB	GND	ZD	2D	1D	ZC
8130	A0 Z	B0 B5	A1 A5	B1 B6	A2 A6	B2 B7	A3 A7	B3 B8	A4 A8	B4 B9	ST A9	GND V_{CC}

NATIONAL SEMICONDUCTOR DM70/80 SERIES *cont*

DM	1 13	2 14	3 15	4 16	5 17	6 18	7 19	8 20	9 21	10 22	11 23	12 24
8131	B1 B5	T1 T6	B2 B6	T2 V_{CC}	B3	T3	$\overline{ST}$	GND	Y	T4	B4	T5
8136	SAME AS DM8131											
8160	A0 B4	B0 A5	A1 B5	B1 V_{CC}	A2	B2	ST	GND	Z	A3	B3	A4
8200	B4 A4	B3 V_{CC}	B2	B1	NC	Z	GND	ST	Y	A1	A2	A3
8210	B A	C V_{CC}	I0	I1	I2	I3	GND	I4	O	I5	I6	I7
8211	B I6	C I7	I0 A	I1 V_{CC}	I2	I3	NC	GND	O	$\overline{ST}$	I4	I5
8214	$\overline{ST1}$ 2C3	B A	1C3 $\overline{ST2}$	1C2 V_{CC}	1C1	1C0	1Y	GND	2Y	2C0	2C1	2C2
8219	E7 C	E6 B	E5 A	E4 E15	E3 E14	E2 E13	E1 E12	E0 E11	ST E10	W E9	D E8	GND V_{CC}
8220	NC H	A V_{CC}	B	C	D	PI	GND	Y	NC	E	F	G
8223	Y0 A3	Y1 A2	Y2 A1	Y3 V_{CC}	Y4	Y5	Y6	GND	Y7	NC	NC	$\overline{D}$
8230	B1 DIA	A2 DIB	A1 B1	Y0 V_{CC}	Y1	Y2	Y3	GND	$\overline{DA}$	$\overline{DB}$	DA	DB
8280	$\overline{ST}$	QC	C	A	QA	CK2	GND	CK1	QB	B	D	QD

8281					SAME AS DM8280							
8288	ST RD	QC V_{CC}	C	A	QA	CK2	GND	CK1	QB	B	D	QD
8511	CK G1	G2 G2	G1 CK	D1 V_{CC}	Q1	$\overline{Q1}$	CR	GND	CR	$\overline{Q2}$	Q2	D2
8512	CK K2	D1 M2	M1 D2	K1 V_{CC}	J1	$\overline{Q1}$	Q1	GND	CR	Q2	$\overline{Q2}$	J2
8520	SI Y	P1 XOO	S/P EXI	P2 P	V_{CC}	P3	P4	CK	XOC	S0	0D	GND
8551	OD1 B	OD2 A	QA CR	QB V_{CC}	QC	QD	CK	GND	ID1	ID2	D	C
8552	OD1 P	OD2 CK	QC TE	QD V_{CC}	QB	QA	TC	GND	CET	CEP	NC	CR
8553	$\overline{R1}$ $\overline{W1}$	$\overline{E}$ $\overline{W2}$	CR $\overline{R2}$	D1 V_{CC}	D2	D3	D4	GND	D5	D6	D7	D8
8554					SAME AS DM8552							
8555	CE C	QD D	QC MC	R V_{CC}	QB	QA	$\overline{L}$	GND	CK	A	B	QD
8556					SAME AS DM8555							
8560	B BO	QB CR	QA A	CKD V_{CC}	CKU	QC	QD	GND	D	C	L	CO (74192)
8563					SAME AS DM8560							(74193)
8570	SA Q8	SB V_{CC}	Q1	Q2	Q3	Q4	GND	CK	CR	Q5	Q6	Q7 (74164)

NATIONAL SEMICONDUCTOR DM70/80 SERIES *cont*

	1	2	3	4	5	6	7	8	9	10	11	12
DM	13	14	15	16	17	18	19	20	21	22	23	24
8573	A6 ME2	A5 ME1	A4 A7	A3 V_{CC}	A0	A1	A2	GND	Y4	Y3	Y2	Y1 (74187) (PP)
8574	SAME AS DM8573											
8575	I4 F1	I5 F2	I6 F3	I7 F4	I8 F5	I9 F6	I10 F7	I11 F8	I12 I1	I13 I2	I14 I3	GND V_{CC}
8576	SAME AS DM8575											
8582	A DI	B H	$\overline{CE1}$ C	$\overline{CE2}$ V_{CC}	$\overline{CE3}$	$\overline{DO}$	D	GND	E	F	G	$\overline{WE}$
8590	L D3	CK D4	D5 CKI	D6 V_{CC}	D7	D8	Q	GND	$\overline{Q}$	SI	D1	D2
8595	A7 O4	A6 O5	A5 O6	A4 O7	A3 O8	A2 E4	A1 E3	A0 E2	O1 E1	O2 NC	O3 A8	GND V_{CC}
8596	SAME AS DM8595											
8597	G ME1	F ME2	E H	D V_{CC}	A	B	C	GND	Y4	Y3	Y2	Y1
8598	Y1 D	Y2 E	Y3 $\overline{ME}$	Y4 V_{CC}	Y5	Y6	Y7	GND	Y8	A	B	C
8599	A0 A3	$\overline{ME}$ A2	$\overline{WE}$ A1	D1 V_{CC}	$\overline{S1}$	D2	$\overline{S2}$	GND	$\overline{S3}$	D3	$\overline{S4}$	D4
8602	1CX $\overline{CD2}$	1 2	$\overline{CD1}$ 2CX	A1 V_{CC}	$\overline{B1}$	Q1	$\overline{Q1}$	GND	Q2	Q2	$\overline{B2}$	A2

8613	CE $\overline{C}$	QD D	QC MC	R V_{CC}	QB	QA	$\overline{L}$	GND	CK	A	B	QD
8670	SI QA	B A	C	V_{CC}	D	MC	CK1	CK2	QD	QC	GND	QB
8675	$\overline{MR}$ Q1	CK Q0	P0 TC	P1 V_{CC}	P2	P3	CEP	GND	$\overline{PE}$	CET	Q3	Q2
8676	SAME AS DM8675											
8693	$\overline{CK2}$ NC	RO1 CK1	RO2	NC	V_{CC}	NC	NC	QC	QB	GND	QD	QA
8695	SAME AS DM8595											
8697	A6 $\overline{ME1}$	A5 $\overline{ME2}$	A4 A7	A3 V_{CC}	A0	A1	A2	GND	Y4	Y3	Y2	Y1
8699	A0 A3	$\overline{ME}$ A2	$\overline{WE}$ A1	D1 V_{CC}	$\overline{S1}$	D2	$\overline{S2}$	GND	$\overline{S3}$	D3	$\overline{S4}$	D4
8800	A1	B1	GND	V3	Y1	Y2	V2	B2	A2	V_{CC}		
8806	$\overline{ST}$ OB	OA V_{CC}	P	NC	GND	IA	GND	GND	IB	GND	NC	DIS
8810	A1 A4	B1 V_{CC}	Y1	A2	B2	Y2	GND	Y3	B3	A3	Y4	B4
8811	Y1 Y4	A1 V_{CC}	B1	Y2	A2	B2	GND	A3	B3	Y3	A4	B4
8812	A1 A6	Y1 V_{CC}	A2	Y2	A3	Y3	GND	Y4	A4	Y5	A5	Y6
8819	SAME AS 8810											

NATIONAL SEMICONDUCTOR DM70/80 SERIES *cont*

	1	2	3	4	5	6	7	8	9	10	11	12
DM	13	14	15	16	17	18	19	20	21	22	23	24
8820	1−	TR1	1+	ST1	RT1	O1	GND	O2	RT2	ST2	2+	TR2
	2−	V_{CC}										
8822	A1			ST1		Y1	GND	Y2		ST2		
	A2	V_{CC}										
8830	A1	B1	C1	D1	Y1	$\overline{Y1}$	GND	$\overline{Y2}$	Y2	D2	C2	B2
	A2	V_{CC}										
8831	B1E	B2E	Y2	B2	YB1	B1	MC1	GND	MC2	A1	YA1	A2
	YA2	A2E	A1E	V_{CC}								
8832	SAME AS 8831											
8833	DO1	DI1	RO1	DO2	DI2	RO2	DE	GND	RE	RO3	DI3	DO3
	RO4	DI4	DO4	V_{CC}								
8834	DO1	DI1	RO1	DO2	DI2	RO2	DE1	GND	DE2	RO3	DI3	DO3
	RO4	DI4	DO4	V_{CC}								
8835	SAME AS 8833											
8836	GND	Y2	Y1	A1	B1	A2	B2	V_{CC}	A3	B3	B4	A4
	Y4	Y3										
8837	A1	Y1	A2	Y2	A3	Y3	DIA	GND	DIB	Y4	B4	Y5
	B5	Y6	B6	V_{CC}								
8838	BS3	A3	Y3	BS4	A4	Y4	DI1	GND	DI2	Y2	A2	BS2
	Y1	A1	BS1	V_{CC}								
8839	SAME AS 8834											

8875A	Y3 ST1	Y2 ST2	Y1 Y4	X4 V_{CC}	X1	X2	X3	GND	P4	P3	P2	P1
8875B	SAME AS DM8875											
8880	B a	C g	PRI f	[3] V_{CC}	RBI	D	A	GND	e	d	c	b
8884A	PRI e	A d	B c	C b	D a	DPI V_{CC}	COI	COO	GND	DPO	g	f
8885	A a	B g	PRI f	D V_{CC}	E	F	G	GND	e	d	c	b
8898	Y1 D	Y2 E	Y3 G	Y4 V_{CC}	Y5	Y6	Y7	GND	Y8	A	B	C
8899	SAME AS DM8898											

[1]1CXR [2]2CXR [3]BI/RBO

SIGNETICS 8200 SERIES

	1	2	3	4	5	6	7	8	9	10	11	12
	13	**14**	**15**	**16**	**17**	**18**	**19**	**20**	**21**	**22**	**23**	**24**
8200	CK1 Q10	D1 Q9	D2 Q8	D3 Q7	D4 Q6	D5 Q5	D6 Q4	D7 Q3	D8 Q2	D9 Q1	D10 CK2	GND V_{CC}
8201	CK1 Q10	$\overline{D1}$ Q9	$\overline{D2}$ Q8	$\overline{D3}$ Q7	$\overline{D4}$ Q6	$\overline{D5}$ Q5	$\overline{D6}$ Q4	$\overline{D7}$ Q3	$\overline{D8}$ Q2	$\overline{D9}$ Q1	$\overline{D10}$ CK2	GND V_{CC}
8202	CK Q10	D1 Q9	D2 Q8	D3 Q7	D4 Q6	D5 Q5	D6 Q4	D7 Q3	D8 Q2	D9 Q1	D10 $\overline{R}$	GND V_{CC}

SIGNETICS 8200 SERIES *cont*

	1	2	3	4	5	6	7	8	9	10	11	12
	13	**14**	**15**	**16**	**17**	**18**	**19**	**20**	**21**	**22**	**23**	**24**
8203	CK	$\overline{D1}$	$\overline{D2}$	$\overline{D3}$	$\overline{D4}$	$\overline{D5}$	$\overline{D6}$	$\overline{D7}$	$\overline{D8}$	$\overline{D9}$	$\overline{D10}$	GND
	Q10	Q9	Q8	Q7	Q6	Q5	Q4	Q3	Q2	Q1	$\overline{R}$	V_{CC}
8204	A3	A4	OPN	A5	A6	A7	O1	O2	O3	O4	OPN	GND
	OPN	O5	O6	O7	O8	ST	CE2	$\overline{CE1}$	A0	A1	A2	V_{CC}
8205	A3	A4	A5	A6	A7	A8	O1	O2	O3	O4	OPN	GND
	OPN	O5	O6	O7	O8	ST	CE2	$\overline{CE1}$	A0	A1	A2	V_{CC}
8206	A1	A0	$\overline{CE1}$	$\overline{CE2}$	$\overline{CE3}$	DO	A4	GND	A5	A6	A7	$R/\overline{W}$
	$\overline{DIN}$	A3	A2	V_{CC}								
8207	SAME AS 8206											
8216	A1	A0	$\overline{CE1}$	$\overline{CE2}$	$\overline{CE3}$	DO	A4	GND	A5	A6	A7	$\overline{WE}$
	DIN	A3	A2	V_{CC}								
8217	SAME AS 8216											
8220	D1	$\overline{A1}$	Y3	NC	Y2	I1	$\overline{W1}$	GND	$\overline{W0}$	$\overline{I0}$	Y1	Y0
	NC	$\overline{A0}$	DO	V_{CC}								
8221	$\overline{WE}$	$\overline{WS0}$	DI0	A4	CE	STR	DO0	GND	DO1	A3	A2	A1
	A0	DI1	$\overline{WS1}$	V_{CC}								
8223	B0	B1	B2	B3	B4	B5	B6	GND	B7	A0	A1	A2
	A3	A4	$\overline{CE}$	V_{CC}								
8224	SAME AS 8223											
8225	A0	$\overline{CE}$	RE	I1	D1	I2	D2	GND	D3	R3	D4	I4
	A3	A2	A1	V_{CC}								

8226	A6 $\overline{CE1}$	A5 $\overline{CE2}$	A4 A7	A3 V_{CC}	A0	A1	A2	GND	O4	O3	O2	O1
8228	A6 A9	A5 A8	A4 A7	A3 V_{CC}	A0	A1	A2	GND	O4	O3	O2	O1
8229						SAME AS 8226						
8230	I0 A2	I1 $\overline{F}$	I2 F	I3 V_{CC}	I4	I5	I6	GND	I7	IN	A0	A1
8231						SAME AS 8230						
8232						SAME AS 8230						
8233	A0 F3	B0 B3	F0 A3	F1 V_{CC}	B1	A1	S1	GND	S0	A2	B2	F2
8234						SAME AS 8233						
8235						SAME AS 8233						
8241	A0 A3	B0 V_{CC}	F0	F1	B1	A1	GND	A2	B2	F2	F3	B3
8242						SAME AS 8241						
8243	I0 S0	I1 S1	I2 S2	I3 Q7	I4 Q6	I5 Q5	I6 Q4	I7 Q3	E2 Q2	B1 Q1	IN Q0	GND V_{CC}
8250	A B	C V_{CC}	D	5	6	7	GND	4	3	2	1	0
8251	C 0	D B	5 A	6 V_{CC}	7	8	9	GND	4	3	2	1
8252			SAME AS 8251						SAME AS 9301			

SIGNETICS 8200 SERIES *cont*

	1 13	2 14	3 15	4 16	5 17	6 18	7 19	8 20	9 21	10 22	11 23	12 24
8260	EI CP	CI CG	CN1 CR	CN2 X4	CN3 Y4	CN4 Y3	CN5 X3	F1 Y2	F2 X2	F3 Y1	F4 X1	GND V_{CC}
8261	G2 P1	P2 V_{CC}	G3	P3	G4	P4	GND	CE	P5	B	G1	A
8262	P1 P8	P2 V_{CC}	P3	P4	P9	O0	GND	I	EO	P5	P6	P7
8263	A1 F2	B1 F3	C1 DC	A0 S1	B0 S0	C0 C3	 B3	 A3	 C2	F0 B2	F1 A2	GND V_{CC}
8264	A1 F2	B1 F3	C1 DC	A0 S1	B0 S0	C0 C3	OE1 B3	OE2 A3	OE3 C2	F0 B2	F1 A2	GND V_{CC}
8266	A0 F3	B0 B3	F0 A3	F1	B1	A1	GND		S0	A2	B2	F2
8267	SAME AS 8266											
8268	$\overline{Y}$ Y2	YC V_{CC}	CI	$\overline{CO}$	Σ	$\overline{\Sigma}$	GND	X1	X2	$\overline{X}$	XC	Y1
8269	B4 A4	B3 V_{CC}	B2	B1		X	GND	ST	Y	A1	A2	A3
8270	DB DC	DA V_{CC}	DS	AO	CK	BO	GND	CO	L	DO	S	DO
8271	RD S	DB DD	DA DC	DS V_{CC}	AO	CK	BO	GND	CO	L	DO	$\overline{DO}$
8273	Q6	Q7	Q8	Q9	Q10	CK1	CK2	GND	$\overline{R}$	D	Q1	Q2

8274	D6 D3	D7 D4	D8 D5	D9 V_{CC}	D10	0	S1	GND	CK	SO	D1	D2
8275	D2 D3	D1 D4	$\overline{Q1}$ E12	Q1 V_{CC}	Q2	$\overline{Q2}$	E34	GND	$\overline{Q4}$	Q4	Q3	$\overline{Q3}$
8276	NC NC	NC V_{CC}	NC	NC	CK	B	GND	A	IX	Q	$\overline{Q}$	NC
8277	R DSB	$\overline{Q7A}$ Q7B	Q7A $\overline{Q7B}$	DSA V_{CC}	DIA	DOA	CKA	GND	CCK	CKB	DOB	DIB
8280	DS R	CO V_{CC}	DC	DA	AO	CK2	GND	CK1	BO	DB	DD	DO
8281						SAME AS 8280						
8284	CE R	CI V_{CC}	CO	Q1	Q2	U/$\overline{D}$	GND	CK	Q3	Q4	$\overline{Q4}$	S
8285						SAME AS 8284						
8288	DS R	CO V_{CC}	DC	DA	AO	CK2	GND	CK1	BO	DB	DD	DO
8290	DS R	CO V_{CC}	DC	DA	AO	CK2	GND	CK1	BO	DB	DD	DO
8291						SAME AS 8290						
8292						SAME AS 8290						
8293						SAME AS 8290						
82112	$\overline{WE}$ O1B	I2 O2B	I1 O3B	A0 O4B	A1 $\overline{SB}$	A2 B2	$\overline{SA}$ B1	O1A B0	O2A I4	O3A I3	O4A WE	GND V_{CC}
82123	B0 A3	B1 A4	B2 $\overline{CE}$	B3 V_{CC}	B4	B5	B6	GND	B7	A0	A1	A2

SIGNETICS 8T00 SERIES

	1	2	3	4	5	6	7	8	9	10	11	12
	13	14	15	16	17	18	19	20	21	22	23	24
8T01	D	B	C	20	30	70	60	GND	40	50	10	00
	80	90	A	V_{CC}								
8T04	a	b	A	B	C	D	RB1	GND	E	1	F	G
	LT	d	c	V_{CC}								
8T05	SAME AS 8T04											
8T06	SAME AS 8T04											
8T09	A1	E1	Y1	E2	A2	Y2	GND	Y3	A3	E3	Y4	E4
	A4	V_{CC}										
8T10	OD1	OD2	O3	O2	O1	O0	CK	GND	ID1	ID2	D0	D1
	D2	D3	CR	V_{CC}								
8T13	A1	A2	A3	A4	B1	B2	Y1	GND	Y2	2A1	2A2	2A3
	2A4	2B1	2B2	V_{CC}								
8T14	A3	B3	R1	S1	A1	B1	FI	GND	F2	R2	S2	A2
	F3	R3	S3	V_{CC}								
8T15	A1	B1	C1	D1	Y1	NC	GND	V_{EE}	Y2	A2	B2	C2
	D2	V_{CC}										
8T16	1M−	Y1	S1	H1	1M+	2	GND	2M−	3	2M+	H2	S2
	Y2	V_{CC}										
8T20	A	PEC	CR	V_{EE}	+I	−I	VR	GND	A	$\overline{Q}$	Q	+CX
	NEC	−CX	RX	V_{CC}								
8T22	A1	A2	B1	B2	NC	$\overline{Q}$	GND	Q	NC	NC	CX	NC
	RX	V_{CC}										

8T23	A1 2A4	A2 2B1	A3 2B2	A4 V_{CC}	B1	B2	Y1	GND	Y2	2A1	2A2	2A3
8T24	A3 F3	B3 R3	R1 S3	S1 V_{CC}	A1	B1	FI	GND	F2	R2	S2	A2
8T25	$\overline{S}$	OA	IA	GND	IB	D	OB	V_{CC}				
8T26	R/E DO4	RO1 RO4	DO1 D/E	DI1 V_{CC}	RO2	DO2	DI2	GND	DI3	DO3	RO3	DI4
8T28	SAME AS 8T26											
8T31	BA7 CLK	BA6 $\overline{RBB}$	BA5 WBB	BA4 BB0	BA3 BB1	BA2 BB2	BA1 BB3	BA0 BB4	$\overline{RBA}$ BB5	$\overline{WBA}$ BB6	$\overline{ME}$ BB7	GND V_{CC}
8T32	UD7 MCLK	UD6 SC	UD5 WC	UD4 1VB0	UD3 1VB1	UD2 1VB2	UD1 1VB3	UD0 IVB4	B0C 1VB5	B1C 1VB6	ME 1VB7	GND V_{CC}
8T33	SAME AS 8T32											
8T37	IN4 IN2	OUT4 OUT1	IN5 IN2	OUT5 V_{CC}	IN6	OUT6	DIS	GND	DIS	OUT3	IN3	OUT2
8T38	BUS3 OUT1	IN3 IN1	OUT3 BUS1	BUS4 V_{CC}	IN4	OUT4	DISA	GND	DISB	OUT2	IN2	BUS2
8T95	DIS4 OUT6	IN1 IN6	OUT1 DIS2	IN2 V_{CC}	OUT2	IN3	OUT3	GND	OUT4	IN4	OUT5	IN5
8T96	DIS4 OUT6	IN1 IN6	OUT1 DIS2	IN2 V_{CC}	OUT2	IN3	OUT3	GND	OUT4	IN4	OUT5	IN5
8T97	SAME AS 8T95											

SIGNETICS 8T00 SERIES *cont*

	1	2	3	4	5	6	7	8	9	10	11	12
	13	14	15	16	17	18	19	20	21	22	23	24
8T98	SAME AS 8T95											
8T100	IN1	Q1	$\overline{Q1}$	IN2	Q2	$\overline{Q2}$	A	GND	B	Q3	$\overline{Q3}$	IN3
	Q4	$\overline{Q4}$	IN4	V_{CC}								
8T101	SAME AS 8T100											
8T110	STR	IN1	$\overline{IN1}$	OUT1	IN2	$\overline{IN2}$	OUT2	GND	OUT3	$\overline{IN3}$	IN3	OUT4
	$\overline{IN4}$	IN4	TSEN	V_{CC}								
8T111	SAME AS 8T110											
8T380	GND	OUT2	OUT1	IN1A	IN1B	IN2A	IN2B	V_{CC}	IN3B	IN3A	IN4B	IN4A
	OUT4	OUT3										

[1]RBO/B1 [2]1EIA [3]2EIA

FAIRCHILD SEMICONDUCTOR 9000 SERIES

	1	2	3	4	5	6	7	8	9	10	11	12	13	14	15	16
9000	JK	$\overline{S}$	K1	J1	J2	Q	GND	$\overline{Q}$	T	K2	K3	J3	$\overline{CR}$	V_{CC}		
9001	JK	$\overline{S}$	K1	J1	$\overline{J2}$	Q	GND	$\overline{Q}$	T	$\overline{K2}$	K3	J3	$\overline{CR}$	V_{CC}		
9002	A1	B1	Y1	A2	B2	Y2	GND	Y3	A3	B3	Y4	A4	B4	V_{CC}		
9003	A1	B1	A2	B2	C2	Y2	GND	Y3	A3	B3	C3	Y1	C1	V_{CC}		
9004	A1	B1	NC	C1	D1	Y1	GND	Y2	A2	B2	NC	C2	D2	V_{CC}		
9005	1A1	2A1	2A2	2B1	2B2	Y2	GND	Y1	1B1	1B2	EX	CX	1A2	V_{CC}		
9006	1B	1C	1D	2A	2B	2C	GND	2D	2CX	2EX	1EX	1CX	1A	V_{CC}		
9007	A	B	C	D	NC	NC	GND	Y	NC	E	F	G	H	V_{CC}		
9008	A2	C1	C2	D1	D2	D3	GND	Y	B1	B2	EX	CX	A1	V_{CC}		
9014	A1	B1	Y1	A2	B2	Y2	$\overline{Y2}$	GND	$\overline{Y3}$	Y3	A3	B3	Y4	A4	B4	V_{CC}
9015	A4	A1	B1	Y1	A2	B2	Y2	GND	Y3	A3	B3	Y4	B4	C4	D4	V_{CC}
9016	A1	Y1	A2	Y2	A3	Y3	GND	Y4	A4	Y5	A5	Y6	A6	V_{CC}		
9017	SAME AS 9016															
9020	$\overline{CR1}$	TC	J1	$\overline{1K2}$	1K1	Q1	$\overline{Q1}$	GND	$\overline{Q2}$	Q2	2K1	$\overline{2K2}$	J2	JKC	$\overline{CR2}$	V_{CC}
9022	$\overline{CR1}$	TC	J1	$\overline{K1}$	$\overline{S1}$	Q1	$\overline{Q1}$	GND	$\overline{Q2}$	Q2	$\overline{S2}$	$\overline{K2}$	$\overline{J2}$	JKC	$\overline{CR2}$	V_{CC}
9024	$\overline{CR1}$	J1	$\overline{K1}$	CK1	$\overline{S1}$	Q1	$\overline{Q1}$	GND	$\overline{Q2}$	Q2	$\overline{S2}$	CK2	$\overline{K2}$	J2	$\overline{CR2}$	V_{CC}
9033	SEE 93433															
9034	SEE 93434															
9035	SEE 93435															

FAIRCHILD SEMICONDUCTOR 9300 SERIES

	1	2	3	4	5	6	7	8	9	10	11	12
	13	14	15	16	17	18	19	20	21	22	23	24
9300	$\overline{MR}$	J	$\overline{K}$	P0	P1	P2	P3	GND	$\overline{PE}$	CK	$\overline{Q3}$	Q3
	Q2	Q1	Q0	V_{CC}								
9301	A2	A3	$\overline{5}$	$\overline{6}$	$\overline{7}$	$\overline{8}$	$\overline{9}$	GND	$\overline{4}$	$\overline{3}$	$\overline{2}$	$\overline{1}$
	$\overline{0}$	A1	A0	V_{CC}								
9302						SAME AS 9301						
9304	$\overline{2A2}$	1A	1B	1C	$\overline{1C0}$	$\overline{1\Sigma}$	1Σ	GND	$\overline{2\Sigma}$	2Σ	2C0	$\overline{2C}$
	2B1	2A1	$\overline{2B2}$	V_{CC}								
9305	$\overline{MS}$	Q3	S0	S1	Q3	Q2	GND	CK1	Q1	CK0	Q0	Q0
	MR	V_{CC}										
9307	A1	A2	$\overline{LT}$	$\overline{RBO}$	$\overline{RBI}$	A3	A0	GND	e	d	c	b
	a	g	f	V_{CC}								
9308	$\overline{1MR}$	$\overline{1E0}$	$\overline{1E1}$	1D0	1Q0	1D1	1Q1	1D2	1Q2	1D3	1Q3	GND
	$\overline{2MR}$	$\overline{2E0}$	$\overline{2E1}$	2D0	2Q0	2D1	2Q1	2D2	2Q2	2D3	2Q3	V_{CC}
9309	ZB	$\overline{ZB}$	S1	B0	B1	B2	B3	GND	A3	A2	A1	A0
	S0	$\overline{ZA}$	ZA	V_{CC}								
9310	MR	CK	P0	P1	P2	P3	CEP	GND	$\overline{PE}$	CET	Q3	Q2
	Q1	Q0	TC	V_{CC}								
9311	$\overline{0}$	$\overline{1}$	$\overline{2}$	$\overline{3}$	$\overline{4}$	$\overline{5}$	$\overline{6}$	$\overline{7}$	$\overline{8}$	$\overline{9}$	$\overline{10}$	GND
	$\overline{11}$	$\overline{12}$	$\overline{13}$	$\overline{14}$	$\overline{15}$	$\overline{E0}$	$\overline{E1}$	A3	A2	A1	A0	V_{CC}
9312	I0	I1	I2	I3	I4	I5	I6	GND	I7	$\overline{E}$	S0	S1
	S2	$\overline{Z}$	Z	V_{CC}								
9313						SAME AS 9312						

9314	$\overline{E}$ Q1	$\overline{S0}$ $\overline{S1}$	D0 Q0	D1 V_{CC}	$\overline{S2}$	D2	D3	GND	$\overline{MR}$	Q3	$\overline{S3}$	Q2
9315	$\overline{8}$ $\overline{4}$	$\overline{9}$ $\overline{5}$	A0 $\overline{1}$	A3 $\overline{0}$	V_{CC}	A1	A2	$\overline{2}$	$\overline{3}$	$\overline{7}$	$\overline{6}$	GND
9316						SAME AS 9310						
9317	A1 $\overline{a}$	A2 $\overline{g}$	$\overline{LT}$ $\overline{f}$	$\overline{RBO}$ V_{CC}	$\overline{RBI}$	A3	A0	GND	$\overline{e}$	$\overline{d}$	$\overline{c}$	$\overline{b}$
9318	$\overline{4}$ $\overline{3}$	$\overline{5}$ $\overline{GS}$	$\overline{6}$ $\overline{E0}$	$\overline{7}$ V_{CC}	$\overline{EI}$	$\overline{A2}$	$\overline{A1}$	GND	$\overline{A0}$	$\overline{0}$	$\overline{1}$	$\overline{2}$
9321	$\overline{1E}$ 2A1	1A0 2A0	1A1 $\overline{2E}$	$\overline{10}$ V_{CC}	$\overline{11}$	$\overline{12}$	$\overline{13}$	GND	$\overline{23}$	$\overline{22}$	$\overline{21}$	$\overline{20}$
9322	S C1	A0 C0	A1 $\overline{E}$	ZA V_{CC}	B0	B1	ZB	GND	ZD	D1	D0	ZC
9324	$\overline{E}$ A0	A < B A = B	B0 A > B	B1 V_{CC}	B2	B3	B4	GND	A4	A3	A2	A1
9328	$\overline{M1}$ 1DS	$\overline{2Q7}$ 1Q7	2Q7 $\overline{1Q7}$	2DS V_{CC}	2D1	2D0	2CK	GND	CKC	1CK	1D0	1D1
9334	A0 D	A1 $\overline{E}$	A2 $\overline{CL}$	Q0 V_{CC}	Q1	Q2	Q3	GND	Q4	Q5	Q6	Q7
9338	B0 A2	B1 A1	B2 A0	ZB V_{CC}	ZC	C2	C1	GND	C0	$\overline{SLE}$	CK	DA
9339	B0 WE	B1 CK	B2 $\overline{EA}$	$\overline{EB}$ V_{CC}	ZB	ZA	Z0	GND	A2	A1	A0	D
9340	COE $\overline{CP1}$	S0 $\overline{CG1}$	S1 $\overline{CP2}$	$\overline{A3}$ $\overline{CG2}$	$\overline{A2}$ $\overline{CG3}$	$\overline{A1}$ $\overline{F0}$	$\overline{AZ}$ $\overline{F1}$	$\overline{B3}$ $\overline{F2}$	$\overline{B2}$ $\overline{F3}$	$\overline{B1}$ 1	$\overline{B0}$ CK	GND V_{CC}

FAIRCHILD SEMICONDUCTOR 9300 SERIES *cont*

	1	2	3	4	5	6	7	8	9	10	11	12
	13	14	15	16	17	18	19	20	21	22	23	24
9341	$\overline{B0}$	$\overline{A0}$	S3	S2	S1	S0	CN	M	$\overline{F0}$	$\overline{F1}$	$\overline{F2}$	GND
	$\overline{F3}$	A = B	P	2	$\overline{G}$	$\overline{B3}$	$\overline{A3}$	$\overline{B2}$	$\overline{A2}$	$\overline{B1}$	$\overline{A1}$	V_{CC}
9342	$\overline{G1}$	$\overline{P1}$	$\overline{G0}$	$\overline{P0}$	$\overline{G3}$	$\overline{P3}$	$\overline{P}$	GND	3	$\overline{G}$	4	5
	CN	$\overline{G2}$	$\overline{P2}$	V_{CC}								
9344	NC	NC	NC	$\overline{Y1}$	$\overline{Y0}$	$\overline{S5}$	$\overline{S4}$	$\overline{S8}$	$\overline{S2}$	$\overline{S1}$	$\overline{S0}$	GND
	NC	$\overline{Q0}$	$\overline{K1}$	$\overline{K2}$	$\overline{K3}$	$\overline{M0}$	$\overline{M1}$	$\overline{X0}$	$\overline{X1}$	$\overline{X2}$	$\overline{X3}$	V_{CC}
9345	$\overline{Q0}$	$\overline{Q1}$	$\overline{Q2}$	$\overline{Q3}$	$\overline{Q4}$	$\overline{Q5}$	$\overline{Q6}$	GND	$\overline{Q7}$	$\overline{Q8}$	$\overline{Q9}$	PD
	PC	PB	PA	V_{CC}						SAME AS 7445		
9348	I5	I6	I7	I8	I9	I10	I11	GND	PO	PE	I0	I1
	I2	I3	I4	V_{CC}								
9350	MS1	NC	MS2	Q2	Q1	NC	GND	Q3	QO	$\overline{CK0}$	$\overline{CK1}$	MR1
	MR2	V_{CC}										
9352	$\overline{0}$	$\overline{1}$	$\overline{2}$	$\overline{3}$	$\overline{4}$	$\overline{5}$	$\overline{6}$	GND	$\overline{7}$	$\overline{8}$	$\overline{9}$	D
	C	B	A	V_{CC}						SAME AS 7442		
9353				SAME AS 9352						SAME AS 7443		
9354				SAME AS 9352						SAME AS 7444		
9356	NC	NC	NC	Q2	Q1	NC	GND	Q3	Q0	$\overline{CK0}$	$\overline{CK1}$	MR1
	MR2	V_{CC}										
9357A	B	C	$\overline{LT}$	6	$\overline{RBI}$	D	A	GND	$\overline{e}$	$\overline{d}$	$\overline{c}$	$\overline{b}$
	$\overline{a}$	$\overline{g}$	$\overline{f}$	V_{CC}						SAME AS 7446		
9357B				SAME AS 9357A						SAME AS 7447		

9358	B	C	$\overline{LT}$	6	$\overline{RBI}$	D	A	GND	e	d	c	b
	a	g	f	V_{CC}						SAME AS 7448		
9359	B	C	$\overline{BI}$	D	A	e	GND	d	c	b	a	g
	f	V_{CC}								SAME AS 7449		
9360	PB	QB	QA	CKD	CKU	QC	QD	GND	PD	PC	$\overline{PL}$	$\overline{TCU}$
	$\overline{TCD}$	MR	PA	V_{CC}						SAME AS 74192		
9362	I0	I1	I2	I3	I8	PO	GND	$\overline{E}$	PE	I4	I5	I6
	I7	V_{CC}										
9366				SAME AS 9360						SAME AS 74193		
9368	A1	A2	$\overline{EL}$	$\overline{RBO}$	$\overline{RBI}$	A3	A0	GND	e	d	c	b
	a	g	f	V_{CC}								
9370	A1	A2	$\overline{EL}$	RBO	$\overline{RBI}$	A3	A0	GND	$\overline{e}$	$\overline{d}$	$\overline{c}$	$\overline{b}$
	$\overline{a}$	$\overline{g}$	$\overline{f}$	V_{CC}								
9372	$\overline{MR}$	D	E	P0	P1	P2	P3	GND	$\overline{PE}$	CK	$\overline{Q3}$	Q3
	Q2	Q1	Q0	V_{CC}								
9374						SAME AS 9370						
9375	Q1	D1	D2	7	V_{CC}	D3	D4	$\overline{Q4}$	Q4	Q3	$\overline{Q3}$	GND
	2	$\overline{Q2}$	Q2	Q1						SAME AS 7475		
9377	D1	D2	1	V_{CC}	D3	D4	NC	Q4	Q3	NC	GND	8
	Q2	Q1										
9380	B*	BC	CN	9	Σ	$\overline{\Sigma}$	GND	A1	A2	A*	AC	B1
	B2	V_{CC}								SAME AS 7480		
9382	$\Sigma1$	A1	B1	V_{CC}	CIN	NC	NC	NC	NC	C2	GND	$\Sigma2$
	B2	A2								SAME AS 7482		

FAIRCHILD SEMICONDUCTOR 9300 SERIES *cont*

	1	2	3	4	5	6	7	8	9	10	11	12
	13	**14**	**15**	**16**	**17**	**18**	**19**	**20**	**21**	**22**	**23**	**24**
9383	A4	Σ3	A3	B3	V_{CC}	Σ2	B2	A2	Σ1	A1	B1	GND
	<IN	C4	Σ4	B4					SAME AS 7483			
9386	A0	B0	Q0	Q1	B1	A1	GND	A2	B2	Q2	Q3	B3
	A3	V_{CC}										
9387	C	A1	Y1	NC	A2	Y2	GND	B	Y3	A3	NC	Y4
	A4	V_{CC}							SAME AS 7487			
9390	$\overline{CK2}$	RO1	RO2	NC	V_{CC}	R91	R92	QC	QB	GND	Q9	QA
	NC	$\overline{CK1}$							SAME AS 7490			
9391	NC	NC	NC	NC	V_{CC}	NC	NC	NC	$\overline{CK}$	GND	B	A
	Q	$\overline{Q}$							SAME AS 7491			
9392	10	NC	NC	NC	V_{CC}	RO1	RO2	OD	OC	GND	OB	OA
	NC	11										
9393	10	RO1	RO2	NC	V_{CC}	NC	NC	OC	OB	GND	OD	OA
	NC	11										
9394	P1A	P1B	P1C	P1D	V_{CC}	PL1	DS	CP	OD	CL	P2D	GND
	P2C	P2B	PL2	P2A								
9395	DS	PA	PB	PC	PD	M	GND	$\overline{CP2}$	$\overline{CP1}$	OD	OC	OB
	OA	V_{CC}										
9396	CP	PA	PB	PC	V_{CC}	PD	PE	PL	DS	OE	OD	GND
	OC	OB	OA	CL								
93141	$\overline{O8}$	$\overline{O9}$	PA	PD	V_{CC}	PB	PC	$\overline{O2}$	$\overline{O3}$	$\overline{O7}$	$\overline{O6}$	GND
	$\overline{O4}$	$\overline{O5}$	$\overline{O1}$	$\overline{O0}$								

93145	$\overline{O0}$ PC	$\overline{O1}$ PB	$\overline{O2}$ PA	$\overline{O3}$ V_{CC}	$\overline{O4}$	$\overline{O5}$	$\overline{O6}$	GND	$\overline{O7}$	$\overline{O8}$	$\overline{O9}$	PD
93150	E7 C	E6 B	E5 A	E4 E15	E3 E14	E2 E13	E1 E12	E0 E11	$\overline{S}$ E10	$\overline{W}$ E9	D E8	GND V_{CC}
93151	D3 D6	D2 D5	D1 D4	D0 V_{CC}	Y	$\overline{W}$	$\overline{S}$	GND	C	B	A	D7
93152	D4 D5	D3 V_{CC}	D2	D1	D0	$\overline{W}$	GND	C	B	A	D7	D6
93153	12 2C3	13 14	1C3 15	1C2 V_{CC}	1C1	1C0	1Y	GND	2Y	2C0	2C1	2C2
93164	A OH	B V_{CC}	OA	OB	OC	OD	GND	CP	$\overline{CL}$	OE	OF	OG
93165	SL C	CP D	E	F	G	H	$\overline{OH}$	GND	OH	S1	A	B
93176	DSTR RD	OC V_{CC}	DC	DA	OA	C2	GND	C1	OB	DB	DD	OD
93177						SAME AS 93176						
93178	DB DC	DA V_{CC}	DS	OA	CLK	OB	GND	OC	16	OD	2	DD
93179	$\overline{RD}$ 17	DB DD	DA DC	DS V_{CC}	OA	CLK	OB	GND	OC	1	OD	$\overline{OD}$
93180	I6 I5	I7 V_{CC}	PE	PO	ΣOE	ΣOO	GND	I0	I1	I2	I3	I4
93183	1A 2A	NC V_{CC}	IB	$1C_n$	18	1Σ	GND	2Σ	NC	19	$2C_n$	2B

FAIRCHILD SEMICONDUCTOR 9300 SERIES *cont*

	1 13	2 14	3 15	4 16	5 17	6 18	7 19	8 20	9 21	10 22	11 23	12 24
93190	B $\overline{R/C}$	OB CP	OA A	$\overline{E}$ V_{CC}	20	OC	OD	GND	D	C	$\overline{L}$	21
93191						SAME AS 93190						
93196	22 $\overline{CLR}$	OC V_{CC}	PC	PA	OA	$\overline{CP2}$	GND	$\overline{CP1}$	OB	PB	PD	OD
93197						SAME AS 93196						
03198	S0 $\overline{CL}$	R OE	PA PE	OA OE	PB PF	OB OG	PC PG	OC OH	P0 PH	OD L	CP S1	GND V_{CC}
93400	A0 Y3	A1 Y4	A2 Y5	A3 V_{CC}	A4	A5	I/O	GND	WE	Y0	Y1	Y2
93400B						SAME AS 93400						
93401	A3 O2	A2 O1	A1 O0	A0 V_{CC}	E0	E1	$\overline{E2}$	GND	$\overline{E3}$	O5	O4	O3
93402	$\overline{WE}$ $\overline{O0}$	D3 $\overline{O2}$	$\overline{D2}$ $\overline{O3}$	$\overline{D1}$ $\overline{A0}$	$\overline{D0}$ $\overline{A1}$	M3 $\overline{A2}$	M2 $\overline{A3}$	M1 $\overline{E0}$	M0 $\overline{E1}$	$\overline{MO}$ $\overline{E2}$	$\overline{O1}$ $\overline{E3}$	GND V_{CC}
93403	A0 A3	$\overline{CS}$ A2	$\overline{WE}$ A1	D0 V_{CC}	$\overline{O0}$	D1	$\overline{O1}$	GND	$\overline{O2}$	D2	$\overline{O3}$	D3
93406	A6 $\overline{CS1}$	A5 $\overline{CS2}$	A4 A7	A3 V_{CC}	A0	A1	A2	GND	$\overline{O3}$	$\overline{O2}$	$\overline{O1}$	$\overline{O0}$

93407	Y1 W1	Y2 Y0	Y3	V_{CC}	X0	X1	X2	X3	W0	GND	$\overline{S0}$	$\overline{S1}$
93410	A0 A5	A1 A6	A2 A7	A3 V_{CC}	$\overline{CS1}$	$\overline{CS2}$	CS3	GND	DIN	$\overline{WE}$	D0	A4
93410A						SAME AS 93410						
93415	$\overline{CS}$ A9	A0 $\overline{WE}$	A1 DIN	A2 V_{CC}	A3	A4	D0	GND	A5	A6	A7	A8
93433	X0 Y0	X1 V_{CC}	X2	X3	W1	$\overline{S1}$	GND	$\overline{S0}$	W0	Y3	Y2	Y1
93434	$\overline{O0}$ A3	$\overline{O1}$ A4	$\overline{O2}$ $\overline{E}$	$\overline{O3}$ V_{CC}	$\overline{O4}$	$\overline{O5}$	$\overline{O6}$	GND	$\overline{O7}$	A0	A1	A2

[1]CO/CG
[2]C_{n+4}
[3]C_{n+z}
[4]C_{n+y}
[5]C_{n+x}
[6]$\overline{BI}$/RBO
[7]CK34
[8]CK12
[9]C_{n+1}
[10]CKBC
[11]CKA
[12]Strobe $\overline{1G}$
[13]Select B
[14]Select A
[15]Strobe $\overline{2G}$
[16]Load
[17]Shift
[18]$1C_{n+1}$
[19]$2C_{n+1}$
[20]Down/Up
[21]Max/Min
[22]Count/Load

FAIRCHILD SEMICONDUCTOR 9400 SERIES

	1 13	2 14	3 15	4 16	5 17	6 18	7 19	8 20	9 21	10 22	11 23	12 24
9401	$\overline{CK}$ ER	$\overline{P}$ V_{CC}	S0	MR	S1	NC	GND	S2	NC	CWE	D	Q
9403	$\overline{IRF}$ TOP	PL $\overline{TOS}$	D0 $\overline{OES}$	D1 [2]	D2 $\overline{EO}$	D3 Q3	DS Q2	[1] Q1	$\overline{IES}$ Q0	$\overline{TTS}$ QS	$\overline{MR}$ $\overline{ORE}$	GND V_{CC}
9404	I0 $\overline{LO}$	I1 O3	I2 $\overline{K3}$	I3 $\overline{O2}$	I4 $\overline{K2}$	$\overline{D0}$ $\overline{Q1}$	$\overline{D1}$ $\overline{K1}$	$\overline{D2}$ $\overline{O0}$	$\overline{D3}$ $\overline{K0}$	$\overline{RO}$ $\overline{EO}$	$\overline{LI}$ $\overline{RI}$	GND V_{CC}
9405	$\overline{EX}$ $\overline{W}$	A0 $\overline{O3}$	A1 $\overline{D3}$	A2 $\overline{O2}$	I1 $\overline{D2}$	I2 $\overline{O1}$	CK $\overline{D1}$	MSS $\overline{O0}$	Z $\overline{D0}$	$\overline{X}$ $\overline{EO}$	$\overline{Y}$ I0	GND V_{CC}
9406	$\overline{EX}$ $\overline{CO}$	I0 $\overline{O3}$	I1 $\overline{D3}$	$\overline{SE}$ $\overline{O2}$	$\overline{SF}$ $\overline{D2}$	$\overline{MR}$ $\overline{O1}$	$\overline{CK}$ $\overline{D1}$	X0 $\overline{O0}$	X1 $\overline{D0}$	X2 $\overline{EO}$	X3 $\overline{CI}$	GND V_{CC}
9407	$\overline{EX}$ $\overline{CO}$	I0 $\overline{O3}$	I1 $\overline{D3}$	I2 $\overline{O2}$	I3 $\overline{D2}$	$\overline{EOX}$ $\overline{O1}$	CK $\overline{D1}$	X0 $\overline{O0}$	X1 $\overline{D0}$	X2 $\overline{EOO}$	X3 CI	GND V_{CC}
9410	$\overline{CS}$ $\overline{D2}$	$\overline{WE}$ $\overline{O1}$	A0 $\overline{D1}$	A1 $\overline{O0}$	A2 $\overline{D0}$	A3 V_{CC}	CK	$\overline{EO}$	GND	$\overline{O3}$	$\overline{D3}$	$\overline{O2}$

[1]CKS1 [2]CKS0

FAIRCHILD SEMICONDUCTOR 9600 SERIES

	1	2	3	4	5	6	7	8	9	10	11	12	13	14	15	16
9600	A1	A2	B1	B2	B3	$\overline{Q}$	GND	Q	CD1	CD2	CX	NC	CXR	V_{CC}		
9601	A1	A2	B1	B2	NC	$\overline{Q}$	GND	Q	NC	NC	CX	NC	CXR	V_{CC}		
9602	1CX	[1]	1CD	1A1	1A2	1Q	1Q	GND	2Q	2Q	$\overline{2A2}$	2A1	$\overline{2CD}$	[2]	2CX	V_{CC}
9603	$\overline{Q}$	NC	$\overline{A1}$	$\overline{A2}$	B	Q	GND	NC	RI	CX	RX	NC	NC	V_{CC}		
μA 9614	1Y	1Y	1Z	1Z	1A	1B	1C	GND	2A	2B	2C	2Z	2Z	2Y	2Y	V_{CC}
μA 9615	1Y	1Y	1S	1RS	+1A	RI	−1A	GND	−2A	RI2	+2B	2RS	2S	2Y	2Y	V_{CC}
μA 9616	A1	A2	IA	OA	C1	IC	GND	V_{EE}	OC	OB	IB	B2	B1	V_{CC}		
μA 9617	OA	HA	RA	A	OC	HC	GND	RC	C	B	RB	HB	OB	V_{CC}		
μA 9620	NC	OA	AD+	A+	A−	AD−	GND	+12	B−	BD−	B+	BD+	OB	V_{CC}		
μA 9621	1Y	IR	1A	1B	1C	1D	GND	[3]	2B	2A	2X	2R	2Y	[4]		
μA 8622	S3	OA	EA	A+	RA	A−	V_{CC}	V_{EE}	B−	RB	B+	EB	OB	GND		
μA 9624	GND	NC	1A	1C	1B	1Y	V_{DD}	2Y	2B	2C	2A	NC	TAP	V_{CC}		
μA 9625	GND	NC	NC	1Y	1A	NC	V_{DD}	NC	NC	2A	2Y	NC	NC	V_{CC}		
μA 9644	1Y	1X	1A	1B	1C	1D	V_{CC}	GND	2Y	2X	2A	2B	2C	2D	S	GND

[1] 1CXR   [2] 2CXR   [3] V_{CC2} [4] V_{CC1}

SPECIAL ABBREVIATIONS USED IN PIN ASSIGNMENTS

Motorola MC660

EX1: expandable input #1
CEX1: external capacitor
RI1: resistance internal 1

Advanced Micro Devices Am 2500

OE: output enable
S/P: serial parallel
SO: select
S: sum or select
SE: sign extend
G1: output enable
A/QA: A or QA
SR: shift right
SL: shift left
RLE: receiver latch enable
BSO: bus O
BE: bus enable
DCK: driver clock
ODP: odd parity

Texas Instruments 54/74

M/M: max/min
RCK: ripple clock
CD: count down
CU: count up
CO: carry out
BO: borrow out
DI: data in
OE: output enable
ODI: odd input
ΣEO: Σ even output
GN1: ground 1
ΣOO: Σ odd output
GN1: ground 1
GN2: ground 2
JI: jam 1
R: reset
DEI: display enable input
DEO: display enable output
UGC: ungated clock
CI: carry in
LS: latch strobe
SCE: serial count enable
PCE: parallel count enable
MXC: max count
DPI: decimal point input
S: select
EP: enable
L: load
ET: enable
S/L: shift/load
CKI: clock inhibit
EO: enable output
U/C: unity/cascade
GR: gate read
GW: gate write
WA: write select A
WB: write select B
C/L: count/load
SH: shift
EVI: even input
PE: preset enable
EI: enable input
Z: zener
P2O: phase comparator 2 out
PP: phase pulses
VCI: voltage controlled oscillator input
DO: demodulator out
IN: inhibit
VCO: voltage controlled oscillator out
CPI: comparator in
Y: output
EX: expand
X2I: signal X2 input/output
CX: common signal X
CY: common signal Y
YOI: signal Y in/out
VEE: second power supply
CC: common C
CB: common B
CA: common A
ST: strobe
DFI: display frequency in
S0 . . . S3: BCD coded inputs
DFO: display frequency out
PD1: parallel data 1
RSD: right shift data
LSD: left shift data
OIO: overflow in/out
FC1: frequency control 1
1RN: range #1
RC: register control
LI: left in/right out
RI: right in/left out
WS: word select
SR: shift right
SL: shift left
REI: recirculation input
CKO: clock out

MC: mode control
PR: preset
S: set
NC: no connection
IV1: invert 1
RBO: ripple blanking output
RBI: ripple blanking input
SI: serial input
SI: signal input
A/S: asynchronous/synchronous
SJ: serial J input
SK: serial K input
T/C: true/complement
W: write
CIN: chip inhibit
RIN: read inhibit
MBY: memory bypass
I1: input 1
01: output 1
PC: polarity control
CR: clear

National Semiconductor DM8XXX

DIA: disable A
XOC: X-OR control
0D: 0000 detect
XOD: X-OR output
EXI: external X-OR input
OD1: output disable 1
ID1: input disable 1
TC: terminal count
CET: count enable
TE: transfer enable
CE: count enable
L or L: load
MC: max count
CO: carry out
BO: borrow out
SI: serial input
CKI: clock inhibit
DIS: disable
OA: output A
IA: input A
TRI: terminating resistor
RT1: response time #1
BS1: bus #1
PRI: programming input
DPI: decimal point input
COI: comma input
COO: comma output
DO: driver out
DI: driver in
DE: driver enable
RO: receiver out
RE: receiver enable
D1: disable 1
D14: disable 1 through 4
S: select
B1: bus input 1
T1: TTL input 1
PI: parity input

Signetics 8200

EI: enable inhibit
CI: carry inhibit or carry in
CN1: carry input #1
CP: carry propagate
CR: carry ripple
CG: carry generate
G1: generated carry input
P1: propagated carry input
CE: carry extend
P1: parity bit 1
OO: odd output
I: inhibit
EO: even output
DC: data complement
OE1: output enable 1
CO: carry out
X: A greater than B
Y: A less than B
XY: A = B
L: load
S: shift or rest
IX: transfer inhibit
CKA: clock A
CCK: common clock
CKB: clock B
DS: data strobe

Signetics 8TXX

OD1: output disable #1
ID1: input disable #1
M—: MIL— input
M+: MIL+ input
1H: hysteresis #1
1EIA: EIA #1 input
PEC: positive edge control
+I: + input
—I: — input
VR: voltage reference
+CX: external capacitor
NEC: negative edge control
RX: external resistor
—CX: external capacitor
OA. output A

IA: input A
D: disable

Fairchild Semiconductor 9000

TC: toggle common
JKC: JK common
CR1: clear 1

Fairchild Semiconductor 9300

CEP: count enable parallel input
CET: count enable trickle input
TC: terminal count
SLE: slave enable
CPC: clock common
COE: carry out enable
CP1: carry propagate from preceding stage
CG1: carry generate from preceding stage
CP2: carry propagate from second preceding stage
CG2: carry generate from second preceding stage
CO/CG: carry out/carry generate output
CN = Cn: carry in
PO: odd parity output
PE: even parity output
CKD: clock down
CKU: clock up
PL: parallel load
TCU: terminal count up
TCD: terminal count down
I/O: input/output

Fairchild Semiconductor 9400

P: preset
CWE: check word enable
ER: error output
IR1: input register full
PL: parallel load
CKSI: clock serial input
IES: serial input enable
TTS: transfer to stack
MR: master reset
TOP: transfer out parallel input
TOS: transfer out serial input
OES: serial output enable
CKSO: serial output clock enable
EO: output enable input
ORE: output register empty output
IO: Instruction work 0
D0: D bus input 0
RO: right shift output
LI: shift left input
LO: shift left output
O0: output 0
K0: K-bus input 0
EX: execute input
MSS: most significant slice input
Z: zero status output
X: carry propagate output
Y: carry generate output

Fairchild Semiconductor 9600

RA: response A
RI: internal resistor
HA: hysteresis A

Index

A

Active bypass
  network, 156
  TTL, 153-154
Adder(s), 97-104
  four-bit, 102
    logic diagram, 103
  gated, 102-104
  two-bit full, 99-102
Address lines, 120, 122-123
Amplifiers, 175
Analog-to-digital converter, 185
AND gates, 28, 173, 183
ANDed J-K flip-flops, 45-46
AND-OR-INVERT gates, 16-17
Applications, TTL, 164-171
Asynchronous, 185

B

Basic
  functions of a decoder circuit, 53
  gate, 10-12
BCD, 9, 54, 86
  output, 87
Binary
  addition, 97
  -Coded-Decimal code, 54
  counter(s)
    four-bit, 79-82, 87
    up/down, 87-94
Bit, 185
  least significant, 187
  parity, 112
Blanking input, 59, 61, 185
Boolean equation, 185
Buffer, 185
  memory, 123
  transistors, 58
Buffering, 15, 45
Building blocks, 8, 9, 32
Byte, 168

C

CAM; *see* content addressable
    memory
Carry, 99
Cascaded comparators, 108
Characteristic impedance, 142
Charge storage, 150
  characteristics, 33
Chip connections, 160
Circuit(s)
  digital, 22
  divide-by-five, 86
  divide-by-two, 79
  input, 12-13
  interface, 134
  logic, 33
  open-collector and wired-OR, 17-18
  output, 10, 13
  Series, 54/74, 9
  true/complement, 104-107
  wired-AND, 18
  wired-OR, 17-18
Clamping diodes, 152
Clear, 186
  input, 186

Clock, 186
rate, 33
signal, 33
Clocked flip-flops, 32-37
CMOS circuits, 161
Code
binary-coded-decimal, 54
Excess-3, 54
Gray, 54
Comparator, 107-109
cascaded, 109
4-bit magnitude, 107-108
Content addressable memory, 127-133
Conventions, digital logic, 173-175
Conversion, serial-to-parallel, 73-75
Converter
analog-to-digital, 185
digital-to-analog, 186
serial-to-parallel, 71, 78
Count-down operation, 79, 87, 91, 93, 94
Counter (s)
decade, 85-87
divide-by-twelve, 82-85
four-bit binary, 79-82
up/down
binary, 87-94
decade, 94
variable-modulo, 94-96
Counting system, up/down, 164-166
Count-Up operation, 79, 87, 89, 93
Current, 23-24
collector, 134
load, 11, 181
shunting, 13-14
sinking, 11, 22-24
spike, 13-14
Cycle, duty, 87, 186

D

Darlington configuration, 136
Data
parallel, 188
selectors, 67-70
serial, 189
transmission system, 166-171
Decade counter, 85-87
up/down, 94
Decoder
circuit
basic functions of, 53
configuration, typical, 54
one-of-four, 52-54
one-out-of ten, 54-58
seven-segment, 58-62
Decoding, 51
system, 168
Delay, propagation, 56-58, 188
Demultiplexing, 67
Detector, zero-crossing, 141-142
Digital
circuit, 22, 32, 51
electronics, 8
families, 8-9
logic conventions, 173-175
signals, 166
systems operating speed, 150
to-analog converter, 186
Diode
Schottky-barrier, 155
-transistor logic, 9
DIP, 186
packages, 160
Display tube, 59
Dissipation
heat, 160
quiescent, 189
Divide-by-twelve counters, 82-85
Driver, interface, 134-135
D-type flip-flop, 38-41
Duty cycle, 87, 186

E

ECL, 9, 161
Edge-triggered, 41
Eight-bit shift register, 71-73
Electronics, digital, 8
Emitter-coupled logic, 9
Enable, 186
Encoder, priority, 115-118
Encoding, 51, 168
Equation, Boolean, 185
Excess-3
code, 54

Excess-3—cont
  Gray code, 54
Excluded inputs, 35
Exclusive
  NOR, 109-110
  OR, 109-110
Expandable gates, 19-22
Expander, 21

F

False statements, 173
Families
  digital, 8-9
  of TTL, 162
Fan-out, 24, 152, 184, 186
File, register, 123-125
Flatpack, 187
Flip-flops
  clocked, 32-37
  D-type, 38-41
  general purpose, 38
  high-speed J-K, 47-50
  J-K Master-Slave, 41-45
  NOR-gate, 31-32
  positive edge-triggered, 50
  set-reset, 29
  TTL, 38-45
Four-bit
  adder, 102
    logic diagram, 103
  binary counters, 79-82
Frequency division, 79, 87
Full adders, 99-102
Functions, memory, 119

G

Gate(s), 187
  AND, 28
  AND-OR-INVERT, 16-17
  basic, 10-12
  expandable, 19-22
  NAND, 9
  NOR, 9, 15
Gated adders, 102-104
Gating
  negative edge, 188
  positive edge, 188
General-purpose flip-flops, 38
Generator, purity, 112-115
Gray code, 55
Guidelines, system design, 183-184

H

Half adders, 99
Heat
  dissipation, 160
  sinks, 152
High
  limit line, 26
  -noise immunity logic, 158
  -speed J-K flip-flop, 47-50
  speed TTL, 150-152
Hysteresis, 148

I

IC, 187
Immunity, noise, 24-27
Impedance
  characteristic, 142
  series, 11
Indicator tube, seven-segment, 59
Inhibit, 187
Input
  buffer, 187
  circuit, 12-13
  clamping, 187
  combinations, 56
  excluded, 35
  gating, 187
  multiple data, 70
  multiple load, 69
  pnp, 157-158
  voltage, 25-26
Integration
  large-scale, 149
  medium-scale, 149
  small-scale, 149
  very large-scale, 150
Interface
  circuits, 134
  driver, 134-135
Inversion, 15-16
Inverters, 15-16, 187
  function, 15

J

J-K Master-Slave flip-flop, 41-45

L

Lamp test and ripple blanking, 62-66
Large-scale integration, 149
Latches, 136-138
Least significant bit, 187
Left-shift register, 75-78
Line drivers and receivers, 142-148
Loading rules, 22-24
Load, unit, 24
Logic
  circuits, 33
  digital, 28, 38
  emitter-coupled, 9
  negative, 173, 188
  positive, 188
  saturated, 154
  transistor-transistor, 9
  Tri-State, 158-159
Low
  limit line, 25
  -power Schottky TTL, 156-157
  -power TTL, 153
LSI; *see* large-scale integration

M

Magnetic core memories, 120
Matrix, 4-by-4, 120
Medium-scale integration, 149
Memory
  content addressable, 127-133
  functions, 119
  magnetic core, 120
  random-access, 120-123
  read-only, 125-127
  semiconductor, 120
Metal oxide semiconductors, 9, 161
Monolithic, 187
MOS, 161
Most significant bit, 188
MSI; *see* medium-scale integration
Multiple
  data input, 70
Multiple—cont
  emitters, 12, 13
  load input, 69
Multiplexing, 67, 188
Multistation operation, 157
Multivibrator, one-shot, 135-136

N

NAND gate, 9, 10-14, 32, 50, 150, 174, 183
Negative
  -edge gating, 188
  logic, 173, 188
Nine's complements, 105
Nixie tube, 58
Noise
  immunity, 24-27
  margin, 26
  spikes, 26-27, 111
NOR gate, 9, 15, 32, 112, 174, 183
  flip-flops, 31-32
Numbering systems, 177-180

O

Octal system, 177
One-of-four decoder, 52-54
One-out-of-ten decoder, 54-58
One-shot multivibrator, 135-136
Open-collector
  and wired-OR circuits, 17-18
  outputs, 157, 188
  transistors, 58
Operating speed, digital systems, 150
OR gate, 174
Oscillator, relaxation, 166
Output
  circuit, 10, 13
  open-collector, 157, 188
  totem pole, 13-14
  voltage, 11, 25-26

P

Pacing signal, 33
Parallel
  data, 188
  operation, 73

Parity
  bit, 112
  generator, 112-115
Pnp inputs, 157-158
Positive
  -edge gating, 188
  edge-triggered flip-flop, 50
  logic, 188
    system, 10
Power supply, TTL, 183-184
Preset, 188
Priority encoder, 115-118
Propagation
  delay, 56-58, 188
  time, 150
Protection, short-circuit, 144
Pull up/pull down, 188

R

Radix, 2, 51
RAM; *see* random-access memory
Random-access memory, 120-123
Read-only memory, 125-127
Reflected wave, 143
Register
  file, 123-125
  left-shift, 75-78
  right-shift, 75-78
Relaxation oscillator, 166
Reset, 33, 46, 80, 83, 87-89
Right-shift register, 75-78
Ringing, 189
Ripple through, 189
Rules, loading, 22-24

S

Saturated logic, 154
Schmitt triggers, 138-140
Schottky
  barrier diode, 155
  -clamped TTL, 154-156
Selectors, data, 67-70
Semiconductors, metal oxide, 9, 161
Serial
  data, 189
  operation, 73
  -parallel shift register, 73-75
Serial—cont
  -to-parallel conversion, 73-75
Series 54/74 circuits, 9
Set, 189
Set-reset flip-flops, 28-31
Seven-segment
  decoder, 58-62
  indicator tube, 59
Shift register
  eight-bit, 71-73
  serial parallel, 73-75
Short-circuit protection, 144
Sink, current, 11
Small-scale integration, 149
SSI; *see* small-scale integration
Strobe, 67, 70
Substrate, 189
Sum, 99
System(s)
  data transmission, 166-171
  design guidelines, 183-184
  numbering, 177-180
Synchronous, 189-190

T

Time, propagation, 150
Totem pole output, 13-14
Transistors, buffer, 58
Transistor-transistor logic, 9
Tri-State
  gate, 190
  logic, 158-159
True/complement circuit, 104-107
Truth table, 190
TTL
  active bypass, 153-154
  applications, 164-171
  families, 162
  flip-flops, 37-44
  high-speed, 150-152
  low-power, 153
    Schottky, 156-157
  power supply, 164
  Schottky-clamped, 154-156
  trends, 159-162
Tube, indicator, 58
Two-bit full adder, 99-102

Typical decoder circuit configuration, 53

U

Unit load, 24, 190
Up/down
  binary counter, 87-94
  counting system, 164-166
  decade counter, 94

V

Variable modulo counter, 94-96
Very large-scale integration, 150
VLSI; *see* very large-scale integration

W

Waveforms, 80, 89, 91
  clock, 43-44, 49
Wave, reflected, 143
Wired-AND
  configuration, 18, 131
Wired-AND—cont
  logic, 62
Wired-OR
  circuits, 17-18
  function, 102, 133, 175
  logic, 62
Word, 190
  digital, 7, 8, 67, 70, 71

X

X address lines, 120, 122-123
X emitters, 122-123

Y

Y address lines, 120, 122-123
Y emitters, 122-123

Z

Zero
  -crossing detector, 141-142
  suppression, 190